The Monograph

The volumes within the *Tall Buildings and Urban Environment* series correspond to the Council's group and committee structure. The present listing includes all current topical committees. Some are collaborating to produce volumes together, and Groups DM and BSS plan, with only a few exceptions, to combine all topics into one volume.

PLANNING AND ENVIRONMENTAL CRITERIA (PC)
Philosophy of Tall Buildings
History of Tall Buildings
Architecture
Rehabilitation, Renovation, Repair
Urban Planning and Design
External Transportation
Parking
Social Effects of the Environment
Socio-Political Influences
Design for the Disabled and Elderly
Interior Design
Landscape Architecture

DEVELOPMENT AND MANAGEMENT (DM)
Economics
Ownership and Maintenance
Project Management
Tall Buildings in Developing Countries
Decision-Making Parameters
Development and Investment
Legal Aspects

SYSTEMS AND CONCEPTS (SC)
Cladding
Partitions, Walls, and Ceilings
Structural Systems
Foundation Design
Construction Systems
High-Rise Housing
Prefabricated Tall Buildings
Tall Buildings Using Local Technology
Robots and Tall Buildings
Application of Systems Methodology

BUILDING SERVICE SYSTEMS (BSS)
HVAC/Energy Conservation
Plumbing and Fire Protection
Electrical Systems

CRITERIA AND LOADING (CL)
Gravity Loads and Temperature Effects
Earthquake Loading and Response
Wind Loading and Wind Effects
Fire
Accidental Loading
Safety and Quality Assurance
Motion Perception and Tolerance

TALL STEEL BUILDINGS (SB)
Commentary on Structural Standards
Methods of Analysis and Design
Stability
Design Methods Based on Stiffness
Fatigue Assessment & Ductility Assurance
Connections
Cold-Formed Steel
Load and Resistance Factor Design (Limits States Design)
Mixed Construction

TALL CONCRETE AND MASONRY BUILDINGS (CB)
Commentary on Structural Standards
Selection of Structural Systems
Optimization
Elastic Analysis
Nonlinear Analysis and Limit Design
Stability
Stiffness and Crack Control
Precast Panel Structures
Creep, Shrinkage, & Temperature Effects
Cast-in-Place Concrete
Precast-Prestressed Concrete
Masonry Structures

High-Tech Buildings
Vertical & Horizontal Transportation
Environmental Design
Urban Services

The basic objective of the Council's Monograph is to document the most recent developments to the state of the art in the field of tall buildings and their role in the urban habitat. The following volumes can be ordered through the Council.

Planning and Design of Tall Buildings, 5 volumes (1978-1981 by ASCE)

Developments in Tall Buildings–1983 (Van Nostrand Reinhold Company)

Advances in Tall Buildings (1986, Van Nostrand Reinhold Company)

High-Rise Buildings: Recent Progress (1986, Council on Tall Buildings)

Second Century of the Skyscraper (1988 Van Nostrand Reinhold Company)

Tall Buildings: 2000 and Beyond, 2 volumes (1990 & 1991, Council on Tall Buildings)

Council Headquarters

Lehigh University, Building 13

Bethlehem, Pennsylvania 18015 USA

Cast-in-Place Concrete in Tall Building Design and Construction

Library of Congress Cataloging-in-Publication Data

Cast-in-place concrete in tall building design and construction / Council on Tall
  Buildings and Urban Habitat, Committee 21D ; Helmut Microys,
  chairman ; Duncan Michael, vice-chairman ; Mehdi Saiidi, editor ;
  contributors L.G. Aycardi ... [et al.].
      p.   cm. — (Concrete and masonry buildings)
  Includes bibliographical references.
  ISBN 0-07-012536-8
  1. Reinforced concrete construction.   2. Tall buildings—Design
and construction.   I. Microys, Helmut F.   II. Michael, Duncan.
III. Saiidi, M. (Medhi)   IV. Council on Tall Buildings and Urban
Habitat.   Committee 21D (Cast-in-Place Concrete)   V. Series.
TA683.4.C37   1991
693'.54—dc20   91-38798
                                                                CIP

1 2 3 4 5 6 7 8 9 0   DOC/DOC   9 8 7 6 5 4 3 2

ISBN   0-07-012536-8

*The sponosring editor for this book was Joel Stein, the editing
supervisor was Peggy Lamb, and the production supervisor was Pamela
A. Pelton. This book was set in Times Roman. It was composed by
McGraw-Hill's Professional Book Group composition unit.*

Council on Tall Buildings and Urban Habitat

Steering Group

Council on Tall Buildings and Urban Habitat

Council Contributors

Boundary Layer Wind Tunnel Laboratory (U. Western Ontario), London
H. K. Cheng & Partners Ltd., Hong Kong
The George Hyman Construction Co., Bethesda
Johnson Fain and Pereira Assoc., Los Angeles
LeMessurier Consultants Inc., Cambridge
W. L. Meinhardt & Partners Pty. Ltd., Melbourne
Obayashi Corporation, Tokyo
Nabih Youssef and Associates, Los Angeles

Contributing Participants

Adviesbureau Voor Bouwtechniele bv, Arnhem
Akitek Perikatan, Negara Brunei Darussalam
Allison, McCormac and Nickolaus, Rockville
American Institute of Steel Construction, Chicago
Anglo American Property Services (Pty) Ltd., Johannesburg
Artech, Inc., Taipei
Austin Commercial, Inc., Dallas
Australian Institute of Steel Construction, Milsons Point
B.C.V. Progetti S.r.l., Milano
Bechtel Corporation, San Francisco
W.S. Bellows Construction Corp., Houston
Alfred Benesch & Co., Chicago
BMP Consulting Engineers, Hong Kong
Bornhorst & Ward Pty. Ltd., Spring Hill
Bovis Limited, London
Bramalea Ltd., Dallas
Brandow & Johnston Associates, Los Angeles
Brooke Hillier Parker, Hong Kong
Campeau Corp., Toronto
CBM Engineers, Houston
Connell Wagner (NSW) Pty. Ltd., Sydney
Construction Consulting Laboratory, Dallas
CPP, Incorporated, Fort Collins
Crane Fulview Door Co., Lake Bluff
Crone & Associates Pty. Ltd., Sydney
Crow Construction Co., New York
DeSimone, Chaplin & Dobryn, New York
Dodd Pacific Engineering, Inc., Seattle
Englekirk, Hart, and Sobel, Inc., Los Angeles
Falcon Steel Company, Wilmington
Fujikawa Johnson and Associates, Chicago
Godfrey Spowers Australia Pty Ltd., Melbourne
Gutteridge Haskins & Davey Pty Ltd., Sydney
T.R. Hamzah & Yeang Sdn Bhd, Selangor
Hayakawa Associates, Los Angeles
Hellmuth, Obata & Kassabaum, Inc., San Francisco
Honeywell, Inc., Minneapolis
INTEMAC, Madrid
International Iron & Steel Institute, Brussels
Johnson & Nielsen, Irvine
Kajima Corp., New York
KPFF Consulting Engineers, Seattle
Leighton Holdings, Ltd., St. Leonards
Lend Lease Design Group Ltd., Sydney
Stanley D. Lindsey & Assoc., Nashville
Lohan Associates, Inc., Chicago
Albert C. Martin & Associates, Los Angeles
Martin & Bravo, Inc., Honolulu
Enrique Martinez-Romero, S.A., Mexico
McWilliam Consulting Engineers, Brisbane

Mitchell McFarlane Brentnall & Partners Intl. Ltd., Hong Kong
Mitsubishi Estate Co., Ltd., Tokyo
Moh and Associates, Inc., Taipei
Mueser Rutledge Consulting Engineers, New York
Multiplex Construction (NSW) Pty. Ltd., Sydney
New York Concrete Construction Institute, New York
Joseph H. Newman, West Orange
Nihon Sekkei, USA, Ltd., Los Angeles
Nikken Sekkei Ltd., Tokyo
Norman Disney & Young, Brisbane
O'Brien-Kreitzberg & Associates, Inc., Pennsauken
Ove Arup & Partners. Sydney
Pacific Atlas Development Corp., Los Angeles
Peddle, Thorp & Walker Arch., Sydney
Perkins & Will, Chicago
J. Roger Preston & Partners, Hong Kong
Projest SA Empreendimentos e Servicos Technicos, Rio de Janeiro
Rahulan Zain Associates, Kuala Lumpur
Ranhill Bersekkutu Sdn Bhd, Kuala Lumpur
Rankine & Hill, Wellington
RFB Consulting Architects, Johannesburg
Rice & Daubney Architects, Planners, North Sydney
Robert Rosenwasser Associates, PC, New York
Emery Roth & Sons Intl, Inc., New York
Rowan Williams Davies & Irwin, Inc., Guelph
Scott Wilson Irwin Johnston, Sydney
Sepakat Setia Perunding (Sdn.) Bhd., Kuala Lumpur
Shimizu Corporation, Tokyo
South African Institute of Steel Construction, Johannesburg
Steel Reinforcement Institute of Australia, Sydney
Steen Consultants Pte. Ltd. Singapore
Stigter Clarey & Partners, Sydney
Studio Finzi, Nova E Castellani, Milano
Taylor Thompson Whitting Pty Ltd., St. Leonards
Tooley & Company, Los Angeles
B.A. Vavaroutas and Associates Ltd., Athens
Pedro Ramirez Vazquez, Arquitecto, Pedregal de San Angel
VIPAC Engineers & Scientists Ltd., Melbourne
Wargon Chapman Partners, Sydney
Weidlinger Associates, New York
Wimberley, Allison, Tong & Goo, Newport Beach
Wong & Ouyang (HK) Ltd., Hong Kong
Woodward-Clyde Consultants, New York
Yapi Merkezi Inc., Istanbul
Zaldastani Associates, Inc., Boston

Other Books in the Tall Buildings and Urban Environment Series

Cladding

Building Design for Handicapped and Aged Persons

Fire Safety in Tall Buildings

Semi-Rigid Connections

Cold-Formed Steel

Fatigue Assessment and Ductility Assurance in Tall Building Design

Stalbility of Tall Steel Buildings

History of Tall Buildings

Concrete and Masonry Buildings

Cast-in-Place Concrete in Tall Building Design and Construction

Council on Tall Buildings and Urban Habitat
Committee 21D

CONTRIBUTORS

L. G. Aycardi
John Bickley
Jan Bobrowski
Joseph P. Colaco
A. R. Cusens
Hans R. Daniel
Zeyad M. El-Shakra
A. Fafitis
Vellore S. Gopalaratnam
Thore Hagberg
M. Nadim Hassoun
Saeed Karshenas
Michael D. Kotsovos
Michael Kreger

M. A. Mansur
Peter Marti
Duncan Michael
Jamshid Mohammadi
D. Moretto
R. Park
T. Paulay
David Rogowsky
Mehdi Saiidi
Kenji Sakino
D. J. Sanders
K. H. Tan
Masahide Tomii
J. Francis Young

Editorial Group

Helmut Microys Chairman
Duncan Michael Vice-Chairman
Mehdi Saiidi Editor

McGraw-Hill, Inc.
New York St. Louis San Francisco Auckland Bogotá
Caracas Lisbon London Madrid Mexico Milan
Montreal New Delhi Paris San Juan Sao Páulo
Singapore Sydney Tokyo Toronto

AUTHOR ACKNOWLEDGMENT

This Monograph was prepared by Committee 21D (Cast-in-Place Concrete) of the Council on Tall Buildings and Urban Habitat as part of the *Tall Buildings and Urban Environment Series*.

Special acknowledgment is due those individuals whose contributions and papers formed the initial contribution to the chapters in this volume. These individuals are:

Duncan Michael, Chapter 1
Saeed Karshenas, Chapter 2
Jamshid Mohammadi, Chapter 3
M. Nadim Hassoun, Section 4.1
Zeyad M. El-Shakra, Section 4.2
Vellore S. Gopalaratnam, Section 4.2
A. Fafitis, Section 4.3
J. Francis Young, Section 4.4
D. H. Sanders, Section 4.5
Peter Marti, Section 5.1
Jan Bobrowski, Section 5.2
Michael D. Kotsovos, Section 5.3
Joseph P. Colaco, Section 6.1
Hans R. Daniel, Section 6.2
Michael D. Kotsovos, Section 6.3

David Rogowsky, Section 6.4
M. A. Mansur, Section 6.5
K. H. Tan, Section 6.5
A. R. Cusens, Section 6.6
Thore Hagberg, Section 6.7
Michael Kreger, Sections 7.1 and 7.2
Masahide Tomii, Section 7.3
Kenji Sakino, Section 7.3
R. Park, Section 7.4
L. G. Aycardi, Section 7.5
T. Paulay, Chapter 8
Mehdi Saiidi, Chapter 9
D. Moretto, Chapter 10
John Bickley, Chapter 11

CONTRIBUTORS

The following is a complete list of those who have submitted written material for possible use in the Monograph, whether or not that material was used in the final version. The Committee Chairman and Editor were given quite complete latitude. Frequently, length limitations precluded the inclusion of much valuable material. The Bibliography contains all contributions. The contributors are: L. G. Aycardi, John Bickley, Jan Bobrowski, Joseph P. Colaco, A. R. Cusens, Hans R. Daniel, Zeyad M. El-Shakra A. Fafitis, Vellore S. Gopalaratnam, Thore Hagberg, M. Nadim Hassoun, Saeed Karshenas, Michael D. Kotsovos, Michael Kreger, M. A. Mansur, Peter Marti, Duncan Michael, Jamshid Mohammadi, D. Moretto, R. Park, T. Paulay, David Rogowsky, Mehdi Saiidi, Kenji Sakino, D. J. Sanders, K. H. Tan, Masahide Tomii, and J. Francis Young.

COMMITTEE MEMBERS

Stephen L. Bakos, John A. Bickley, Joseph P. Colaco, Hans Daniel, Apostolos Fafitis, Jose Grases, Thore Hagberg, Gert F. Konig, Michael D. Kotsovos, Mohammad A. Mansur, Peter Marti, Ignacio Martin, Duncan Michael, Helmut F. Microys, Oreste Morette, R. Park, Thomas Paulay, Mehdi Saiidi, Joseph Schwaighofer, Manfred Stiller, and Masahide Tomii.

GROUP LEADERS

The committee on Cast-in-Place Concrete is part of Group CB of the Council, "Tall Concrete and Masonry Buildings." The leaders are:

W. Gene Corley, Group Chairman

Sven Sahlin, Group Vice-Chairman

Paul Zia, Group Editor

Jose Calavera, Group Editor

Ti Huang, Group Advisor

Foreword

This volume is one of a series of Monographs prepared under the aegis of the Council on Tall Buildings and Urban Habitat—Monographs aimed at updating the documentation of the state-of-the-art of the planning, design, construction, and operation of tall buildings and also their interaction with the urban environment of which they are a part.

The original Monographs contained 52 major topics collected in 5 volumes:

Volume PC: *Planning and Environmental Criteria for Tall Buildings*
Volume SC: *Tall Building Systems and Concepts*
Volume CL: *Tall Building Criteria and Loading*
Volume SB: *Structural Design of Tall Steel Buildings*
Volume CB: *Structural Design of Tall Concrete and Masonry Buildings*

Following the publication of a number of updates to these volumes, the Steering Group of the Council decided to develop a new series based on the original effort but more strongly focused on the individual topical committees rather than on the groups. This would do two things. It would free the Council committees from restraints as to length. Also it would permit material on a given topic to more quickly reach the public.

This particular Monograph was prepared by the Council's Committee 21D, *Cast-in-Place Concrete*. Although based on the original chapter in Volume CB, it concentrates on these important issues:

• An in-depth discussion of construction loads, including material, shoring, and reshoring
• New materials and techniques, including fiber-reinforced and high-strength concrete
• Structural analysis
• Alternate design methods

The Monograph series is intended to be of value to those responsible for planning and design practice. It is prepared for those who plan, design, construct, or operate tall buildings, and who need the latest information as a basis for judgment decisions. It includes a summary and condensation of research findings for design use, it provides a major reference source to recent literature and to recently developed design concepts, and it identifies needed research.

It is not intended to serve as a primer. Its function is to communicate to all knowledgeable persons in the various fields of expertise the state of the art and most advanced knowledge in those fields. Our message has more to do with setting design policies and general approaches than with detailed applications. It aims to provide adequate information for experienced general practitioners confronted with their first high-rise, as well as opening new vistas to those who have designed them in the past.

Direct contributions to this Monograph have come from many people in many countries. One further notable characteristic is that much of the material has been prepared by practicing designers. More than half of the initial chapter drafts came from the nonacademic sector.

The Council has seen considerable benefit accrue from the mix of professions, and this is no less true of the Monograph series itself. The new series of Monographs, *Tall Buildings and the Urban Environment*, will be international in scope and interdisciplinary in treatment. This gives each committee full rein to explore all aspects of their subject as it relates to other nations and to other fields of interest. This broadened view, it is hoped, will further bring tall buildings into proper perspective in all disciplines.

Tall Buildings

A tall building is not defined by its height or number of stories. The important criterion is whether or not the design is influenced by some aspect of "tallness." It is a building in which "tallness" strongly influences planning, design, construction, and use. It is a building whose height creates different conditions from those that exist in "common" buildings of a certain region and period.

The Council

The Council is an activity sponsored by engineering, architectural, construction, and planning professionals throughout the world, an organization that was established to study and report on all aspects of planning, design, construction, and operation of tall buildings.

The sponsoring societies of the Council are the American Institute of Architects (AIA), American Society of Civil Engineers (ASCE), American Planning Association (APA), American Society of Interior Designers (ASID), International Association for Bridge and Structural Engineering (IABSE), International Union of Architects (UIA), Japan Structural Consultants Association (JSCA), and the Urban Land Institute (ULI).

The Council is concerned not only with buildings themselves but also with the role of tall buildings in the urban environment and their impact thereon. Such a concern also involves a systematic study of the whole problem of providing adequate space for life and work, considering not only technological factors, but social and cultural aspects as well. The Council is not an advocate for tall buildings per se; but in those situations in which they are viable, it seeks to encourage the use of the latest knowledge in their implementation.

Units, Symbols, References, and Other Details

The general guideline was to use SI metric units first, followed by U.S. Customary System units in parentheses, and also "old" metric when necessary. A conversion table for units is supplied at the end of the volume. A list of symbols also appears at the end of the volume.

The spelling was agreed at the outset to be "American" English.

A condensation of the relevant references and bibliography will be found at the end of each chapter. Full citations are given only in a composite list at the end of the volume.

From the start, the Tall Building Monograph series has been the prime focus of the Council's activity, and it is intended that its periodic revision and the implementation of its ideas and recommendations should be a continuing activity on both national and international levels. Readers who find that a particular topic needs further treatment are invited to bring it to our attention.

Acknowledgment

This work would not have been possible but for the early financial support of the National Science Foundation, which supported the program out of which this Monograph developed. More recently the major financial support has been from the organizational members, identified in earlier pages of this Monograph as well as from many individual members. Their confidence is appreciated.

Acknowledgment is next due the headquarters staff at Lehigh University with whom it has been our pleasure to be associated. Special mention is due Dr. Ti Huang as Group CB Advisor, who provided technical assistance on this Monograph. Other staff members involved were Jean Polzer (secretary) and Elizabeth Easley (student assistant).

All those who had a role in the authorship of the volume are identified in the acknowledgment page that follows the title page. Especially important are the contributors whose papers formed the essential first drafts—the starting point.

The primary conceptual and editing work was in the hands of the leaders of the Council's Committee 21D, Cast-in-Place Concrete. The Chairman is Helmut Microys of M. S. Yolles and Partners, Toronto, Canada. The Vice-Chairman is Duncan Michael of Ove Arup Partnership, London, England. Comprehensive editing was the efforts of Mehdi Saiidi, University of Nevada-Reno, Reno, Nevada, USA.

Overall guidance was provided by the Group Leaders Gene Corley of Construction Technology Labs, Skokie, Illinois, USA; Sven Sahlin of the Royal Institute of Technology, Stockholm, Sweden; Paul Zia of North Carolina State University, Raleigh, North Carolina, USA; and Jose Calavera of Intemac, Madrid, Spain.

Lynn S. Beedle
Editor-in-Chief

Dolores B. Rice
Managing Editor

Lehigh University
Bethlehem, Pennsylvania
1991

Preface

This Monograph emphasizes the design aspects of cast-in-place concrete in tall buildings. It endeavors to present material that is not readily found in current text books but is essential to any practitioner in the area of tall structures. While much of the information has its roots in tall buildings, a large part is equally applicable to other structures.

The content and treatment of the material is intended to appeal to practicing members of the structural engineering profession who have a working knowledge of the theory and design practices of reinforced and prestressed concrete. Furthermore, it should be kept in mind that this is one volume of a multivolume Monograph and the reader will find it useful to cross-reference to appropriate sections of other volumes.

The chapter on *Loads* concerns itself primarily with construction loads. These are loads not easily quantified during the design process. They have importance because concrete structures have to provide full support before they have attained full strength.

Structural Analysis gives a brief overview of how the particular characteristics of rigid and monolithic behavior of cast-in-place concrete influence its analysis and in turn the design.

Materials and Techniques considers the constituent materials of reinforced concrete. It examines the characteristics of fiber-reinforced and high-strength concrete and how additives are used to improve the properties of fresh as well as hardened concrete. It looks at high-strength concrete—the major influence in the design of ever taller reinforced concrete structures—and how its properties require special attention in design. While creep and shrinkage are present in all concrete structures, they pose particular problems in tall buildings. The design must assure that these effects are duly considered.

Alternate Design Methods examines design procedures which are able to predict element behavior more realistically and accurately than conventional approaches. These methods are being applied elsewhere in this volume and are particularly useful where the basic design assumptions of reinforced concrete are no longer valid. An understanding of these methods is extremely useful in designing elements for which no ready solutions exist.

Chapters 6 and 7, *Horizontal Members* and *Vertical Members,* are extensive and deal with basic element design and a variety of commonly recurring problems. This is practical design-oriented material.

Seismic Design of Reinforced Concrete Systems is a comprehensive discussion of this topic. It presents numerous specific recommendations, stresses the importance of proper detailing, and provides appropriate examples.

Connections, Chapter 9, focuses on rigid, moment-resisting joints and their behavior. It comments upon design considerations, makes recommendations, and again mentions the importance of proper detailing.

Foundations reviews the various foundation systems which may be encountered in the design.

The final chapter, *Quality Control by In-Place Testing at Early Ages,* talks about the need for better methods than the standard cylinder test to establish strength. Early stripping of formwork, the use of high-strength concrete (often based on 56- or 91-day strength) and other construction requirements demand quick and reliable means to determine the in-situ concrete strength at early ages. This chapter outlines the options presently available to the practitioner.

Helmut Microys, Chairman

Contents

1. Introduction 1

1.1. Condensed References/Bibliography 3

2. Construction Loads 5

2.1. Overview 5
2.2. Slab Formwork Loads 6
2.3. Concrete Slab Loads During Construction 8
2.4. Research Needs 9
2.5. Condensed References/Bibliography 9

3. Structural Analysis 11

3.1. Current Structural Analysis Methods 11
3.2. Shear and Moments Envelopes 13
3.3. Approximate Analysis Methods 13
3.4. Special Considerations 14
3.5. Research Needs 18
3.6. Condensed References/Bibliography 18

4. Materials and Techniques 21

4.1. Reinforcement 21
4.2. Fiber Reinforced Concrete 25
4.3. High-Strength Concrete and Related Topics 40
4.4. Additives 57
4.5. Creep and Shrinkage 59
4.6. Condensed References/Bibliography 63

5. Alternate Design Methods 67

5.1. Truss Models 67
5.2. Design Utilizing Multiaxial Stress States 81
5.3. Appendices 113
5.4. Condensed References/Bibliography 119

6. Horizontal Members 123

6.1. Concrete Floor Systems 123
6.2. Posttensioned Slabs and Beams 135
6.3. Shear Considerations 146

6.4. Deep Beams   157
6.5. Openings through Beams   164
6.6. Stairs   170
6.7. Brackets and Short Foundation Beams   171
6.8. Condensed References/Bibliography   189

7. Vertical Members   195

7.1. Short Columns   195
7.2. Slender Columns   199
7.3. Concrete-Filled Steel Tubes   202
7.4. Detailing Practice for Reinforced Concrete Columns   222
7.5. Retaining Walls   250
7.6. Condensed References/Bibliography   251

8. Seismic Design of Reinforced Concrete Systems   253

8.1. The Concepts of Capacity Design   254
8.2. Moment-Resisting Ductile Frames   255
8.3. Ductile Structural Walls   289
8.4. Conclusions   311
8.5. Condensed References/Bibliography   312

9. Connections   315

9.1. Types of Failure   316
9.2. Recommendations for Design of Beam-Column Joints   321
9.3. Recommendations for Design of Slab-Column Joints   322
9.4. Detailing Practices   324
9.5. Research Needs   325
9.6. Condensed References/Bibliography   326

10. Foundations   327

10.1. Shallow Foundations   327
10.2. Deep Foundations   335
10.3. Bracing of Foundations   339
10.4. Suggestions for Further Research   340
10.5. Condensed References/Bibliography   340

11. Quality Control by In-Place Testing at Early Ages   341

11.1. Specifications and Interpretations   342
11.2. Creep and Curing Factors in Early Stripping of Form Work   345
11.3. Accelerated Programs   346
11.4. Condensed References/Bibliography   348

Nomenclature   349

   Glossary   349

Symbols 355
Abbreviations 357
Units 358

References/Bibliography 361
Contributors 389
Name Index 391
Subject Index 397

Cast-in-Place Concrete in Tall Building Design and Construction

1

Introduction

Cast-in-Place Concrete in Tall Building Design and Construction focuses on the engineering design of cast-in-place concrete for tall buildings. The original publication of a chapter on the subject in the volume *Structural Design of Tall Concrete and Masonry Buildings* in 1978 (Council on Tall Buildings, 1978) was followed by supplementary material in 1983 and 1986 (Council on Tall Buildings, 1983, 1986). This present publication is a new effort made by a largely new membership of topical Committee 21D, Cast-in-Place Concrete, of the Council. The aim has been to bring the knowledge, developments, and practice of the last decade into the publication in an integrated way.

Many textbooks and journal papers of quality are available to practitioners and other interested parties. The criterion in selecting topics for this Monograph has been matters which needed special emphasis or which are of particular current interest.

Specific sections of this Monograph have now been created for the subjects of loads, including construction forces; structural analysis; materials; truss analogy; and quality assurance and control. These support the core sections devoted to horizontal members, vertical members, connections, and foundations.

In the total design of tall concrete buildings the key feature has been the continued progressive increase in the height of buildings where the use of concrete can be appropriate. This capability derives directly from two sources: first, the successful manufacture of high-strength concrete has become less of a special event and much more of a norm; and second, the cleverness of construction techniques, both the process systems and the ingenuity of the equipment, has kept advancing.

Possibly the next major issues for cast-in-place concrete are those concerning the materials. The higher-strength availabilities are an obvious technical and economical benefit. The long-term performance of concrete, its durability, and the chemical actions which will occur both within the concrete and from its environmental experiences call for priority study at present. Reinforcing materials are becoming an interesting area, with special metals and nonmetals being promoted for more general use.

The movements of concrete, including its own particular phenomena of shrinkage and creep, become more critical issues. The higher strengths, taller constructions, and earlier loadings all come together in affecting significantly the movements of the building.

The direct consequences of subjects such as vibration magnitudes, periods of the total building and of its slender elements, as well as member instability are clear enough and are being studied. In addition, the performance of the building is controlled by long-term structural movements. The design of cladding, of internal divisions and all fixings for fittings, and of the equipment plant have to take into account these cumulative structural movements. The study of this subject is becoming more informed and rationalized at the present.

Developments in electronics are having a wide range of effects on tall concrete structures. Telecommunications towers are often very tall and have multiple performance requirements. This stimulation provides a source of engineering ideas for general buildings. The ways in which project teams work together and inform each other are being modified significantly by new communication techniques, so that methods of interaction not previously contemplated are now emerging. Some results are the viability of project teams created worldwide, a great increase in the potential speed of project activity, and much more reliable, higher-quality information.

The direct effect of electronic developments for the structural engineer in working on a building design is the use of computers for structural analysis, detailed element design, and the making of drawings. These changes have complex consequences. For structural analysis the total reliance on good modeling before the analysis becomes critical. This is serious engineering, where art dominates the science, and there is no safety net. Nonetheless modeling skills are teachable and will be central to engineers' training. Detailed design becomes more standardized with the use of computers. This is a trend to be encouraged, as it leads to cheaper and more reliable construction and reduces a tedious activity. Where computer-aided drafting may take the industry in terms of fundamental changes is not yet at all apparent.

One issue not yet fully resolved is the inconsistency among the various established engineering procedures for analysis and detailed design because of the history of how those activities developed: Mathematicians led in analysis; the production shop led in detailed design. We still attempt the most perfect elastic analyses, whereas detailed design is an amalgam of customary rules justified with semiscience. The general acceptance of limit states with different performance criteria provides some of the framework for the rationalization which will evolve. We may eventually bring nonlinearity and time into our routine design considerations. This issue appears not to be manifesting itself in dangerous structures, but it does cause unnecessary inefficiencies in engineering design.

The influence of seismicity on tall building design has increased. In locations with recognized seismic activities, development of design and analysis has continued, focusing on risk assessment, analysis of structural performance near collapse, and behavior of actual design details. The relatively low risks arising in other locations are now also being recognized, and corresponding design approaches are being defined. All this activity has created a better appreciation of the benefits of robustness in all major structures. This applies irrespective of the seismic imperative.

Today's more ambitious construction processes often affect the design directly. The specific construction loading and force configurations may be the critical design limit. These will occur when the concrete is young. Its strength can be evaluated and used as the controlling criterion for construction progress. The other significant physical properties of the concrete may not be directly related to the compressive strength. Thus hidden damage to the concrete can occur. In its construction phase the structure is incomplete and may not have the eventual total restraint system available to resist the construction forces. Hence rigorous modeling of the partial structure as it will exist at each construction stage is needed. This has to be seen through the construction period, so that the structure is able to accommodate spontaneous changes of plan.

1.1 CONDENSED REFERENCES / BIBLIOGRAPHY

Council on Tall Buildings 1978, *Structural Design of Tall Concrete and Masonry Buildings*
Council on Tall Buildings 1983, *Developments in Tall Buildings*
Council on Tall Buildings 1986, *Advances in Tall Buildings*

2

Construction Loads

The original Monograph publications by the Council included a volume on loading for tall buildings. The Council's volume on reinforced concrete (the CB publication) did not specifically address loads. New information has become available on construction loads. Given the importance of these loads, it was decided to present a summary of the available information.

The loads for which a reinforced concrete structure needs to be designed may be placed into two categories: (1) those that are clearly defined in design codes, and (2) those with no standard guidelines for their determination. Examples of the first category are live loads, wind loads, and the like. The second category includes loads due to temperature changes, creep of concrete, and construction loads, among others.

Most designers are aware of the loads in the second category. However, a lack of specific and widely accepted guidelines makes them resort to the use of typically unproven and judgmental quantities for these loads. Given the relatively certain nature of the loads in the first category, no attempt was made to discuss them in this Monograph. Of the loads in the second group, construction loads were believed to be somewhat more critical, as they have led to many failures. The focus of this chapter is to review the available procedures to take construction loads into account and to point out the areas where research data are lacking.

2.1 OVERVIEW

Concrete construction loads include those loads that are applied to a concrete building during construction and the loads that are supported by temporary structures used in the process of construction. The study of construction loads has received very little attention. Only recently have researchers begun to address the problem of structural safety during construction and to investigate construction loads and resistances.

In the construction of multistory concrete structures, it is a common practice to support a newly poured floor by a system of shores and reshores resting on lower floors that have not yet attained their full strength. The magnitudes of the loads applied to the slabs, shores, and reshores during construction depend on a number of factors, including the speed of construction, the number of levels of shore and reshore, and the type and size of the construction equipment used. Careful preconstruction planning and analysis should include these factors.

The assurance of the safety of a concrete building during construction requires careful consideration of two main problems: (1) the adequacy of the formwork and shoring systems to transfer the imposed loads during various stages of construction, and (2) the ability of the partially cured slabs to resist the applied loads. Failure of the shores or reshores supporting a floor can cause the collapse of part or all of the floor, which may result in a progressive collapse of the entire structure. Overloading of a partially cured slab, if it does not result in failure of the slab, can induce excessive long-term creep deflections (Gosh, 1982).

To investigate these problems, the engineer must analyze a structure at various stages of construction. Among the requirements for such an analysis is a knowledge of the construction loads on formworks and partially completed concrete structures.

2.2 SLAB FORMWORK LOADS

In the United States, the two main sources of specifications for formwork loads are the American Concrete Institute Standard 347-78 (ACI 347, 1978) and the American National Standard Institute Standard A10.9 (ANSI A10.9, 1983). Another source of guidelines for formwork safety is OSHA's *Safety and Health Regulations for Construction* (OSHA, 1983). However, OSHA refers to ANSI A10.9 for formwork design.

ACI 347 divides formwork loads into three categories: vertical loads, lateral loads, and special loads. The minimum design load requirements for these categories are reviewed in this chapter. It must be emphasized that compliance with the minimum requirement does not guarantee safety in all circumstances. A designer should be alert to provide for unusual loading conditions.

Vertical loads include dead and live loads. The dead load consists of the weight of the formwork together with the weight of the concrete slab. ANSI A10.9 specifies a minimum of 0.48 kPa (10 psf) for formwork dead load. There is no minimum dead load requirement by ACI 347. Slab formwork live loads include the weight of workers, equipment, material storage, and impact when placing concrete. ANSI A10.9 does not specify a minimum design live load for slab formworks. However, ACI 347 recommends that the design live load be at least 2.4 kPa (50 psf) of horizontal projection. The minimum design load specified by ACI 347 for combined dead and live loads is 4.8 kPa (100 psf). These ACI design loads must be increased by 1.2 kPa (25 psf) when concrete is placed by motorized carts.

There is no documentation supporting these minimum design loads. The basis of these requirements seems to be mainly engineering judgment and experience (Lew, 1976, 1985). To investigate and model actual concrete construction live loads, over 30 concrete construction project sites around the country were visited between 1987 and 1989. During these visits data on equipment, material storage, and worker loads were collected for two stages of construction: (1) before the concrete slab had been poured and (2) after the slab had been poured and preparations for the construction of the next floor were under way (Karshenas and Ayoub, 1989). Figure 2.1 shows a sample of the construction loads surveyed.

For each load item, data on weight, dimensions of the contact area with the floor, and location relative to a reference coordinate system were collected.

These data were used to draw the plan of each floor surveyed, with all objects shown to scale at their original locations. The weights of the objects were determined by inventory technique (Culver and Kushner, 1975) and direct weighing.

To analyze the collected data, the surveyed floors were divided into successive sets of grids of various sizes, and the loads within each grid were recorded. Table 2.1 shows the observed mean load intensities and the load intensities at 90, 99, and 99.5% probability levels for five different grid sizes. The load intensities in Table 2.1 are for material, equipment, and personnel loads on newly poured slabs supported by formwork. These load intensities show that the 2.4-kPa (50-psf) minimum design load specified by ACI 347 is exceeded about 0.5% of the time for grid sizes of about 9.25 m^2 (100 ft^2) or smaller. Further analysis of the collected data is under way, with the ultimate goal of developing probability-based loading criteria for slab formworks.

Another category of loads that should be considered in formwork design is lateral loads. Lateral loads are due to wind, impact of material placement, starting and stopping of equipment such as forklifts or motorized carts, cable tensions, and earthquake. Both ANSI A10.9 and ACI 347 specify a minimum lateral design load, in any direction, of 1.5 kN/m (100 lb/ft) along the floor edge or 2% of the total dead load of the floor, whichever is greater. It must be emphasized that these design loads are largely based on judgment, and there is no published document to substantiate the values (Lew, 1985). In some cases the actual loads may exceed these values. For example, depending on the location, exposed area, size, duration of exposure, and dynamic characteristics of a formwork, the wind load can exceed these loads.

The category of special loads includes all loads that can occur during construction and are not included in the two categories of vertical and lateral loads. Among these loads are accidental impacts and unsymmetrical placement of heavy

Fig. 2.1 Example of material storage loads on newly poured slab.

material. For instance, if a crane operator is not careful when placing construction material on formworks, large vertical and horizontal impacts may be created. Placing heavy material or equipment on a formwork system may also result in instability of the formwork if it is not designed properly.

Both ANSI A10.9 and ACI 347 require that the designer provide against special loads; however, neither of the two documents specifies a minimum design load. To mitigate the effect of these types of loads on a slab formwork, the form elements must be properly connected and braced in both directions so that groups of formwork members work together in sharing the loads.

2.3 CONCRETE SLAB LOADS DURING CONSTRUCTION

It is a common practice in cast-in-place building construction to support a freshly cast floor by a system of shores and reshores that rest on the floors below. Depending on the procedure used, the supporting slabs may be subjected to loads greater than the service loads for which they were designed. In addition to the high imposed loads, the supporting· slabs may not have developed their full strength capabilities.

To ensure the safety of a concrete structure during construction, a load analysis must be performed for each stage of construction to determine the applied loads on various slabs interconnected by shores and reshores. If the load imposed on a partially cured slab is higher than its capacity, the construction procedure must be changed to either reduce the slab loads or increase the concrete strength at the age at which the maximum load occurs.

Neither ANSI A10.9 nor ACI 347 prescribes a method for calculating the loads transferred to interconnected concrete slabs during construction. However, *Formwork for Concrete* (Hurd, 1979), reviewed and guided by ACI Committee 347, suggests a simplified method developed by Grundy and Kabaila (1963). This method is based on a few simple assumptions. Nonetheless, both experimental (Agarwal and Gardner, 1974) and theoretical (Liu et al., 1985) studies have shown that the results obtained using this method of load analysis are less than 10% in error.

The slab loads determined by a load analysis are used to calculate various load effects, such as bending moments and shear forces in the slab. To ensure a safe construction procedure, the calculated slab load effects must be compared with the corresponding slab resistances. ANSI A10.9 requires that for safety analysis, slab resistances must be determined in accordance with ACI 318-89 (1989). For

Table 2.1 Observed live loads for different grid sizes

(1)		(2)		(4)		(5)		(6)	
Grid size		Mean load		90% load		99% load		99.5% load	
m²	ft²	kPa	psf	kPa	psf	kPa	psf	kPa	psf
2.32	25	0.31	6.5	1.08	22.7	2.93	61.3	3.34	69.8
5.95	64	0.3	6.24	0.92	19.3	2.0	41.8	2.39	50
9.25	100	0.29	6.03	0.80	16.8	2.18	45.6	2.68	56
20.9	225	0.3	6.16	0.73	15.2	1.58	33	1.94	40.5
37.16	400	0.28	5.83	0.72	15	1.43	30	1.46	30.5

construction loads ANSI A10.9 recommends a load factor no less than 1.3. Hurd and Courtois (1986), Gross and Lew (1986), and Gardner (1985) suggest a more conservative 1.4 construction load factor. None of these values seems to be based on an analysis of the actual construction loads.

When calculating the maximum slab load effects for safety analysis, a slab load distribution representative of the actual shore loads must be used. Truss-supported flying-form systems usually apply two rows of concentrated loads to the supporting slab rather than the approximately uniform loads experienced in most evenly spaced hand-set shores (Scott, 1985).

2.4 RESEARCH NEEDS

A partially completed concrete structure and its formwork system must support all applied loads during various stages of construction. The design loads currently specified by various standards are largely based on judgment and experience. They are only the minimum requirements, and in some cases they may be exceeded by the actual construction loads. The requirements are usually very general and leave many decisions regarding loads and load combinations to the designer. Extensive research is required to develop rational and consistent design load criteria for the construction stage of structures.

2.5 CONDENSED REFERENCES / BIBLIOGRAPHY

ACI 318 1989, *Building Code Requirements for Reinforced Concrete and Commentary*
ACI 347 1978, *Recommended Practice for Concrete Formwork*
Agarwal 1974, *Form and Shore Requirements for Multistory Flat Slab Type Buildings*
ANSI A10.9 1983, *American National Standard for Construction and Demolition Opera-*

Culver 1975, *A Program for Survey of Fire and Live Loads in Office Buildings*

Gardner 1985, *Shoring, Reshoring and Safety*
Gosh 1982, *Deflections of Two-Way Reinforced Concrete Shoring System*
Gross 1986, *Analysis of Shoring Loads and Slab Capacity for Multistory Concrete Con-*
Grundy 1963, *Construction Loads on Slabs with Shored Formwork in Multistory Buildings*

Hurd 1979, *Formwork for Concrete*
Hurd 1986, *Method of Analysis for Shoring and Reshoring in Multistory Buildings*

Karshenas 1989, *An Investigation of Live Loads on Concrete Structures During Construc-*

Lew 1976, *Safety During Construction of Concrete Buildings—A Status Report*
Lew 1985, *Construction Loads and Load Effects in Concrete Building Construction*
Liu 1985, *Construction Load Analysis for Concrete Structures*

OSHA 1983, *Safety and Health Regulations for Construction*

Scott 1985, *Reshoring a Multistory Concrete Frame: A Practical Approach, Analysis and*

3

Structural Analysis

A distinct characteristic of cast-in-place concrete structures is their capability to behave as nearly perfect rigid frames. Cast-in-place concrete structures are monolithic systems. The reinforcement detail of individual members consists of a series of steel bars extended over the joints into the adjacent members. This type of detailing provides the joint rigidity and continuity needed for a structural system to behave as a rigid frame. In contrast to this, most structures made of steel or timber can only partially satisfy the joint continuity, even though connecting elements such as bolts, rivets, welds, and nails are theoretically designed to maintain the continuity of the structure at the joints. Because of their monolithic characteristics, cast-in-place reinforced concrete structural systems often require more detailed and, to some extent, diverse structural analysis methods so that the correct estimation of internal forces can be made with the effect of continuity at the joints properly included in the analysis procedure. Aside from conventional structural analysis methods using the elastic theory, cast-in-place concrete structures in many cases also need to be analyzed using the more elaborate limit analysis method to further evaluate and ascertain specific collapse mechanisms that otherwise may be overlooked in a conventional analysis. In this chapter, a brief review of current structural analysis methods from the viewpoint of cast-in-place reinforced concrete structures is presented. Specifically, areas where a more rigorous analysis would be needed to incorporate the behavior of the structure properly in evaluating the internal forces are described. A discussion of needed research in the area of structural analysis, especially an analysis of structural systems for certain *limit state* modes of failure (in other words, incremental collapse and shakedown) and for specific design objectives (for example, strength requirement versus serviceability requirement), is also presented.

3.1 CURRENT STRUCTURAL ANALYSIS METHODS

In the conventional methods of analysis, cast-in-place reinforced concrete structural systems are analyzed as rigid frames. The joint continuity is taken into account using the effect of all possible elastic rotations and translations expected at the joints. Appropriate equations describing the force-deformation relations, equilibrium, and deformation compatibility are then used, and boundary conditions are applied to obtain all potential nodal displacements and rotations. These data are then utilized in the analysis of individual members to obtain their internal forces (moment, shear, and axial force).

Figure 3.1 illustrates the influence of an elastic rotation at a joint and the influence of interstory horizontal relative displacement on the internal forces of an orthogonal frame. A rotation at joint i is identical to all four members joined at i. This satisfies the compatibility of the system's deformation. The rotation θ_i at the node i of member ij produces the bending moment M_{ij}. At node j, the member will experience a rotation θ_j and a moment M_{ji}. The relationship between the two moments and their corresponding nodal rotations can be found easily using conventional methods, such as the slope-deflection method (Meyers, 1983). In the case of a lateral deformation (Fig. 3.1b), the relative displacement of joints i and k is $\delta_k - \delta_i$, which produces moments M_{ik} and M_{ki} in element ik. Again relationships between these moments and the relative lateral displacement can be obtained using the slope-deflection method. The force-deformation equations for each member, considering all possible nodal rotations and joint translations, can be written in the following matrix form:

$$k_{ij}U_{ij} = p_{ij} \qquad (3.1)$$

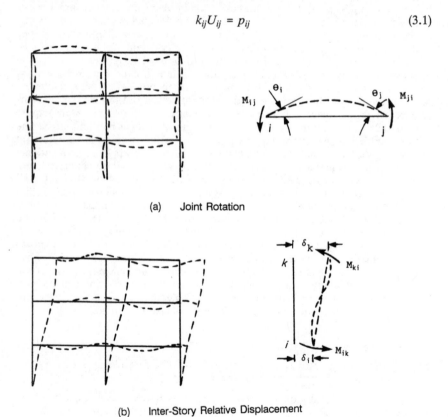

(a)   Joint Rotation

(b)   Inter-Story Relative Displacement

Fig. 3.1 Deflection patterns of a rigid frame.

in which the matrix k_{ij} and the vectors u_{ij} and p_{ij} represent, respectively, the matrix of the stiffness coefficients, and the vectors of the deformation components and of the internal forces of the element (say, ij).

Using the relationship between the internal forces and the corresponding rotations and translations (Eq. 3.1) for all of the members in the frame and further using the equilibrium of the internal moments at the joints and of the interstory shear forces, a series of force-deformation relations is written for the entire structural system. These relations can be presented in the following matrix format:

$$KU = P \qquad (3.2)$$

in which K is the system stiffness matrix, U is the vector of all rotations and translations, and P is the vector of all external nodal forces, including creep, shrinkage, and differential temperature loads. Equation 3.2 is then solved for U after the boundary conditions are implemented. Once U is known, all internal forces can be evaluated using equations similar to Eq. 3.1. The reader is referred to Meyers (1983) for a more detailed discussion on this method of structural analysis.

3.2 SHEAR AND MOMENT ENVELOPES

Like most other structures, cast-in-place reinforced concrete structures are designed for the most severe live load combination. Accordingly, the live loads are positioned at different locations in a given structural frame to obtain the most critical live load combination which produces the worst effect on the structure and the internal force distribution. This procedure, which is known as *pattern loading,* calls for loading the alternative spans in a continuous-beam nonsymmetric loading and, occasionally, for loading only a portion of a given span. Furthermore, different live load patterns may be needed to estimate the maximum negative moment, positive moment, and shear. Wang and Salmon (1985) present several such load combinations for typical continuous concrete structures to obtain maximum design bending moments.

Upon completion of the structural analysis using pattern loading, the envelope design bending moment and shear diagrams are fabricated and plotted, showing the maximum values obtained at different locations. The pattern loading procedure requires several rounds of structural analyses. Today's efficient computer techniques allow for rapid calculations of internal forces using the aforementioned matrix structural analysis. Thus development of shear and bending moment design envelopes can be accomplished more thoroughly and accurately using such computer techniques.

3.3 APPROXIMATE ANALYSIS METHODS

Approximate analyses of cast-in-place reinforced concrete structures are possible and are usually helpful in cases where a preliminary design of members is desired. Furthermore, when the quick checking of exact solutions is sought, approximate analysis methods can be used effectively.

A preliminary design of structural members is especially required to determine the sizes of beams and columns needed for more detailed and accurate analyses. The approximate design values recommended by the American Concrete Institute code 318-89 for continuous structures (ACI, 1989) are especially useful for this purpose. However, a more elaborate analysis will be needed to determine more accurate values for moments and shears at the final stages of design.

3.4 SPECIAL CONSIDERATIONS

The available structural analysis methods are equally applicable to cast-in-place concrete structures. However, there are certain specific analysis requirements related to the cast-in-place concrete structures and their behavior under service conditions as well as under limit state conditions. These are explained in this section.

1 Implementation of design objectives in structural analysis

The design bending moment and shear envelopes explained in previous sections should be evaluated carefully to ascertain their consistency with the structural design and design objectives. This may require several different structural analyses to meet different design objectives. Cast-in-place concrete structural members are designed for strength and serviceability. Design for a required strength is conducted for dynamic loads (seismic and wind loads) as well as for the static dead load and quasistatic live load. Design for serviceability, on the other hand, is concerned with deflections and cracking of structural members. Each type of design objective not only requires a different structural analysis but may also need a different loading pattern.

When a desired strength is the design objective, the structural analysis follows the conventional procedures explained earlier. However, special analyses may be needed to further investigate the potentials for the formation of *plastic hinges* and redistribution of internal moments. This is further explained later in this chapter.

When the objective of design concerns a serviceability requirement, such as control of deflection or floor vibration, the structural analysis method should be consistent with the specific serviceability requirement. The deflection of a cast-in-place concrete member consists of two components: instantaneous and long-term deflections. Instantaneous deflection occurs under live load, whereas long-term deflection is the result of a sustained load (such as dead load). Generally two different analyses are required to fully determine the critical deflections of a cast-in-place structure. Long-term deflection requires analysis of the structure under dead load. In this case, the effective moment of inertia of each beam should be used. The effective moment of inertia is given in ACI 318 and depends on the modulus of rupture of the concrete, the service bending moment, the moment of inertia of the gross section and that of the cracked section, and the maximum service load moment. Because of its dependence on the service bending moment, the effective moment of inertia for the dead load will be different from that for a combination of dead load and live load. Calculation of the instantaneous deflection requires analysis of the structure under live load. However, because the live load cannot act without the presence of the dead load, first the deflection under the combined service dead load and live load is obtained, and then the deflection due to the dead load is deducted to obtain the instantaneous deflection (Wang and Salmon, 1985). The procedure for calculating the deflection of cast-in-place beams, however, may require several rounds of structural analyses. Because of the dependence of the effective moment of inertia on the service moments, a preliminary analysis will be needed to obtain a first round of estimates for these moments. This is followed by a second analysis with the more accurate effective moments of inertia of each beam. A more elaborate analysis technique for deflection is, however, the finite-element method. With the finite-element method, each beam can be divided into several flexural elements, each with its own effective moment of inertia. Since the effective moment of inertia depends on the section properties as well as on the applied service moment, it changes along a given beam. Thus the beam idealization as a series of finite flexural elements is expected to produce more accurate deflection results.

Cast-in-place concrete structures supporting floor systems which are subject to severe floor vibrations should be analyzed for any potential damage arising from such vibrations. The design in this type of loading generally considers a tolerable vibration level (in terms of amplitude and frequency range) for a specific reason. Floor systems supporting sensitive optical devices (used, for example, in microsurgery applications) would require a lower design amplitude than those in an ordinary apartment building. In the latter case, the vibration tolerance level follows human perception and comfort. In any case, where the floor vibration imposes a serviceability design issue, a dynamic analysis of the structural frames supporting the floor system will be needed only to ascertain the frequency contents and the amplitude of vibration of the frame's response and their relations with the frequency and amplitude specified as the tolerance levels in the design objectives. For more discussion on the issue of floor vibration, the reader is referred to the proceedings of recent conferences on the serviceability of structures. (For example, see National Research Council of Canada, 1988.)

2 Consideration for critical cracking

Structural members with potentials for extensive cracking should be analyzed in view of changing the distribution of the internal stresses. Ordinary cracks, which occur as part of the curing process of concrete, merely constitute a serviceability issue and are not expected to cause any significant change in the structural analysis procedure. However, if a structure is expected to experience a severe load reversal (as in the case of an earthquake), the structural analysis should consider the potentials for extensive cracking and a reduction in the stiffness of individual members.

Cast-in-place concrete structures are analyzed to resist lateral loads due to earthquakes and winds. In the case of an earthquake, where a more rigorous load reversal situation in a relatively short period of time is expected, structural analyses should consider the hysteretic behavior of concrete and a partial deterioration and loss of stiffness of structural members. Analysis techniques considering the hysteretic behavior can be found in Saiidi and Sozen (1979) and Anderson and Townsend (1977), among others.

3 Effect of ultimate states on structural analysis

It is common practice to analyze reinforced concrete structures using the elastic method. Current design practice, on the other hand, emphasizes the strength method, which uses ultimate stress conditions, for both the reinforcing steel and the concrete. The elastic method of analysis, even though it appears to be somewhat in contradiction with the strength method, provides a safe, conservative, and convenient procedure for finding the design moments and shear forces of structural members. However, an analysis technique more consistent with the strength method is limit analysis. The basis of limit analysis is the same as that of the plastic analysis approach used in steel structures. The idea is to determine the most critical combination of plastic hinges in a given structural frame that causes collapse. A plastic hinge at a point describes the change in the flexural rotation of the section at that point from the elastic state into the plastic state. Generally upon load increase on a given structural member, a critical section (which is often the section that carries the maximum bending moment) would approach the yield level. The section stays at this yield level, but will not fail. At this stage, the load-bearing capability of the entire structural member increases due to the redistribution of internal bending moments. This means that the load is now distributed to other sections with lesser stresses. This redistribution of internal forces continues until a sufficient number of plastic hinges are formed to cause instability of the structure and formation of a *collapse mechanism.*

The formation of a plastic hinge in a cast-in-place reinforced concrete frame depends on the moment-curvature, or moment-rotation, behavior of the structural members. Figure 3.2 depicts a typical moment-rotation curve. As seen in this figure, between points B (where the first yielding occurs) and C (where concrete crushes) there is a delay in collapse, but the rotation increases without any appreciable increase in the resisting moment. This behavior depends to a great extent on the percentage of reinforcing steel. With a lower steel ratio ρ (or $\rho - \rho'$ where there is also compression steel in the section), the moment-rotation behavior is more ductile and closer to the idealized elastic-plastic type used in conventional plastic analysis. More discussion along this line can be found in McCormac (1986).

The complexity in limit analysis lies in the determination of the critical collapse mechanism of the structure. An incremental load analysis may be conducted for this purpose. In this method the load is applied in several increments. At each increment the structure is evaluated for the formation of plastic hinges. The incremental load application is continued until the structure becomes unstable, thereby indicating that a collapse mechanism has occurred. This method is only practical if there are a limited number of loads on the system and, further-

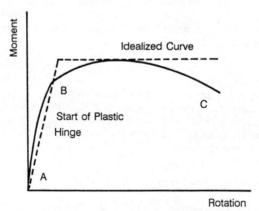

Fig. 3.2   Moment-rotation relationship.

more, if the ratios between these loads remain constant throughout the loading process. A more popular method is the analysis of all potential collapse mechanisms using the virtual work theorem and then selecting as *the* critical mechanism the one that occurs under the smallest load intensity. This method becomes tedious in the case of structures made of several bays and stories. However, the method has been used successfully in simpler structures such as slabs, for which the critical collapse mechanism is often well known.

As described earlier, the conventional method of structural analysis is often sufficient for a safe and conservative design. However, the redistribution of bending moments, expected when the maximum capacities of critical sections have been reached, cannot be determined using the conventional analysis methods. The redistribution of moments is an important issue in the design of cast-in-place structures and cannot be simply overlooked. One important feature of the limit analysis is its capability of describing the redistribution accurately. In order to include this redistribution in a conventional analysis, ACI code 318 permits a limited amount of redistribution of moments obtained through elastic analysis. The ACI provision can be used in lieu of the more elaborate limit analysis and the more accurate calculation of the rotation capacity of critical sections. The ACI-recommended moment redistribution depends on an approximate measure of the member's ductility. The ratio $(\rho - \rho')/\rho_b$ is used as a measure of the rotation capacity of the critical section, where ρ_b is the balanced steel ratio. When the steel ratio is nearly equal to ρ_b (that is, $\rho - \rho' = \rho_b$), the rotation beyond the yield level (in other words, the BC region in the curve of Fig. 3.2) is very limited, whereas in cases where $\rho - \rho'$ is low, the rotation is significant. Accordingly, the ACI code allows the maximum negative moments of continuous structures to be increased or decreased by not more than $20[1 - (\rho - \rho')/\rho_b]\%$. It is emphasized that such a modification can only be applied to moments obtained through an elastic analysis (not through ACI approximate formulas) and for cases where $\rho - \rho'$ is equal to or less than $0.50\rho_b$. Furthermore, this redistribution cannot be applied to slabs for which the direct method of analysis is used nor for structures designed according to the alternate design method (ACI, 1989).

4 Structural analysis for incremental collapse and shakedown

One other consideration in the limit analysis of structures is the potential for incremental collapse and shakedown. These modes of failure are especially possible in structures subjected to cyclic loading, such as seismic loading. Incremental collapse occurs where a sufficient number of plastic hinges is formed in the frame and each hinge accumulates additional rotation as the load cycles repeat, until collapse occurs. Shakedown, on the other hand, occurs under a load intensity less than the ultimate capacity of the frame. These are further explained below.

In a cyclic load environment, a given frame undergoes incremental changes in its plastic hinge formation and the amount of rotation experienced by the individual plastic hinges. In the early stages of loading, when only a few hinges begin to form and the plastic rotation at each hinge is small, if the loads are removed, a certain amount of residual bending moments will be locked in the already formed hinges. When the loads reapply, depending on their intensities and locations, one of the following two conditions may occur:

1. When the intensity of the loads is below a certain limit (say L), and especially when the loads reapply at locations different from those at the previous cycles, the already formed plastic hinges will experience only small plastic rota-

tions while other plastic hinges can also form. This trend repeats as the cyclic load application continues. At a certain number of load cycles there will be a sufficient number of hinges to cause instability of the frame and a collapse mechanism to occur. However, because these hinges (or at least a majority of them) are not fully developed, the collapse load is expected to be less than the limit state capacity of the structure. This is a shakedown.

2. When the load intensity is greater than the limit L, and especially when the cyclic loads do not change their points of application, the rotations at the existing plastic hinges will continue, increasing until they reach their full capacities. The collapse mechanism in this case follows when a sufficient number of fully developed plastic hinges form. Thus the collapse load is equal to the limit state capacity of the structure. This is an incremental collapse.

Comprehensive discussions of these modes of failure and of the methods of structural analysis to identify the demarcation load intensity level L can be found in Guralnick et al. (1984) and Guralnick et al. (1988). The method of analysis explained in these studies is based on energy methods which provide a powerful computer-based analysis technique for multibay, multistory elastic–perfectly plastic structures. These methods have been applied successfully to steel structures. With the proper idealization of the moment-rotation behavior of concrete (Fig. 3.2) and the existence of an adequate ductility level, these methods can also be applied to cast-in-place reinforced concrete structures.

3.5 RESEARCH NEEDS

The preceding sections have presented an overview of different structural analysis methods to be considered for cast-in-place concrete structures. However, in certain cases these methods must be investigated further before they can be applied specifically to cast-in-place concrete structures. The application of these methods to cast-in-place concrete structures is especially important in developing simplified analysis and design tools for the practicing engineer. This section identifies two specific areas where additional research will be needed or the existing state-of-the-art knowledge needs to be extended to cover cast-in-place concrete structures:

1. Development of analysis techniques consistent with design objectives. Needed are distinct separate analysis methods for limit state design, including serviceability requirements (deflection, floor vibration, and cracking).

2. Structural analysis for incremental collapse and shakedown. Potential structures for which these modes of failure may become critical need to be identified. Current methods, which are used mainly in steel structures, shall be evaluated for application to cast-in-place concrete structures. Limit boundaries between incremental collapse, plastic failure, and shakedown should also be investigated and ascertained using energy methods.

3.6 CONDENSED REFERENCES / BIBLIOGRAPHY

ACI 318 1989, *Building Code Requirements for Reinforced Concrete and Commentary*
Anderson 1977, *Models for RC Frames with Degrading Stiffness*

Guralnick 1984, *Plastic Collapse, Shakedown and Hysteresis*
Guralnick 1988, *Energy Methods for Incremental Collapse of Framed Structures*

McCormac 1986, *Design of Reinforced Concrete*
Meyers 1983, *Matrix Analysis of Structures*
Mohammadi 1990, *Strategies for Bridge Inspection Using Probabilistic Models*

National Research Council of Canada 1988, *Proceedings, Symposium/Workshop on Ser-*

Saiidi 1979, *Simple and Complex Models for Nonlinear Seismic Response of Reinforced*
Shah 1982, *Fatigue of Concrete Structures*

Wang 1985, *Reinforced Concrete Design*

4

Materials and Techniques

The previous Monographs, published in 1978, did not specifically include the material behavior in reinforced concrete systems. A considerable amount of research has been conducted on the material aspect of reinforced concrete since that time. High-strength concrete, admixtures, and, in some cases, fiber-reinforced concrete are receiving significant application in today's tall building construction. It was therefore decided to include a summary of the important considerations related to these materials.

Although the first impression that the term *reinforced concrete* conveys is that of the familiar composite material, which consists of steel bars and concrete, recent developments in its constituent materials make reinforced concrete an ever-changing construction material. In the area of concrete, different chemical and physical admixtures are constantly attempted and investigated with the hope of improving one or more characteristics of concrete, be it its workability or its freeze-thaw resistance. Or it might be the tensile strength of concrete, which is being improved to avoid excessive shrinkage cracks. In some cases, portland cement is completely replaced with different types of polymer resins, which function quite differently than a cement paste.

In the area of reinforcement, current developments, although far from being widely accepted and used, are in fiber-reinforced plastic bars and other types of advanced composites, which show better resistance against environmental effects than the conventional steel bars and cables.

The purpose of this chapter is to present an overview of the properties of the more conventional materials as well as of some types of concrete which are gaining acceptance in the construction of tall buildings. The coverage is general and broad. Readers are provided with a list of references to obtain more detail.

4.1 REINFORCEMENT

Reinforcement, usually in the form of steel round bars or wires, is used in concrete members mainly to resist tensile stresses. Reinforcement is also used to increase the member's compression resistance. Steel costs more than concrete, but it has a yield strength about 10 times the compressive strength and about 100 times the tensile strength of concrete.

Longitudinal bars resisting either tensile or compressive forces in a reinforced

concrete beam are called *main reinforcement. Stirrups* are another type of reinforcement used in beams. The direction of the stirrups is transverse to the direction of the main steel, and they are bent in a box or U shape, as shown in Fig. 4.1.
Similar reinforcement is used in columns, where it is called *ties. Secondary reinforcement* is additional steel, usually used in slabs in a direction perpendicular to
the main reinforcement.

1 Round bars

Round bars are available in a large range of diameters from 6 to 36 mm (¼ to 1⅜ in.),
plus two special types of 45 mm (1¾ in.) and 57 mm (2¼ in.). Round bars, depending
on their surfaces, are either plain or deformed bars. Plain bars are used mainly for
secondary reinforcement or in stirrups and ties. Deformed bars have projections or
deformations on the surface for the purpose of improving the bond with concrete and reducing the width of cracks opening in the tension zone.

For a deformed bar, a nominal diameter is used, which is the diameter of a
circular surface with the same area as the section of the deformed bar. Requirements of surface projections on bars are specified by ASTM specification A305
(ASTM, 1964) or A615 (ASTM, 1987). The bar sizes are designated by numbers 3
through 11, corresponding to the diameters in eighths of an inch. The two largest
sizes are designated no. 14 and no. 18. Table 4.1 lists the designations, areas,
perimeters, and weights of standard U.S. bars.

Special marks on the steel of standard U.S. bars indicate the initial of the producing mill, the bar size, and the type of steel (Fig. 4.2). The grade of the reinforcement is indicated on the bars by either the continuous-line system or the
number system. In the first system, one longitudinal line is added to the bar, besides the main ribs, to indicate the high-strength grade of 420 MPa (60 ksi) according to ASTM specification A617 (ASTM A617, 1987). If only the main ribs
are shown on the bar without any additional lines, the steel is of the ordinary
grade, according to ASTM A615 [f_y = 280 MPa (40 ksi)] (ASTM A615, 1967).
In the number system, the yield strength of the high-strength grades is marked
clearly on every bar. For ordinary grades, no strength marks are given. Both
types are shown in Fig. 4.2.

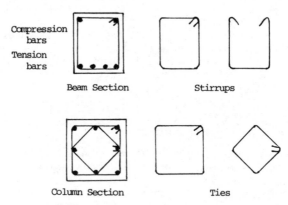

Fig. 4.1   Beam and column reinforcement.

2 Grades and strength

Different grades of steel are used in reinforced concrete. Reinforcing bars with a yield strength of 420 MPa (60 ksi) are the most commonly used; bars with yield strengths of 280 and 350 MPa (40 and 50 ksi) are the least used in reinforced concrete design. A higher strength is recommended to achieve an economical design

Table 4.1 Designations, areas, perimeters, and weights of standard U.S. bars

	Diameter*			Cross-sectional area			
Bar no.	mm	in. nominal	in. actual	mm^2	in.^{2}	Perimeter, in.	Unit weight, lb/ft
3	9.5	⅜	0.375	71	0.11	1.18	0.376
4	12.7	½	0.500	129	0.20	1.57	0.668
5	15.9	⅝	0.625	200	0.31	1.96	1.043
6	19.1	¾	0.750	284	0.44	2.36	1.502
7	22.2	⅞	0.875	387	0.60	2.75	2.044
8	25.4	1	1.000	510	0.79	3.14	2.670
9	28.7	1⅛	1.128	645	1.00	3.54	3.400
10	32.3	1¼	1.270	820	1.27	3.99	4.303
11	35.8	1⅜	1.410	1010	1.56	4.43	5.313
14	43.0	1¾	1.693	1450	2.25	5.32	7.650
18	57.3	2¼	2.257	2580	4.00	7.09	13.600

*25.4 mm (1 in.).

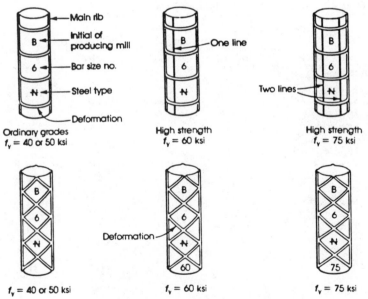

Fig. 4.2 Some types of standard U.S. bars.

and to reduce congestion of steel bars in the forms. Table 4.2 lists the available reinforcing steels and the ASTM limitations on yield strength and ultimate strength. The American Concrete Institute code 318-89 (ACI, 1989) permits the use of reinforcing bars in reinforced concrete members up to a yield strength of 550 MPa (80 ksi).

3 Stress-strain curves

Variations in the chemical composition of steel have a great effect on the mechanical properties and the stress-strain relationship in a steel specimen. For example, the introduction of carbon and alloying additives in steel increases its strength but reduces its ductility. Commercial steel rarely contains more than 1.2% carbon; the proportion of carbon used in structural steels varies between 0.2 and 0.3%. Figure 4.3 shows typical stress-strain curves of steel reinforcing bars.

Two other properties of interest in the design of reinforced concrete structures are modulus of elasticity and yield strength. The modulus of elasticity E_s has been shown to be constant for all types of steel. ACI code 318 has adopted a value of 2.0×10^5 MPa (29×10^6 psi) for E_s. The modulus of elasticity is the slope of the stress-strain curve in the elastic range up to the proportional limit.

A typical stress-strain curve for a bar of low-carbon steel with a yield strength f_y of 350 MPa (50 ksi) or less usually shows an elastic portion followed by a definite yield point at the yield stress level (Fig. 4.3). Immediately after the yield stress is reached, the strain increases by about 8 to 15 times the initial yield strain ϵ_y.

In high-tensile steel, a definite yield point may not show on the stress-strain curve. In this case, ultimate strength is reached gradually under an increase of

Table 4.2 Grades of ASTM reinforcing steel bars

Steel	Minimum yield strength f_y		Ultimate strength f_{su}	
	MPa	ksi	MPa	ksi
Billet steel, A615 (ASTM, 1967)				
Grade 40	276	40	483	70
Grade 60	414	60	621	90
Grade 75	518	75	690	100
Rail steel, A616 (ASTM, 1987)				
Grade 50	345	50	551	80
Grade 60	414	60	621	90
Deformed wire, A496 (ASTM, 1985)				
Reinforcing	518	75	586	85
Fabric	483	70	551	80
Cold-drawn wire, A82 (ASTM, 1985)				
Reinforcing	483	70	551	80
Fabric	448	65	518	75
Fabric	386	56	483	70

stress. The yield strength of proof stress is considered as that stress which leaves a residual strain of 0.2% on the release of load, or a total strain of 0.5 to 0.6% under load.

4 Welded wire fabric

Welded wire fabric consists of a series of longitudinal and transverse cold-drawn steel wires, generally at right angles and welded together at points of intersection in square or rectangular grids. This type of reinforcement is mostly used in two-dimensional concrete members such as slabs and walls. The short time needed to place a large amount of welded wire fabric makes it very economical to use.

Smooth as well as deformed wires can be used to fabricate welded wire fabric mesh. The diameter of the wires used ranges from about 3 to 15 mm (0.125 to 0.625 in.). The minimum yield strengths of smooth and deformed wires are 448 and 483 MPa (65 and 70 ksi), while the ultimate tensile strengths are 518 and 552 MPa (75 and 80 ksi) according to A497 (ASTM, 1986). The yield stresses are measured at a strain of 0.5%. Table 4.3 gives the properties of some standard smooth and deformed wire reinforcements.

4.2 FIBER-REINFORCED CONCRETE

Useful improvements in the mechanical behavior of tension-weak concrete (or mortar) matrices can be achieved by the incorporation of short discrete fibers

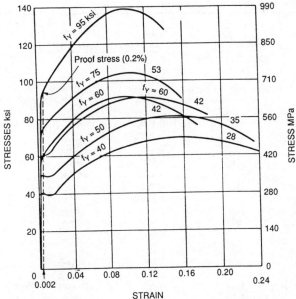

Fig. 4.3 Typical stress-strain curves for some reinforcing steel bars.

(steel, polypropylene, glass, carbon). The resulting composite, generically termed fiber-reinforced concrete (FRC), has been found to have numerous potential applications. It can either complement conventional materials in improving the engineering performance of a structure or structural component (for example, the shear and torsion resistance of beams, repair of cracks in dams, ductile hinges in reinforced concrete frames) or, in some instances, be better suited for particular applications than some conventional materials (for example, in tunnel linings, secondary energy-absorbing barriers, pavements, on-grade slabs, footings). The volume of use of FRC has increased tremendously in the last few years. Proliferation of several new fiber manufacturers and increased sales of fibers both serve as evidence of this fact.

Most notable among the improved mechanical characteristics of FRC are its superior fracture resistance and resistance to fatigue, impact, and impulsive loads. The flexural and tensile strengths are also enhanced, although to a lesser extent, for the relatively small amounts of fibers normally used. Strength and toughness are two mechanical performance parameters presently being used in design specifications. Toughness is generally accepted as a measure of the energy-absorbing capacity of the material.

Depending on the fiber geometry, fiber type, fiber volume fraction, and properties of the matrix, different types of failure mechanisms can be engineered. Analytical models in general are available to describe one or more types of failure mechanisms observed. Although there is now a good understanding of the mechanical properties of FRC, its fracture and failure mechanisms, and analytical modeling aspects, systematic design procedures are as yet unavailable.

A chapter such as this cannot be both exhaustive and brief. While the scope of this chapter is exhaustive in that historical perspectives, constituent materials,

Table 4.3   Standard wire reinforcement*

Smooth	Deformed	Nominal diameter, in.	Nominal area, in.^{2}	Nominal weight, lb/ft
W31	D31	0.628	0.310	1.054
W30	D30	0.618	0.300	1.020
W28	D28	0.597	0.280	0.952
W26	D26	0.575	0.260	0.934
W24	D24	0.553	0.240	0.816
W22	D22	0.529	0.220	0.748
W20	D20	0.504	0.200	0.680
W18	D18	0.478	0.180	0.612
W16	D16	0.451	0.160	0.544
W14	D14	0.422	0.140	0.476
W12	D12	0.390	0.120	0.408
W11	D11	0.374	0.110	0.374
W10	D10	0.356	0.100	0.340
W9	D9	0.338	0.090	0.306
W8	D8	0.319	0.080	0.272
W7	D7	0.298	0.070	0.238
W6	D6	0.276	0.060	0.204
W5	D5	0.252	0.050	0.170
W4	D4	0.225	0.040	0.136
W3	D3	0.195	0.030	0.102
W2	D2	0.159	0.020	0.068

*1 in. = 25.4 mm; 1 in.^{2} = 645.1 mm^2; 1 lb/ft = 14.57 N/m.

fracture and failure mechanisms, mechanical properties, analytical models, and applications are detailed, the references cited are by no means exhaustive. References cited are recent and should serve as a good starting point for an interested reader. A fairly exhaustive bibliography by Hoff (1987) should be of interest to the research-oriented reader.

1 Historical background

Fibers have been used to reinforce brittle materials since ancient times. In the earlier days, straw was used to reinforce sunbaked bricks (Shah, 1974). This type of reinforcement is found in many of the early civilizations (Egyptian, Indian, and more). In more recent times, horse hair has been used to reinforce plaster, and until just recently, asbestos fibers were used to reinforce portland cement (ACI, 1973). Patents for various methods of incorporating wire segments or metal chips into concrete have been granted since the turn of the century. The use of closely spaced wires and random fibers was researched in the late 1950s and early 1960s by Romualdi and Batson (1963) and by Romualdi and Mandel (1964). Their research led to a patent (ACI, 1973). The Portland Cement Association (PCA) investigated FRC in the late 1950s. With the surge in fiber reinforcing, new materials other than steel were investigated. Recently, organic and synthetic fibers such as acrylic, aramid, carbon, nylon, polyester, polyethylene, and polypropylene have also been used. Although FRC has been around for some time, only in the last two decades has it received systematic attention in terms of its mechanics of failure and toughening and with regard to design and performance evaluation.

Area per foot of width for different spacings, in.^{2}						
2 in.	3 in.	4 in.	6 in.	8 in.	10 in.	12 in.
1.86	1.24	0.93	0.62	0.465	0.372	0.31
1.80	1.20	0.90	0.60	0.45	0.366	0.32
1.68	1.12	0.84	0.56	0.42	0.336	0.28
1.56	1.04	0.78	0.52	0.39	0.312	0.26
1.44	0.96	0.72	0.48	0.36	0.288	0.24
1.32	0.88	0.66	0.44	0.33	0.264	0.22
1.20	0.80	0.60	0.40	0.30	0.24	0.20
1.08	0.72	0.54	0.36	0.27	0.216	0.18
0.96	0.64	0.48	0.32	0.24	0.192	0.16
0.84	0.56	0.42	0.28	0.21	0.168	0.14
0.72	0.48	0.36	0.24	0.18	0.144	0.12
0.66	0.44	0.33	0.22	0.165	0.132	0.11
0.60	0.40	0.30	0.20	0.15	0.12	0.10
0.54	0.36	0.27	0.18	0.135	0.108	0.09
0.48	0.32	0.24	0.16	0.12	0.096	0.08
0.42	0.28	0.21	0.14	0.105	0.084	0.07
0.36	0.24	0.18	0.12	0.09	0.072	0.06
0.30	0.20	0.15	0.10	0.075	0.06	0.05
0.24	0.16	0.12	0.08	0.06	0.048	0.04
0.18	0.12	0.09	0.06	0.045	0.036	0.03
0.12	0.08	0.06	0.04	0.03	0.024	0.02

2 Constituent materials

Matrix mix. Commercially used mixes for the matrix in FRC are often not very much different from what is used for conventional reinforced concrete construction. In applications where thin sections of FRC have to be cast, the maximum aggregate size is typically limited to 9.5 to 19.0 mm (⅜ to ¾ in.). The coarse aggregate content is varied (lowered) depending on the type of application (for example, thin sections). FRC mixes are somewhat cement-rich (6 bags to 1 yd³). It may be necessary to use superplasticizers with mixes containing larger fiber volume fractions (1% or more). Since the addition of fibers reduces the workability, one needs to account for this in the mix design (water content adjustment, adjustment of the coarse to fine aggregate content, and use of admixtures). After the addition of fibers, typical slumps obtained for workable mixes are in the 50- to 100-mm (2- to 4-in.) range. Air-entraining agents can also be used with FRC to improve its ability to resist freeze-thaw cycling under load (typical in pavement applications). The usefulness of FRC has been aided in general by new developments in the concrete field (use of high-range water reducers, addition of silica fume to reduce permeability, and the like).

Reinforcing parameters. The mechanical properties of FRC are influenced significantly by the fiber aspect ratio, fiber volume fraction, fiber type, fiber orientation and distribution, and the properties of the fiber-matrix interface.

   Fiber aspect ratio. Fiber aspect ratio is defined as the ratio of the length to the equivalent fiber diameter l/d. (For noncircular fiber cross sections, for example, the equivalent diameter is the diameter of the circle whose cross-sectional area equals that of the fiber.) The aspect ratio is a dimensionless number that influences both the workability of the wet mix and the mechanical properties of the hardened composite. To avoid fiber balling in conventional mixing, and to provide a near uniform distribution of fibers in the mix, a maximum aspect ratio of 100 is usually recommended. With special mixing and fabrication techniques (such as spinning for pipes) one can use fiber aspect ratios five times as high.

   Fiber volume fraction. The volume fraction of fibers is described as the percentage of the fiber volume to the total volume of the mix. Practically used fiber volumes in conventional FRC range from 0.1 to 2.0%. Higher volumes (up to 15%) may be incorporated using special fabrication techniques (SIFCON-slurry infiltrated fibrous concrete, described in Subsection 6.

   Fiber types. Fibers currently being used in concrete can be classified broadly into two types.

   The first type is low-modulus, high-elongation fibers (synthetic polymeric fibers) such as acrylic, aramid, nylon, polyester, polyethylene, and polypropylene. The common forms of these are smooth-monofilament or fibrillated fibers. Monofilament fibers are approximately 0.25 mm (0.01 in.) in diameter and 12 to 50 mm (0.5 to 2 in.) in length, with aspect ratios of 50 to 100. Special cutting processes used on thin film sheets of polypropylene yield fibrillated fibers (bundles of small-diameter fibers cross-linked along their length). During the mixing process, the fibrillated fibers are broken up into smaller individual fibers by the aggregates. They are chemically inert and do not react with admixtures. Typical fiber volumes used vary from 0.1 to 2.0%.

   The second type is high-modulus, high-strength fibers, such as steel, glass, and carbon. Steel fibers are available in a number of shapes, sizes, and metal types. The most commonly used ones are produced by one of three different processes.

1. Square or rectangular fibers are produced by cutting or slitting sheets of metals.

2. Collated fibers are produced by chopping cold-drawn wires into the desired lengths. They are glued together by a cellulose glue in collated bundles. This provides larger apparent diameters, thus improving the ease of initial mixing and eliminating the necessity to manually loosen the fibers before mixing.

3. Melt-extracted fibers are produced by a process where a rotating cooled disk with indentations of the size of the fiber is dipped in the surface of a molten pool of high-quality metal.

Glass fibers are usually round and straight with diameters of 0.005 to 0.015 mm (0.0002 to 0.0006 in.). They could also be bonded together to produce glass fiber bundles with bundle diameters of up to 1.3 mm (0.050 in.). The major drawback of glass fiber is its high vulnerability in the alkaline cementitious environment, which affects the long-term performance characteristics of the composite adversely. Alkali-resistant glass fibers can, however, be used to overcome this problem. Carbon fibers are produced in large volumes from petroleum pitches. They are typically very small in diameter and length. They are also manufactured as continuous mats or continuous straight fibers. Compared with the other fiber types, uniform dispersion of these fibers is more difficult to achieve.

3   Fracture and failure mechanisms

Similar to the behavior of plain concrete, composite failure under most types of loading is initiated by the tensile cracking of the matrix along planes where the normal tensile strains exceed the corresponding permissible values. This may be followed by multiple cracking of the matrix prior to composite fracture if the fibers are sufficiently long (or continuous). However, when short strong fibers are used (steel, polypropylene, glass), once the matrix has cracked, one of the following types of failure will occur (Fig. 4.4):

1. The composite fractures immediately after matrix cracking. This results from inadequate fiber content at the critical section or from insufficient fiber lengths to transfer stresses across the matrix crack.

2. Although the maximum load on the composite is not significantly different from that of the matrix alone, the composite continues to carry decreasing loads after the peak. The postcracking resistance is primarily attributed to fiber pullout. While no significant increases in composite strength are observed, considerable enhancement of the composite fracture energy and toughness is obtained.

3. Even after matrix cracking, the composite continues to carry increasing loads. The peak load-carrying capacity of the composite and the corresponding deformations are significantly greater than that of the unreinforced matrix. During the prepeak inelastic regime of the composite response, progressive debonding and softening of the interface together with multiple cracking of the matrix may be responsible for the energy absorption processes.

If the fibers are very long, after multiple cracking of the matrix has occurred, fiber fracture at or near the critical section will precipitate composite failure. At the other extreme, short fibers will tend to pull out of the matrix before they

reach their breaking strain. It is often advantageous to use lengths that are intermediate so that both constituents of the composite are optimally used and the
composite exhibits both strengthening and toughening. The fiber length at which
there is a transition in the mechanism of composite failure from fiber fracture to
a fiber pullout-type failure is the critical fiber length l_c. Although the implications
of the critical fiber length are not very significant as far as strength is concerned,
the ductility or the energy absorption capacity of the composite is influenced a
great deal by changes in the failure mechanism of the composite.

4 Mechanical properties

Due to the fact that there has been more experience with the use of steel-fiber-
reinforced concrete (SFRC) and also since the largest body of knowledge on FRC
relates to SFRC, much of what is discussed in this subsection is based on the
mechanical response of SFRC. Although much of what applies to SFRC is also
valid in general for mixes with other fiber types, some differences in the mechanical response are to be expected.

Tensile behavior. Since composite failure is often initiated by local tensile failure, knowledge of the tensile response is essential to a good understanding of the
failure mechanisms. Three stages can be distinguished in typical tension tests of
short-fiber composites: (1) elastic response until the initiation of matrix cracking,
(2) nonlinear response, which results from multiple matrix cracking, fiber-matrix
debonding, and frictional slip, and (3) postpeak softening response.

Based on numerous stable fracture tests in direct tension, Gopalaratnam and
Shah (1987b) suggested that in short (steel) fiber composites, (1) composite failure

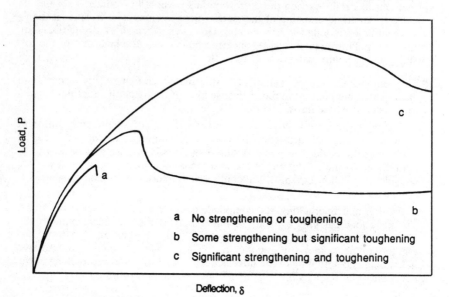

a   No strengthening or toughening
b   Some strengthening but significant toughening
c   Significant strengthening and toughening

Deflection, δ

Fig. 4.4   Strengthening and toughening mechanisms observed in FRC.

is precipitated by the formation of a single matrix crack across the specimen, (2) fibers bridging this critical section start debonding during opening of the matrix crack, (3) a sudden drop in load results at the composite peak stress (which is larger than the matrix strength), indicating some sort of instability, and (4) the postpeak response of the composite is essentially a frictional-type pullout behavior (Fig. 4.5). Due to displacement localization, the composite stress-strain response in the postcracking regime is gage-length dependent. It is hence more appropriate to describe the material response in this regime by a stress–crack-width relationship (Gopalaratnam, 1985; Gopalaratnam and Shah, 1987a, 1987b; Hillerborg, 1980). The composite peak stress and the corresponding displacements (or strains) are larger than the values for the unreinforced matrix mix (up to 25 to 30% over the corresponding unreinforced matrix for 1.5% steel FRC mix). The load-carrying capacity abruptly drops to a postcracking strength, following composite peak stress, at which time a single crack becomes visible at the critical section. A further increase in displacement results in a gradual (almost linear) decrease in the load-carrying capacity. It was also observed that the composite strength is related linearly to the fiber content. The tensile strength increases from 2.79 MPa (405 psi) for plain concrete to 3.00, 3.22, and 3.61 MPa (435, 467, and 524 psi) for composites containing, respectively, 0.5, 1.0, and 1.5 vol% of fibers with an aspect ratio of 62.5. Similar observations were made by Naaman et al. (1974).

Compressive behavior.   Incorporating fibers in a plain concrete matrix has little effect on its precracking behavior in compression. However, it enhances its postcracking behavior substantially, resulting in greatly improved ductility and toughness. From static compression tests the following has been observed (Gopalaratnam, 1985):

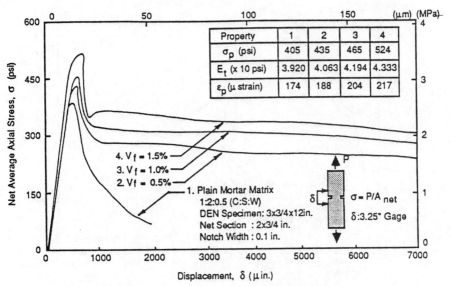

Fig. 4.5   Typical stress-displacement response obtained from direct tension tests on plain mortar matrix and FRC mixes. (*From Gopalaratnam and Shah, 1987b.*)

1. The inclusion of fibers in the matrix enhances the compressive strength (an increase of 16 and 35% for 0.5 and 1.5% fiber volume fraction, respectively, over plain concrete) and the corresponding strain. Also for the same aspect ratio, the strength increases are linearly related to the fiber volume content.

2. The initial tangent modulus in compression measured experimentally obeys the law of mixture prediction quite well.

3. The inclusion of fibers has an effect comparable to confining unreinforced concrete.

Although the presence of fibers influences the load-deformation behavior in the ascending portion, its major contribution is realized only beyond the peak loads, where the slope of the descending portion is more shallow than that of plain concrete, resulting in substantially higher toughness (Fig. 4.6). Fanella and Naaman (1985) have confirmed the effects of fiber volume content noted earlier. They also observed that an increase in the aspect ratio at a constant volume fraction of fibers leads to similar results. They concluded that aspect ratio and fiber length play important roles in improving the peak strain and the toughness of the composite, and also that, everything else being equal, improvements due to fiber addition were relatively more significant at the lower matrix compressive strengths.

However, toughness, or energy absorption, in compression is not as well understood or important, mainly because the significant benefit obtained with the use of fibers is in the tensile and flexural modes. Nonetheless, toughness in com-

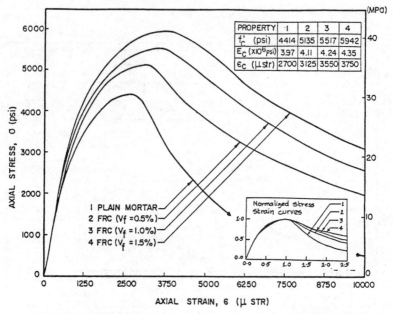

Fig. 4.6   Results from static uniaxial compression tests on plain mortar matrix and FRC specimens. (*From Gopalaratnam, 1985.*)

pression due to the incorporation of fibers is useful in preventing spalling and explosive failure under static or dynamic compressive loadings.

Flexural behavior.   Since in most practical applications FRC is likely to be subjected to flexural loads, its performance in flexure needs to be clearly understood. There are two commonly reported strength values associated with flexure, first-crack strength and ultimate flexural strength. First-crack strength is defined as the flexural tensile strength of the composite at the point where the load-deflection curve deviates from linearity. The ultimate flexural strength is evaluated as the flexural tensile strength at the peak load-carrying capacity of the composite beam. Both the first-crack strength σ_f and the ultimate flexural strength σ_u (or the modulus of rupture, MOR) are calculated based on the elastic behavior of an uncracked section. While these conditions are approximately satisfied for the first-crack strength, the assumptions are often violated at the peak-load levels. These assumptions, however, are still used for computing the ultimate strength, if only for comparisons and relative performance evaluations.

While first-crack strength is not significantly influenced by the incorporation of fibers, the ultimate flexural strength is greatly influenced by the fiber type, fiber aspect ratio, and fiber volume content (Johnston, 1980). Shah and Rangan (1971) have investigated the influence of fiber aspect ratio and fiber volume content on the flexural strength of FRC. They conducted experiments on FRC beams tested under midpoint loading and concluded that while the flexural strength is influenced somewhat by the fiber aspect ratio and volume content, the incorporation of fibers enhances the flexural toughness of plain mixes by over an order of magnitude (Fig. 4.7). Their results showed an increase of 50 to 70% in the composite flexural strength over that of plain concrete for 1 vol% content of fibers. The corresponding increase in flexural toughness is 1400 to 1600%. Johnston (1980) has reported that the ultimate flexural strength increases in relation to the product of fiber volume fraction V_f and aspect ratio l/d. He concluded that a low concentration (less than 0.5% fiber content) and a low aspect ratio (less than 50) have negligible effects on the static strength properties. Higher percentages of hooked- or enlarged-end (higher-anchorage) fibers have produced flexural strength increases over unreinforced matrices of as much as 100%. Ramakrishnan et al. (1980) have investigated the influence of fiber volume content and fiber aspect ratio on the age-dependent flexural strength (MOR) of FRC. They conducted experiments on 102- by 102- by 356-mm (4- by 4- by 14-in.) specimens with a span length of 305 mm (12 in.) using collated hooked-end steel fibers in two sizes. The specimens were tested at an age of 7 and 28 days. Based on their experimental investigation, they concluded that the 7-day flexural strength was between 80 and 90% of the 28-day flexural strength.

Toughness.   Improved resistance to both fracture and crack growth and resistance to impact loads are recognized as important attributes of FRCs. Fracture, fatigue, and impact resistance are related to the toughness of the material. Toughness is generally accepted as the energy absorption capacity of the composite. All of the popularly used tests for toughness measurements (ACI, 1978, 1988; ASTM, 1984, 1989; Japan Concrete Institute, 1983) use a static third-point (that is, four points) bending configuration. Besides being a relatively simple test to conduct, this configuration closely represents the stress conditions that the composite is most likely to experience in many of the practical applications.

Johnston (1982a) has provided a good description of the different toughness measurement techniques. A more recent interuniversity study by Gopalaratnam et al. (1990) and El-Shakra and Gopalaratnam (1990) includes discussions of the merits and drawbacks of some of these methods. Figure 4.8 gives a schematic representation of the methods proposed for toughness measurement. In all of these methods, the energy absorbed by the specimen is computed from the area under the load-deflection response. Nondimensional indices are used to compare the flexural toughness of different FRC mixes. Energy absorbed up to the prescribed displacement levels in addition provides more basic information on the absolute toughness of the composite (Japan Concrete Institute, 1983).

While strength increases with the incorporation of fibers are in the 25 to 50% range, toughness increases of a couple of magnitudes are not uncommon (FRC toughness compared to that of plain concrete). Based on an exhaustive interuniversity study, Gopalaratnam et al. (1990) and El-Shakra (1989) report energy absorption capacities of 5300 J/m^2 of cross-sectional area (30 lb · in./in.^{2}) up to the deflection limit of 1.5 percent of the span, compared to 79 J/m^2 (0.45 lb · in./in.^{2}) for complete fracture of plain concrete. If FRC were tested up to complete failure, this value would be expected to be significantly higher.

Shear behavior. The shear capacity of FRC can be used to augment the capacity of vertical stirrups in reinforced concrete beams substantially. The advantages are that (1) the random distribution of fibers throughout the volume of concrete allows reinforcement at much closer spacing than is practical for the smallest reinforcing bars, (2) the first-crack tensile strength and the ultimate tensile strength

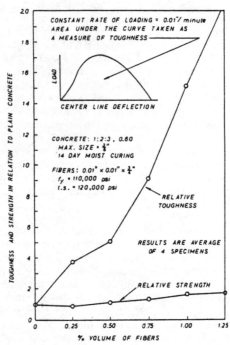

Fig. 4.7   Flexural strength and toughness enhancements with addition of fiber. (*From Shah and Rangan, 1971.*)

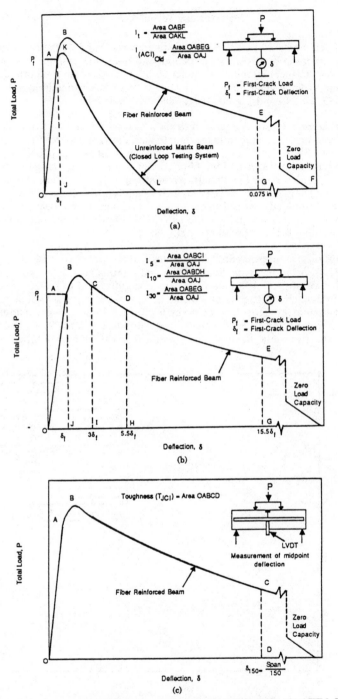

Fig. 4.8 Presently used toughness measures. (a) ACI 544 (1978, 1988). (b) ASTM C1018 (1984, 1989). (c) JCI SF4 (1983).

35

of concrete are increased by the fibers, as stated earlier, and (3) the shear friction strength is increased by resistance to pullout and fibers bridging the cracks. Figure 4.9 shows the shear strength as a function of the shear-span-to-depth ratio for SFRC beams from several published investigations (ACI Committee 544, 1973; Batson, 1985; Umoto and Fujino, 1981; Williamson, 1978).

Fatigue resistance.   Experimental studies show that for a given type of fiber there is a significant increase in the fatigue strength with increasing percentage of fibers (Batson et al., 1972; Kormeling et al., 1980; Ramakrishnan and Josifek, 1987). Depending on the fiber type and the fiber volume fraction used, fatigue strengths of between 65 and 90% of the static flexural strengths (at 2 million cycles when nonreversed loading is used) can be obtained. Slightly lower fatigue strengths are obtained with full-load reversal. The addition of fibers to conventionally reinforced beams increases the fatigue life and decreases the crack width under fatigue loading (Fig. 4.10) (Kormeling et al., 1980).

Impact resistance.   Instrumented impact tests have been used by Suaris and Shah (1983), Gopalaratnam and Shah (1986), and Banthia et al. (1987) to study the impact behavior of FRC. Plain matrices have been observed to be rate-sensitive. Increases in dynamic strengths (strain rate of approximately 1/sec) of 40 to 60% over static flexural strengths have been reported. FRC is more rate-sensitive than the plain matrix, showing improvements in flexural strength of 79, 99, and 111% over the respective static flexural strengths for 0.5, 1.0, and 1.5% (fiber volume

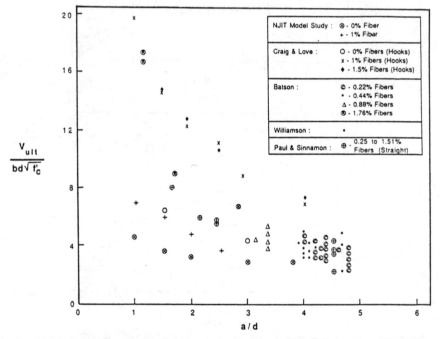

Fig. 4.9   Shear behavior of reinforced fibrous concrete beams. (*From ACI Committee 544, 1973.*)

content) composites (aspect ratio of 62.5) when the rate of straining was increased from 1×10^{-6} to 0.3/sec (Fig. 4.11). In addition to improved strengths at the higher rates of loading, the deflection at ultimate load at these rates was consistently higher than the corresponding values at static loading. Up to 50% increases in these deflection values were recorded for the various plain and reinforced composites tested. Energy absorption of FRC (generally a couple of orders of magnitude larger than that of the unreinforced composites) up to a fixed deflection value of 3 mm (0.1 in.) at dynamic rates of loading increased by 70 to 80% over the corresponding static values. For the same aspect ratio of fibers used, composites made with higher fiber contents showed greater rate sensitivity, perhaps due to the characteristics of cracking in these composites and the rate sensitivity associated with such a process. Also, low-strength matrices exhibited more rate sensitivity than high-strength matrices, again perhaps due to the changes in the cracking mechanisms in these two types of mixes.

Bond characteristics.   The behavior of the fiber-matrix interface plays a very important role in the failure of short-fiber FRC (Wei et al., 1986). The fiber-matrix bond in typical fiber-matrix systems presently in use is largely mechanical in nature (adhesion, friction, bearing, or combinations of these mechanisms). In most fiber-matrix interfaces, the adhesion capacity is much smaller than the frictional and bearing capacities. While bearing plays a dominant role in hooked, deformed, and fibrillated fibers, the mechanics of stress transfer are complex and difficult to analyze. Often equivalent bond strength based on uniform frictional stress transfer is computed and reported in such cases. Frictional pullout of smooth fibers is much better understood and researched (Gopalaratnam and Abu-Mathkour, 1987; Naaman and Shah, 1976; Wei et al., 1986).

Studies of the effects of fiber orientation on pullout strength have been performed by Naaman and Shah (1976). From their studies conducted on the pullout of steel fibers from mortar matrix, they concluded that the peak pullout load for fibers in the loading direction is almost as high as that for fibers parallel to the loading direction (Fig. 4.12). However, the postpeak load-carrying capacity for a

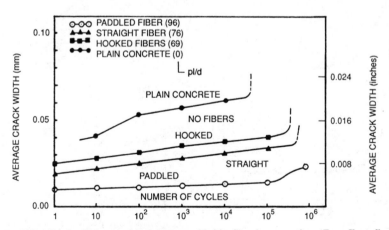

Fig. 4.10   Crack-width control in fatigue provided by fiber incorporation. (*From Kormeling et al., 1980.*)

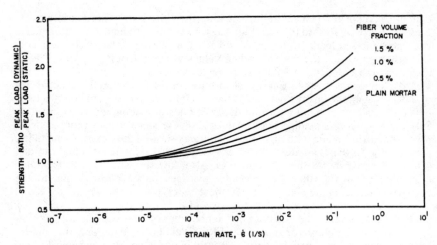

Fig. 4.11   Effect of strain rate on flexural strength of unreinforced and fiber-reinforced mortar specimens. (*From Gopalaratnam and Shah, 1985b.*)

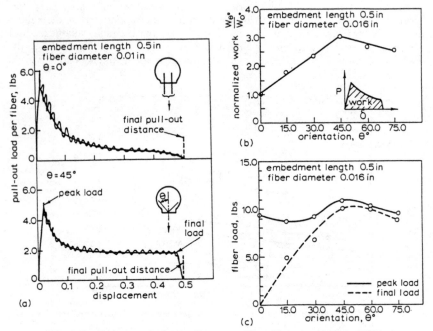

Fig. 4.12   Typical results from pullout tests. (*From Naaman and Shah, 1976.*)

fiber inclined to the loading direction, as observed by them, is higher than that for a parallel fiber. The highest value was observed for a 45° orientation. As a result, the work required to pull out completely is higher for the inclined fibers.

In slip-controlled pullout tests, Gopalaratnam and Abu-Mathkour (1987) minimized the adverse effects of some of the gripping forces by using an annular cylindrical specimen which allows the simultaneous pullout of 18 fibers embedded in a mortar matrix. From their tests, they reported that the average interfacial bond strength decreases as the fiber embedment length increases, while it increases as the fiber diameter increases. The energy absorbed at any given fiber slip level increases as the fiber embedment length or diameter increases. As expected, they also noted that fibers with embedment lengths less than the critical embedment length pull out, while those with embedment lengths greater than the critical embedment length fracture before pulling out.

5 Analytical models

As discussed earlier, the mechanical behavior of tension-weak concrete matrices can be improved by the incorporation of fibers. Depending on the fiber geometry and type, a number of failure mechanisms can be achieved. In general, analytical models are formulated on the basis of one or more of these mechanisms of failure. The primary types of failure mechanisms in FRC composites were described in an earlier section.

Based in part of the fundamental approach in their formulation, analytical models can be categorized as models based on the theory of multiple fracture, composite models, and micromechanics models. Fairly exhaustive reviews of these models are available elsewhere (Gopalaratnam and Shah, 1987a; Mindess, 1983).

6 Applications

Fibrous concrete has a broad range of potential uses in both cast-in-place and precast applications where durability and crack control are major considerations. In tall buildings FRC can be used for exterior panels, shear walls, floors that carry vehicle traffic (parking levels in tall buildings), columns (minimize spalling, avoid congestion of reinforcement), beams (shear strength enhancement), foundations and footings (shear resistance and dynamic loads), and at beam-column joints (to provide ductility and avoid congestion of reinforcement). Precast fibrous concrete has been used in precast garages, where fibers reduce cracking and spalling damage during transportation and handling, and in precast pipes, where fibers increase the strength and cracking characteristics of the pipe.

7 Future research needs

Research is needed in the following areas to promote the knowledge base as well as to provide sound scientific bases for the use of FRC.

1. Measurement of toughness and its relation to fracture, fatigue, and impact resistance of FRC

2. Bond characteristics of the fiber-matrix interface for different fiber-matrix systems

3. Shrinkage characteristics of fresh and hardened FRC
4. Analytical models for the fracture and toughening mechanisms of FRC
5. Design procedures for specific applications (such as pavements, shear resistance in reinforced concrete beams, ductile hinges in reinforced concrete frames, tunnel linings, bridge-deck and pavement overlays, and partial depth patching).

4.3 HIGH-STRENGTH CONCRETE AND RELATED TOPICS

According to the American Concrete Institute Committee 363, concretes with design compressive strengths of 41 MPa (6000 psi) or greater can be characterized as high-strength concretes (ACI 363, 1984). In general, high-strength concrete contains a higher cement content, a low water-to-cement ratio, and stronger aggregates than lower-strength concretes. Water-reducing agents, pozzolans, and fly ash are also common admixtures.

1 Behavior

Concrete exhibits a complex response to loading. Nonlinear stress-strain relationship, strain softening, and stiffness degradation are some of its characteristics. A key to understanding this behavior is the study of the interaction between the two phases of the material, the aggregate and the mortar. A critical role in this interaction is played by the internal microcracks, which are initially bond cracks between aggregates and mortar, and which grow and propagate with increasing stress. Experimental research has revealed that for high-strength concrete, the amount of bond microcracks is less due to a better compatibility of the strength and the elastic properties of mortar and coarse aggregate and to a higher tensile bond strength (Carrasquillo et al., 1981a, 1981b). Also, the sustained load strength of high-strength concrete is higher, and the stress-creep relationship is linear to a higher percentage of the compressive strength than that of normal-strength concrete (Ngab et al., 1981a, 1981b; Schmidt and Hoffman, 1975).

2 Uses of high-strength concrete

The major reason for using high-strength concrete is that it will carry a compression load at less cost. It is recommended primarily for columns and shear walls. For slabs, higher-strength concrete will result in reducing the thickness and increasing the amount of steel reinforcement, which will probably offset concrete savings. Other applications include precast and prestressed elements, where increased concrete strength is a most desirable feature. Also less creep, which is associated with higher strengths, may reduce the losses due to prestressing.

Current ultimate-strength design methods as they are reflected in the American Concrete Institute code ACI 318, as well as in other codes, are based on experimental information from concretes of compressive strengths ranging from 21 to 41 MPa (3000 to 6000 psi). Although higher-strength concrete elements can be designed using the same provisions as those used for normal-strength concrete, some of the requirements of the code may have to be revised (Nawy and Balaguru, 1983; Ahmad and Shah, 1985).

The primary goal of present research is to understand the behavior of high-strength concrete, to establish its engineering properties (elastic modulus, tensile strength, Poisson's ratio, creep coefficient, and the like), and to study the behavior of reinforced and prestressed structures made of high-strength concrete. Some of the conclusions reached so far are briefly mentioned in the following subsections.

3   Stress-strain relations

Uniaxial compressive stress.   The response of high-strength concrete to compressive stress is quite different from the response of normal-strength concrete (Ahmad and Shah, 1985; Nilson, 1985). The initial slope of the σ versus ε curve is steeper, the ascending part of the curve is more linear and steeper, and the strain at maximum stress is slightly higher. However, the slope of the descending part is steeper, and therefore the useful strain limit is lower. Typical stress-strain curves of high-strength concrete are shown in Fig. 4.13 together with a typical low-strength-concrete curve for comparison.

Various analytical models have been developed, and mathematical formulas have been proposed to express the stress-strain curves of concrete. Some of them are summarized in the following.

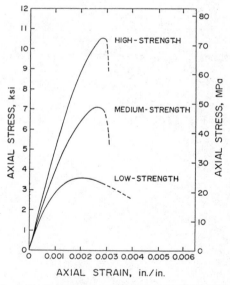

Fig. 4.13   Typical stress-strain curves of plain concrete.

1. Fractional equation:

$$f = f'_c \frac{A(\varepsilon/\varepsilon_0) + (B - 1)(\varepsilon/\varepsilon_0)^2}{1 + (A - 2)(\varepsilon/\varepsilon_0) + B(\varepsilon/\varepsilon_0)^2} \qquad (4.1)$$

where

$$A = E_c \frac{\varepsilon_0}{f'_c} \qquad (4.2)$$

$$E_c = 27.55 w^{1.5} \sqrt{f'_c} \qquad (4.3)$$

$$B = 0.88087 - 0.57 \times 10^{-4} f'_c \qquad (4.4)$$

$$\varepsilon_0 = 0.001648 + 1.14 \times 10^{-7} f'_c \qquad (4.5)$$

and in which w is the unit weight of concrete in pcf and f'_c is the 28-day cylinder strength in psi. The constants were obtained from experimental data for concrete from f'_c = 21 MPa (3000 psi) to f'_c = 76 MPa (11,000 psi) (Ahmad and Shah, 1985).

2. Exponential equation:

$$f = f'_c \left[1 - \left(1 - \frac{\varepsilon}{\varepsilon_0} \right)^A \right], \qquad \text{ascending part, } \varepsilon < \varepsilon_0 \qquad (4.6)$$

$$f = f'_c \exp[- k(\varepsilon - \varepsilon_0)^{1.15}], \qquad \text{descending part, } \varepsilon \geq \varepsilon_0$$

$$(4.7)$$

where

$$k = 0.17 f'_c \qquad (4.8)$$

in which A and E_c are given by Eqs. 4.2 and 4.3 and f'_c is in psi. The strain ε_0 is the strain at peak stress (Fafitis and Shah, 1982; Shah et al., 1983). The experimental data for Eqs. 4.5 and 4.6 ranged from 21 to 76 MPa (3000 to 11,000 psi).

3. CEB formula (CEB-FIP, 1978, Gopalaratnam and Shah, 1985a):

$$f = f'_c \frac{k\eta - \eta^2}{1 + (k - 2)\eta} \qquad (4.9)$$

in which

$$\eta = \frac{\varepsilon}{\varepsilon_{c_1}} \qquad (4.10)$$

$$\varepsilon_{c_1} = 0.0022 \qquad (4.11)$$

$$k = 1.1 \frac{E_c \varepsilon_{c_1}}{f'_c} \qquad (4.12)$$

Plottings of these stress-strain relations (Eqs. 4.1, 4.6, 4.7, and 4.9) are shown in Fig. 4.14.

The ACI code allows the approximation of the actual stress-strain curve by a rectangular stress block of depth equal to $a = \beta_1 c$, where c is the depth to the neutral axis and β_1 is a constant which, for $f'_c > 8000$ psi, is equal to 0.65 (ACI 318, 1989). Experimental data, however, indicate a higher value of β_1. In Swartz et al. (1985) this value was found to be equal to about 0.8, and the ultimate compressive strain recommended was 0.0025 instead of the 0.003 value accepted by the ACI code.

Uniaxial tensile stress. The uniaxial tensile strength is determined either directly by uniaxial tensile test or indirectly by split cylinder test or beam test in flexure (modulus of rupture test). The complete stress-strain curve of concrete in tension is difficult to obtain, and as a result there are only limited data available. From some recent experimental data it appears that a good approximation to uniaxial strength is given by the expression $6.5\sqrt{f'_c}$, where f'_c is the compressive strength psi (Gopalaratnam and Shah, 1985a). The tensile splitting strength f'_{sp} does not vary much with increasing compressive strength. The expression recommended for splitting strength is (ACI 363, 1984):

$$f'_{sp} = 7.4\sqrt{f'_c} \qquad (4.13)$$

and the modulus of rupture is given by

$$f_r = 11.7\sqrt{f'_c} \qquad (4.14)$$

where f'_c is in psi. Figure 4.15 shows the experimental data on which these expressions are based.

Two other expressions proposed in Ahmad and Shah (1985) are

$$f'_{sp} = 4.34 f'^{0.55}_c \qquad (4.15)$$

$$f_r = 2.3 f'^{2.3}_c \qquad (4.16)$$

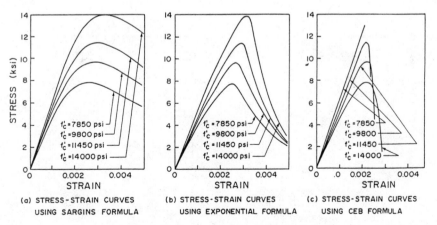

(a) STRESS-STRAIN CURVES USING SARGINS FORMULA

(b) STRESS-STRAIN CURVES USING EXPONENTIAL FORMULA

(c) STRESS-STRAIN CURVES USING CEB FORMULA

Fig. 4.14 Stress-strain curves of various models for plain concrete.

where f'_c is in psi. A comparison of the predictions of expressions 4.15 and 4.16 with experimental data is shown in Fig. 4.16, together with the curves of Eqs. 4.13 and 4.14.

Elastic modulus and Poisson's ratio. Based on a large number of experimental data it was found that the ACI code formula

$$E_c = 33w^{1.5}\sqrt{f'_c} \qquad (4.17)$$

overestimates the modulus of elasticity of concrete for strengths greater than about 34 to 41 MPa (5000 to 6000 psi). The following formula gives a better value for the modulus of elasticity of high-strength concrete (Carrasquillo et al., 1981a; Nilson, 1985):

$$E_c = (40{,}000\sqrt{f'_c} + 10^6)\left(\frac{w_c}{145}\right)^{1.5} \text{psi} \qquad (4.18)$$

In both Eqs. 4.17 and 4.18, w is the weight of the concrete in pcf and f'_c is the compressive strength in psi. A comparison of Eqs. 4.17 and 4.18 with experimental data is given in Fig. 4.17.

There are very limited data available on values of Poisson's ratio for high-strength concrete. However, it appears that within the elastic range, the values are comparable to those of lower-strength concrete (for example, about 0.2).

Behavior under multiaxial stress. There is an increase in the strength, stiffness, and proportional limit of concrete under biaxial compression (Chen et al., 1985). This is due to the confinement of internal microcracking. However, the experimental data on high-strength concrete are very limited, and no conclusion on the effect of multiaxial stress on the behavior of high-strength concrete can yet be drawn.

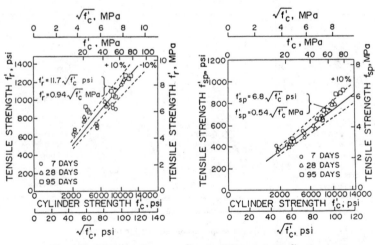

Fig. 4.15   Modulus of rupture f'_r and splitting strength f'_{sp} of concrete.

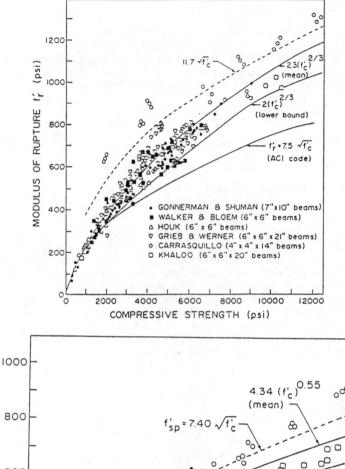

Fig. 4.16　Comparison of experimental and analytical values for splitting strength and modulus of rupture.

4 Shrinkage and creep

There is not much information available on the shrinkage behavior of high-strength concrete. From studies it appears that the shrinkage of high-strength concrete may be greater than that for normal-strength concrete, but not significantly. Creep is given by the creep coefficient and the specific creep. The creep coefficient C_c is defined as the ratio of creep strain to initial elastic strain,

$$C_c = \frac{\text{creep strain}}{\text{initial elastic strain}} \tag{4.19}$$

and the specific creep is the creep per unit stress,

$$\delta_c = \text{creep strain per unit stress} \tag{4.20}$$

They are related through the elastic modulus,

$$C_c = E_c \delta_c \tag{4.21}$$

The creep coefficient and the specific creep are smaller for concretes with higher compressive strength (ACI 318, 1989; Ngab et al., 1981a). It is believed that this is due primarily to the amount of water, which is less in high-strength concrete. Under drying conditions, the specific creep of high-strength concrete is 20 to 25% that of normal-strength concrete. Under nondrying conditions, it is 30 to 35%. The creep coefficient under drying conditions is 50 to 75% that of normal-strength concrete, and under nondrying conditions, it is 75 to 90%. The relationship of creep coefficient C_c and time is shown in Fig. 4.18.

The ratio of the sustained load strength to the short-term strength is higher in high-strength than in normal-strength concrete. For high-strength concrete, this

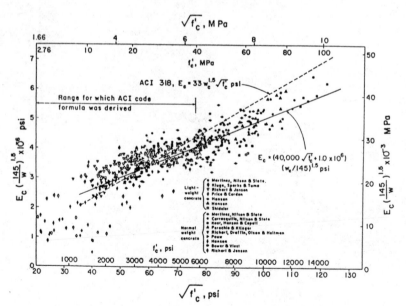

Fig. 4.17 Variation of elastic modulus with compressive strength.

ratio is about 0.85 to 0.95, whereas in normal-strength concrete it is about 0.70 and 0.75 (Ngab et al., 1981a).

Although high-strength concrete exhibits lower creep than normal-strength concrete, the stresses in high-strength concrete are higher, and therefore the total creep deformations are approximately the same (ACI 363, 1984).

5 Columns with high-strength concrete

Axially loaded columns. The axial strength of reinforced concrete columns according to ACI code 318-89 (ACI, 1989) is

$$P = 0.85f'_c A_c + f_y A_s \qquad (4.22)$$

in which f'_c is the concrete compressive strength of the cylinder, f_y is the yield strength of steel, and A_c and A_s are the areas of concrete and steel, respectively. The factor 0.85 accounts for observed differences in the strength of the concrete in columns compared with the strength of cylindrical specimens of the same mix. The same factor can be used for high-strength concrete (ACI 363, 1984; Martinez et al., 1982).

Steel confinement. To assure adequate ductility of reinforced concrete columns the ACI code requires lateral reinforcement (ACI 318, 1989). For circular columns the volume of spirals per unit volume of confined core is

$$\rho_s \geq 0.45\left(\frac{A_g}{A_c} - 1\right)\frac{f'_c}{f_y} \qquad (4.23)$$

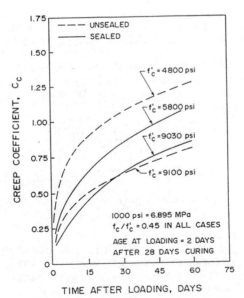

Fig. 4.18 Variation of creep coefficient with time.

and for square columns to be considered as confined,

$$A_{sh} \geq 0.3 s h_c \frac{f_c'}{f_y}\left(\frac{A_g}{A_c} - 1\right) \tag{4.24}$$

$$A_{sh} \geq 0.09 s h_c \frac{f_c'}{f_y} \tag{4.25}$$

where A_g and A_c are the gross and confined concrete areas, respectively, f_c' is the cylinder compressive strength of concrete, f_y is the yield strength of steel, A_{sh} is the cross-sectional area of ties including cross ties, s is the spacing of the ties, and h_c is the cross-sectional dimension of the column core measured center to center of the confining reinforcement.

The basic philosophy of the ACI code is that the increase in strength of the core due to confinement must be sufficient to offset the loss due to spalling of the unconfined cover, and also that the column must be able to sustain large deformations without loss of its load-carrying capacity.

The increase in strength of the core is calculated assuming that the lateral steel has yielded. Then the lateral pressure (or confinement index) provided by the hoop tension (in the case of circular columns) is

$$f_2' = \frac{2A_{sp}f_y}{d_c s} \tag{4.26}$$

in which A_{sp} is the area of the spiral steel, d_c is the diameter of the concrete core, and s is the pitch of the spiral. The confined concrete strength $\bar{f}_c'$ is given by the empirical equation

$$\bar{f}_c' = f_c'' + 4f_2' \tag{4.27}$$

in which $\bar{f}_c'$ is the strength of the confined column, f_c'' is the strength of the unconfined column, and f_2' is the confining pressure given by Eq. 4.26 (ACI 363, 1984).

Experiments have shown that spiral reinforcement is less effective in high-strength concrete and also that the lateral steel may not have yielded at peak load (Ahmad and Shah, 1982; Martinez et al., 1982). An improved version of Eq. 4.27 is (Martinez et al., 1982)

$$\bar{f}_c' = f_c'' + 4f_2'\left(1 - \frac{s}{d_c}\right) \tag{4.28}$$

for normal-weight concrete and

$$\bar{f}_c' = f_c'' + 1.8f_2'\left(1 - \frac{s}{d_c}\right) \tag{4.29}$$

for lightweight concrete.

In Eqs. 4.27 through 4.29 the strength enhancement due to confinement is assumed independent of the concrete strength. However, experimental data indicate that the strength enhancement depends also on the concrete strength. Based on experiments on small cylindrical specimens of concrete from about 28 to 65.5 MPa ($\approx$ 4000 to 9500 psi), an empirical expression was derived:

$$\bar{f}'_c = f''_c + \left(1.15 + \frac{3048}{f''_c}\right)f'_2 \qquad (4.30)$$

The strain ε_0 corresponding to the peak stress $\bar{f}'_c$ is

$$\varepsilon_0 = 1.027 \times 10^{-7}f''_c + 0.0296\frac{f'_2}{f''_c} + 0.00195 \qquad (4.31)$$

The stress in Eqs. 4.30 and 4.31 is in psi.

For circular columns the confinement index f'_2 is calculated using Eq. 4.26. For square columns, however, the confining mechanism is not clear. Based on experimental data (Sheikh and Uzumeri, 1980) with square columns of various tie and longitudinal steel configurations, it was found (Fatitis and Shah, 1985a, 1985b) that if the section is well designed, namely, if there are longitudinal bars at the four corners and the intermediate bars are supported laterally by ties (Fig. 4.19), the confinement index can be estimated by the formula

$$f'_2 = \frac{A_{sh}f_y}{sd_e} \qquad (4.32)$$

in which d_e is the equivalent diameter of the square section and is equal to the side of the square core that is the section within the external stirrup (or tie). A_{sh} is the area of ties (including cross ties) as defined in Eqs. 4.24 and 4.25.

Based on available evidence, one may conclude that the level of confinement stress corresponding to spirals designed by ACI code 363 (1984) (given by Eq. 4.23) is rather low and becoming significantly lower for larger-diameter columns.

There is very little information about lightweight concrete columns with ties or spirals. Therefore the design of such columns should receive special consideration.

Columns with axial load and bending moment. The concept of a rectangular stress block with average stress equal to $0.85f'_c$ and depth $a = \beta_1c$, where c is the depth to the neutral axis, has been based on experimental results on concrete of rather low strength. Experimental research has confirmed that alternatives to the rectangular stress block may be necessary when high-strength concrete is used. A more accurate modeling of the stress distribution in the compressive zone of columns may be important. A comparison of the interaction diagrams using the rect-

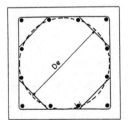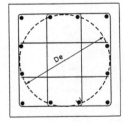

EQUIVALENT DIAMETER

Fig. 4.19 Equivalent-diameter concept for square concrete columns.

angular stress block as recommended by the ACI code (1984) and a trapezoidal stress block is shown in Fig. 4.20. From this figure it seems that the difference is probably not large enough to justify more exact calculations. This seems to be true for compressive strains not higher than 0.003. For higher strains, a recent study revealed that there may be considerable differences between the ultimate moment predicted by the rectangular stress block and more accurate stress-strain relations (Fafitis and Shah, 1985a, 1985b). The internal force distribution of a circular column subjected to an external force equal to 80% of its axial capacity is shown in Fig. 4.21 for maximum compressive strains equal to 0.004, 0.035, and 0.05. The concrete inside the external ties is treated as confined, whereas the cover concrete is modeled as unconfined. The contributions of the longitudinal steel, the confined concrete, and the unconfined concrete are given in the Tables of Fig. 4.21. Figure 4.22 shows the predicted moment capacity of the same column (subjected to a constant axial load P_u) when it is subjected to deformations up to 0.05. It is seen that for maximum strain (at the top fiber) equal to about 0.003, the prediction of the ACI code is conservative. However, when the column is subjected to larger deformations (as during a severe earthquake), the capacity may be much smaller than the ACI prediction. Similar behavior was obtained for higher concrete strengths and also for square columns (Fafitis, 1984). From Fig. 4.22 it is apparent that the contribution of the confined core concrete is the major one. Therefore confinement improves the capacity and the ductility of compressive structural elements. It seems, however, that confinement in high-strength concrete is not as effective as in normal-strength concrete (Nilson, 1985).

6 Shear

The present design methods for shear as they are reflected in the ACI code were developed for concretes up to about 41 MPa (6000 psi). Experimental investiga-

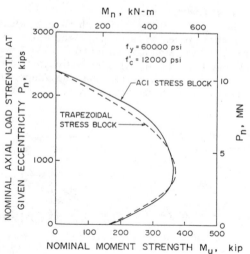

Fig. 4.20   Comparison of interaction diagrams for column using rectangular and trapezoidal stress blocks.

tions indicate that there is a need to develop improved design procedures for high-strength concrete.

The shear strength of beams without stirrups is given according to ACI code 318 (1989) by the following two equations:

$$V_c = 2\sqrt{f_2'}b_w d \qquad (4.33)$$

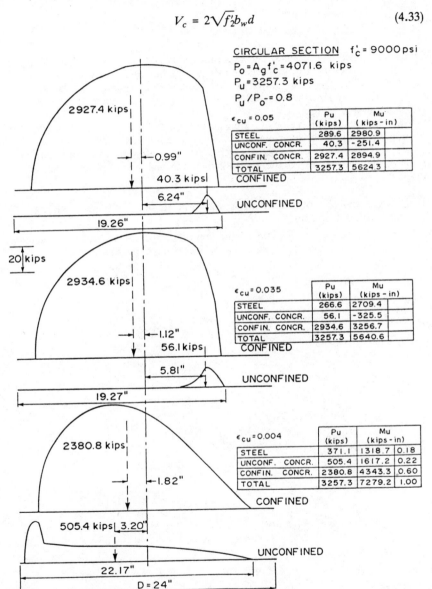

Fig. 4.21 Internal force distribution of circular column subjected to constant axial load and flexural deformation.

$$V_c = \left(1.9\sqrt{f'_c} + 2500\rho_w\frac{V_u d}{M_u}\right)b_w d \qquad (4.34)$$

where b_w = web width

d = effective depth

ρ_w = steel ratio based on web width

The shear strength obtained by experiments is not always smaller than the strength predicted by Eq. 4.34, as shown in Fig. 4.23. Therefore Eq. 4.34 is not always conservative. The effect of longitudinal reinforcement ρ_w is not adequately accounted for in the ACI code (Eq. 4.33), as indicated in Fig. 4.24 (Elzanaty et al., 1986).

Several equations have been proposed to replace Eqs. 4.33 and 4.34 and also to predict the ultimate shear capacity of beams reinforced with stirrups and longitudinal steel. However, more research is needed before a design procedure for shear is developed. From the existing data the following conclusions can be drawn:

1. The ACI code is not always conservative in predicting the shear strength of beams without stirrups.

2. The ACI code may underestimate the importance of longitudinal reinforcement ρ_w and the shear span ratio a/d and may overestimate the importance of f'_c.

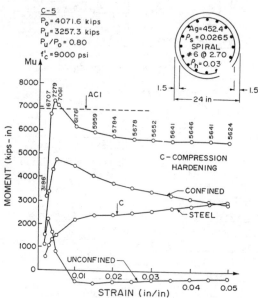

Fig. 4.22   Moment capacity of circular column subjected to constant axial load and flexural deformation.

3. For beams with stirrups, the shear strength increases with the increase of concrete strength.

7 Beams and slabs

Flexural analysis of beams (except for deep beams) and slabs is based on the assumption that plane sections remain plane and that at ultimate moment, the

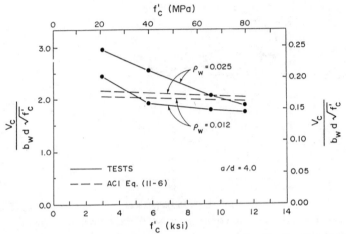

Fig. 4.23 Comparison of shear resistance of concrete predicted by Eq. 11-6 of ACI 318 with experimental data.

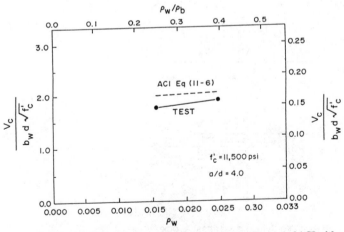

Fig. 4.24 Comparison of shear strength of concrete predicted by Eq. 11-6 of ACI with experimental data for various longitudinal steel ratios.

maximum compressive strain is equal to 0.003. From experimental data (Fig. 4.25) it appears that this limiting strain is satisfactory for high-strength concrete (ACI 363, 1984).

The ultimate moment of singly reinforced sections is based on the stress block concept. The nonlinear stress distribution in the compressive zone of a section is replaced by an equivalent rectangular stress block, as shown in Fig. 4.26. The

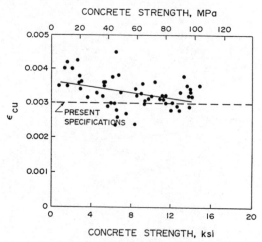

Fig. 4.25 Comparison of ACI 363 ultimate strain ($\varepsilon_{cu} = 0.003$) with experimental values.

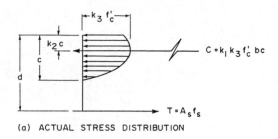

(a) ACTUAL STRESS DISTRIBUTION

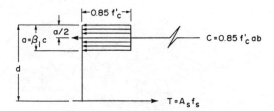

(b) EQUIVALENT STRESS BLOCK

Fig. 4.26 Equivalent stress block concept.

depth of the stress block is taken as $a = \beta_1 c$, where c is the depth to the neutral axis and β_1 is an empirical coefficient that varies with the concrete strength. It does not become less than 0.65 or greater than 0.85 (ACI 318, 1989). The other parameters in Fig. 4.26 (k_1, k_2, and k_3) depend on the concrete strength as well. It can be shown that the nominal flexural strength of a single underreinforced beam is

$$M_n = A_s f_y d \left(1 - \frac{k_2}{k_1 k_3} \rho \frac{f_y}{f_c'} \right)$$

(4.35)

in which A_s is the steel area, f_y is the yield stress of the steel, d is the effective depth, $\rho = A_s/bd$, and f_c' is the compressive strength of the concrete (ACI, 1984). Experimental data indicate that the quantity $k_2/k_1 k_3$ is not sensitive to the compressive strength of concrete and has a value approximately equal to 0.59, as shown in Fig. 4.27 (ACI, 1984; Leslie et al., 1976).

The ACI code requires a minimum amount of longitudinal steel

$$\rho_{min} = \frac{200}{f_y}$$

(4.36)

The purpose of this minimum is to ensure that a very lightly reinforced beam will not fail suddenly upon flexural cracking, when the tension carried by the concrete prior to cracking is transferred to the steel after cracking. For a concrete strength above about 35 MPa (5000 psi), Eq. 4.36 is not conservative. An alternative formula was proposed as follows (ACI 363, 1984; Nilson, 1985):

$$\rho_{min} = \frac{2.7\sqrt{f_c'}}{f_y}$$

(4.37)

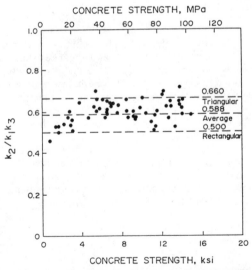

Fig. 4.27 **Effect of concrete strength in predicted nominal moment capacity of singly underinforced beams.**

With respect to short-term deflections, it was found experimentally (Nilson, 1985) that the ACI code effective moment-of-inertia formula

$$I_e = \left(\frac{M_{cr}}{M_a}\right)I_g + \left[1 - \left(\frac{M_{cr}}{M_a}\right)^3\right]I_{cr} \tag{4.38}$$

in which M_{cr} and M_a are the cracking and maximum moments, respectively, and I_g and I_{cr} are the gross and cracked-section moments of inertia, respectively, gives good results for lower- and higher-strength concrete provided that the elastic modulus of the concrete is estimated correctly.

8 Applications of high-strength concrete to tall buildings

High-strength concrete has found numerous applications in structural engineering (such as bridges, offshore platforms, and pavements). Some of its main characteristics make high-strength concrete an ideal material for tall buildings. The higher compressive strength permits a considerable reduction in column size and an increase in the rentable area per floor. The higher elastic modulus reduces the elastic deformations and the drift of buildings with shear walls of high-strength concrete.

Due to higher early strength, the forms can be removed and reused faster; and the construction time, which is often critical in high-rise buildings, can be reduced. Other factors that may contribute to a better performance of tall buildings of high-strength concrete include a somewhat lower creep deformation, higher durability, and smaller prestressing losses due to reduced creep and lower elastic shortening. These advantages are realized at minimal increase in the concrete cost.

9 Further research

The relatively smooth planes of failure of high-strength concrete result in a considerable reduction of the aggregate interlock and shear resistance. The most urgent area of research is perhaps the study of the shear characteristics of high-strength concrete. Bond and development length are also areas for further research. The brittle failure of high-strength concrete and methods to improve its performance (such as by confinement) need additional study.

The interface of columns with beams and slabs (which are usually made of lower-strength concrete) is also an area that needs to be investigated, and some rules for the detailing of such connections need to be established.

Other areas for future research may include the nonlinear behavior of structures with high-strength concrete and their postbuckling capacity. The response of tall buildings of high-strength concrete to cyclic loadings (wind, earthquakes) is an interesting and important research area.

10 Summary

While lateral steel provides ductility to structural elements, lateral reinforcement may not be as effective in high-strength concrete as in lower-strength concrete.

Columns of high-strength concrete may exhibit a sharp drop-off of load after peak, which may need special consideration.

The long-term deflection, as calculated for lower-strength concrete, does not reflect the lower creep coefficient of high-strength concrete nor the reduced efficiency of compression reinforcement. In columns, the capacity as calculated based on a rectangular stress block and an ultimate strain of 0.003 may not be conservative for the larger deformations occurring during an earthquake.

The available experimental data indicate that the shear design procedure recommended by the ACI code for lower-strength concretes needs to be modified to include higher-strength concretes. Additional information is needed in areas such as diagonal tension, torsion, bond, development length, and the effects of repeated loading (ACI 363, 1984).

4.4 ADDITIVES

1 Admixtures

Admixtures are defined as any material, which is not cement, water, aggregates, or reinforcement, that is added to the concrete during, or immediately after, batching and mixing. Such materials are added for a variety of specific purposes, but can be assigned to one of several general categories. Admixtures may be used to improve the properties of fresh concrete so that it is better suited for placement, consolidation, finishing, and such; they may be used to improve the properties of hardened concrete, such as freeze-thaw durability and increased compressive strength; they may be used to make more economical concrete; or they may be used for any combination of these purposes.

Admixtures are assigned to one of two general classifications, chemical or water-soluble admixtures, and mineral or solid admixtures. ASTM standard specifications cover most admixtures that are in common use. For further information about the admixtures described in this section, the reader is referred to the technical reports issued by the relevant technical committees of the American Concrete Institute (ACI).

2 Chemical admixtures

Included under chemical admixtures are air-entraining agents, set-modifying admixtures, and water-reducing agents. Air-entraining agents are used to provide protection against frost damage and should be used whenever concrete is going to be exposed to freezing and thawing in the presence of moisture. Air-entraining agents are detergent-type materials, which form a system of very fine air bubbles within the cement paste. This air void system relieves internal stress, which can occur during freezing.

Set-modifying agents are used to either increase or decrease the rate of setting and early hardening. Although calcium chloride was the most commonly used set accelerator, it has been implicated in the corrosion of reinforcing steel. Thus its use should be avoided in reinforced concrete and particularly in prestressed or posttensioned concrete. Nonchloride accelerators are available. Accelerators are particularly useful in offsetting the detrimental effects of low ambient temperatures on the rate of early strength gain, but may also be used to speed up the removal of formwork and allow earlier imposition of construction loads. However, accelerators will not increase the long-term strength of concrete and may even slightly reduce it. Also, concrete containing an accelerating admixture may show somewhat higher drying shrinkage and creep.

Set retarders are mostly organic materials that act to inhibit the normal sequences of early hydration, so that the time during which the concrete remains in the plastic state is extended. Consequently set retarders are used to offset the effects of high ambient temperatures and to extend the useful working time of concrete during long transit times or difficult placements. Set retarders can also be used to eliminate cold joints between adjacent lifts.

Water-reducing admixtures are surface active agents which adsorb onto the surfaces of the cement grains and thereby prevent them from sticking together. This has the effect of reducing the amount of water that is needed to achieve a desired slump. In this way the workability of the concrete can be improved without the addition of extra water, which would lower the compressive strength of the concrete and its quality in general. Water-reducing agents may also act to entrain air and retard setting, and thus their rates of addition must be limited. High-range water-reducing agents, commonly known as superplasticizers, can be used at higher dosage rates and therefore provide a greater reduction in water content without undesirable side effects. Superplasticizers can be used to make "flowing" concretes [slumps > 152 mm (6 in.)], which can be placed without vibration and without danger of excessive segregation or bleeding. Water-reducing agents, superplasticizers in particular, are needed to provide high-strength concrete with compressive strengths in excess of 69 MPa (10,000 psi).

3 Mineral admixtures

Mineral admixtures are finely divided solids that take part in the cementitious reactions that underlay the hardening of concrete. They can thus be used to replace part of the cement and are sometimes referred to as supplementary cementing materials. The most common materials used are fly ash, (condensed) silica fume, and granulated blast furnace slag.

Fly ash is the inorganic residue left over from burning powdered coal. It consists of particles of cement fineness composed of an aluminosilicate glass in which are embedded crystalline phases such as quartz and hematite. The glass is pozzolanic, which means that it will react with the calcium hydroxide which is formed during hydration of the cement. Additional cementing products are thus produced. Fly ash will improve the workability of fresh concrete without increasing the heat or chemical durability and permeability of hardened concrete. The composition of fly ash depends on its origin. Type F is formed from bituminous coals east of the Mississippi River and is low in calcium. Type C is formed from lignitic western coals and is high in calcium. Some type C fly ashes are not suitable for use in concrete, since they contain significant quantities of uncombined lime and sulfate-bearing phases.

Silica fume is a by-product from the manufacture of silicon and ferrosilicon. It is extremely fine material (100 times finer than fly ash) and has a higher content of reactive amorphous silica. As such it is a very reactive pozzolan and reacts much more rapidly than fly ash, but its reaction chemistry is similar. As a result it can be used for the same purposes at a lower replacement level. This partially offsets the much higher cost of silica fume.

Granulated blast furnace slag is a calcium aluminosilicate glass formed by quenching molten slag in water. The slag is ground to cement fineness. When activated by alkalis, the slag will react with water to develop strength, and its hydration chemistry is similar to the hydration of portland cement. Slag can be activated by portland cement. Slag-cement blends of up to 70% slag will provide good strength development with low heat of hydration to provide a concrete with good chemical durability and low permeability. Thus slag and fly ash provide similar benefits.

4.5 CREEP AND SHRINKAGE

Deformations caused by creep and shrinkage occur in all buildings, but present unique problems for tall buildings. Differential shortening between adjacent columns caused by creep and shrinkage may be very small between two floors, but the sum of all the axial deformations for a line of columns can cause a column height difference of several inches in the upper floors of a building. The differential height between adjacent columns can cause structural as well as nonstructural problems. Long-term slab deflections must also be addressed when designing tall buildings. The objectives of this section are to present the basic principles and variables influencing creep and shrinkage, to discuss the influences of creep and shrinkage on building design, and to describe the preventive measures that can be taken to reduce or design for creep and shrinkage.

1 Properties of creep and shrinkage

Creep and shrinkage are caused by significantly different mechanisms. Shrinkage is caused by a reduction in the moisture content in either fresh or hardened concrete, or it is caused by temperature changes. Creep is induced by section stresses.

Shrinkage that is caused by moisture loss is unique to concrete when compared to steel. Shrinkage that occurs in fresh concrete is called *plastic shrinkage,* while *drying shrinkage* occurs in hardened concrete. Plastic shrinkage occurs when the rate of water evaporation exceeds the rate at which bleed water is reaching the surface of the concrete. Plastic shrinkage cracking is most common on horizontal surfaces, where evaporation can occur rapidly. Plastic shrinkage can be controlled by restricting the rate of evaporation. This can be accomplished by keeping the concrete surface moist until the surface is finished and curing has begun.

Drying shrinkage is much more critical to buildings. Many variables affect the rate and magnitude of drying shrinkage. They include the cement characteristics, water-cement ratio, rate of hydration, curing conditions, admixtures, moisture content, aggregate, reinforcement, volume-to-surface ratio, thickness, and humidity. Since there are many variables influencing drying shrinkage, it has been difficult to isolate the fundamental processes.

It has been found that there is an optimum gypsum content for each particular cement to minimize shrinkage. In addition, aggregate and reinforcement are significant restraints to shrinkage. A general rule is that the larger the volume of aggregates and reinforcement, the smaller the shrinkage. Concretes consisting of aggregates such as granite, dolomite, limestone, and rocks rich in quartz and feldspar with a high modulus of elasticity and virtually no shrinkage have lower amounts of shrinkage than concretes consisting of sandstone or slate. Another major variable is the specimen geometry, which can be evaluated by measuring the volume-to-surface ratio. The less volume a section has per amount of surface area, the greater is the area of evaporation and, therefore, the shrinkage. Admixtures can also affect shrinkage, but the effects vary depending on the composition of the admixture.

Two other types of shrinkage, which are considered special cases of drying shrinkage, are *carbonation* shrinkage and *autogenous* shrinkage. Carbonation shrinkage occurs when hydrating cement reacts with carbon dioxide in the air. It is believed that carbon dioxide reacts with calcium silicate hydrate (a hydration product) to effectively lower the relative humidity within the concrete. Autogenous shrinkage occurs in low water-cement-ratio concretes. Since there is very little free water, the concrete "dries out" through chemical processes. The end effect is a lower relative humidity for the concrete. Problems caused by autogenous shrinkage are fairly rare. They occur most frequently in mass concrete.

ACI Committee 209 (1982) has a set of empirical equations that predict the amount of shrinkage. The major variable is time, but there are correction factors for humidity, thickness of members, concrete slump, percentage of fines, air content, and cement content. The basic trend for each of the variables is as follows. As the humidity and element thickness decrease, the amount of shrinkage increases. As the percentage of fines, air content, cement content, and slump increases, the amount of shrinkage increases. The CEB-FIP (1978) also has recommendations for the prediction of shrinkage.

Shortening due to creep differs from shrinkage because creep is induced by stress on the member. The list of variables that affect creep is identical to the list for shrinkage, with the addition of the magnitude and duration of the load. When the load is applied to a member, there is instantaneous elastic shortening. From the time the load is applied, there is also long-term creep. When the load is removed, most of the elastic shortening, but only a portion of the long-term creep will be recovered. The difference between the initial elastic shortening and what is recovered is due to the increase in the modulus of elasticity of the concrete. ACI Committee 209 has developed an equation for the prediction of creep, which includes time under load, age when loaded, concrete strength, modulus of elasticity, relative humidity, section thickness, concrete slump, percentage of fines, and air content. The load history is very critical in predicting creep. Therefore the construction sequence and speed can greatly affect the total amount of creep.

2 Effects on buildings

The major effects of creep and shrinkage on tall buildings are shortening of columns and deflection of slabs. The differential shortening of columns can cause slab tilt between adjacent columns. Tilt in the slab can induce nonstructural problems with interior walls or exterior cladding. Slab movement will also induce moments in the slab. Since those movements occur over a long period of time, it has been estimated that 50% of the deflection-induced slab moment will "creep out" over time (Ghali et al. 1969). The type of slab system used influences the effects of the differential support deformation. If the building has a stiff slab system, the slab will transfer a portion of the column load from the shorter column to the taller column. This has the positive effect of decreasing the differential shortening. The reduction in load in the shorter column helps to decrease the amount of creep shortening, while the increase in load on the taller column increases the load-induced creep on that column. Buildings of less than 30 stories which have a flexible slab system (flat plate) typically will not be adversely affected by column movements (Fintel and Khan, 1971).

Thermal effects, unlike creep and drying shrinkage, occur year after year and will not diminish as the structure ages. Thermal effects typically create problems between exterior exposed columns and interior columns. The exterior columns are exposed directly to fluctuations in temperature, while the interior columns experience only small changes in temperature. Fintel and Khan (1971) observed in the 1960s that thermal effects became significant for buildings taller than 20 stories which had exposed exterior columns.

Vertical slab deflections caused by creep and shrinkage can become critical, especially in fast-track high-rise concrete buildings, buildings with long slab spans, and buildings with slender members. A finite-element analysis investigation, which included the effects of creep and shrinkage, was performed by El-Sheikh and Chen (1988). The authors compared deflections for a flat-plate–column system constructed at two rates: one floor every two days and one floor every seven days. They determined that, as long as concretes with high early strength (type III) and nominal strength above 48 MPa (7000 psi) were used, the fast-track construction would not increase the short- or long-term deflections. If normal-strength concrete $[f'_c = 34.5$ MPa (5000 psi)] was used in a fast-track construction process, they found that deflections would increase by as much as 50%. Slab deflections typically do not cause structural problems but reveal themselves in nonstructural problems, such as cracking in partitions, around windows, and around doors. Potential structural problems can occur on the roof due to ponding.

Horizontal deflections and cracking can also be caused by creep and shrinkage. Cracking occurs when a portion of the member is restrained from changing its length.

3 Solutions to problems

Some of the problems caused by creep and shrinkage can be mitigated during construction; others must be analyzed before construction. Many of the problems can be minimized through design details. In the case of cast-in-place construction, adjustment in the forms can be used to remove the column shortening that occurs in the structure during construction. An analysis must be used to determine the postcast column shortening. If columns are prefabricated, all adjustment must be planned in advance. Fintel and Khan (1971) developed a method for analyzing the differential shortening of columns. Their method was compared with field observations and found to have acceptable agreement. Bakoss et al. (1985) compared the results from a method developed by Warner (1975) for the estimation of column shortening and the method developed by Fintel and Khan with the measured column deflections of a 120-m (394-ft) building. Bakoss et al. found acceptable agreement for two out of the three floor levels that were investigated, and they did not find a substantial difference between the two methods. A field and analytical study was also conducted by Pfeifer et al. (1971). Their conclusion was that either their own method or that developed by Fintel and Khan could be utilized for estimating column deformations. It is possible to reduce the creep and shrinkage effects by proportioning members so that there is not a great difference in the nonelastic movements of adjacent columns. If columns are the same size, the lightly loaded columns should have a lower percentage of reinforcement or should be loaded at an earlier concrete age to equilibrate creep levels between heavily loaded and lightly loaded columns.

When movement cannot be avoided, precautions must be taken. Horizontal members must be strong enough to resist the additional loads caused by differential movement. Slabs can be cast with an initial tilt so that the slab will be level after the predicted column shortening has occurred. The decision of when the slab will be level is one of engineering judgment. Typically it is when the building is first occupied or within 5 years of first occupation. Partitions must be flexible or have compressible layers to prevent them from becoming load-bearing members. Mechanical systems must allow for movement.

The estimation of slab and beam deflections due to creep and shrinkage was investigated by Trost (1982). He found reasonable agreement with tests, most of his predictions being within 20% of the test results. Yu and Winter (1960) also established a method for estimating long-term deflection through the modification of elastic deflections.

Horizontal movement and cracking can be minimized by the use of proper detailing. Well-distributed reinforcement will keep cracks small. Another choice is the utilization of joints or control strips. Expansion joints allow for the free movement of the members on either side of the joint. Control joints are used to concentrate the cracking to one location. This is done by weakening the concrete section at a particular location. Control strips are constructed by casting strips of the slab several weeks after the main slab is cast. While the strip is open, the initial shrinkage can occur without inducing cracks and the concrete gains tensile strength. When the control strips are cast, continuity is established.

4 Research needs for creep and shrinkage

New materials and new concrete modifiers may have a significant effect on the magnitude of creep and shrinkage. Products such as high-strength concrete, superhigh-strength concrete, silica fume, slag cement, polymers, fibers (metallic and nonmetallic), high-range water reducers, and advanced composite materials need to be investigated to study their effects. It is not sufficient to look at each parameter individually, but their effects must be investigated when they are working together. Creep and shrinkage effects can be predicted using several methods. The accuracy of the present methods is usually sufficient for current building design. As buildings move into the ultrahigh-rise level, more accurate prediction procedures may be needed, along with new design procedures and details. One of the methods used for reducing the effects of creep and shrinkage for horizontal elements is the casting of control strips after adjacent portions have been cast. A rational approach to the spacing of these control strips, and the spacing of expansion and control joints, needs to be developed. Additional correlation studies are needed between what occurs in a building during construction and during its lifetime and the ability of models to predict these movements.

5 Conclusions

The problems caused by creep and shrinkage in tall buildings can be solved through the use of proper detailing and advance planning. Most of the problems involving creep and shrinkage are adequately addressed in the literature. Current analytical methods provide sufficient accuracy so that, when used in combination with proper detailing practices, they have eliminated or significantly reduced creep- and shrinkage-induced problems.

4.6 CONDENSED REFERENCES / BIBLIOGRAPHY

ACI Committee 209 1982, *Prediction of Creep, Shrinkage, and Temperature Effects in Con-*
ACI 318 1989, *Building Code Requirements for Reinforced Concrete and Commentary*
ACI 363 1984, *State-of-the-Art on High-Strength Concrete*
ACI Committee 544 1973, *State of the Art Report on Fiber Reinforced Concrete*
ACI Committee 544 1978, *Measurements of Properties of Fiber Reinforced Concrete*
ACI Committee 544 1988, *Measurements of Properties of Fiber Reinforced Concrete*
Ahmad 1982, *Stress-Strain Curves of Concrete Confined by Spiral Reinforcement*
Ahmad 1985, *Structural Properties of High Strength Concrete and Its Implications for Pre-*
Ahmad 1986, *Shear Capacity of Reinforced High-Strength Concrete Beams*
ASTM A82 1985, *Standard Specification for Steel Wire, Plain, for Concrete Reinforcement*
ASTM A496 1985, *Standard Specification for Steel Wire, Deformed, for Concrete Rein-*
ASTM A497 1986, *Standard Specification for Steel Welded Wire Fabric, Deformed, for*
ASTM A305 1964, *Standard Specs for the Minimum Requirements for the Deformation of*
ASTM A615 1967, *Standard Specification for Deformed and Plain Billet-Steel Bars for*
ASTM A616 1987, *Standard Specification for Rail-Steel Deformed and Plain Bars for Con-*
ASTM A617 1987, *Standard Specification for Axle-Steel Deformed and Plain Bars for Con-*
ASTM C1018 1984, *Standard Test Method for Flexural Toughness of Fiber Reinforced*
ASTM C1018 1989, *Standard Test Method for Flexural Toughness and First-Crack*

Bakoss 1985, *Measured and Predicted Long-Term Deformations in a Tall Building Deflect-*
Banthia 1987, *Steel Fiber Reinforced Concrete Under Impact*
Batson 1972, *Flexural Fatigue Strength of Steel Fiber Reinforced Concrete Beams*
Batson 1985, *Use of Steel Fibers for Shear Reinforcement and Ductility*
Bazant 1984, *Size Effect in Shear Failure of Longitudinally Reinforced Beams*

Carrasquillo 1981a, *Microcracking and Behavior of High Strength Concrete Subjected to*
Carrasquillo 1981b, *Properties of High Strength Concrete Subject to Short-Term Loads*
CEB-FIP 1978, *Model Code for Concrete Structures*
Chen 1985, *Behavior of High-Strength Concrete Under Uniaxial and Biaxial Compression*

El-Shakra 1989, *Toughness and Flexural Response of Fiber Reinforced Concretes*
El-Shakra 1990, *Effect of Deflection Measurements on Toughness Evaluations of Fiber Re-*
El-Sheikh 1988, *Effects of Fast Construction on Deflections of R.C. Buildings*
Elzanaty 1986, *Shear Capacity of Reinforced Concrete Beams Under High-Strength Con-*

Fafitis 1982, *Discussion on: A Comparative Study of Confinement Models*
Fafitis 1984, *Response of Confined Concrete Subjected to Earthquake Type Loadings*
Fafitis 1985a, *Predictions of Ultimate Behavior of Confined Columns Subjected to Large*
Fafitis 1985b, *Lateral Reinforcement for High-Strength Concrete Columns*
Fanella 1985, *Stress-Strain Properties of Fiber Reinforced Concrete in Compression*
Feineck 1988, *Theoretical Considerations and Experimental Evidence on Web Compres-*

Fintel 1971, *Effects of Column Creep and Shrinkage in Tall Structures*
Frenay 1987, *Shear Transfer in High-Strength Concrete*
Frenay 1990, *Theory and Experiments on the Behavior of Cracks in Concrete Subjected to*

Ghali 1969, *Time-Dependent Forces Induced by Settlement of Supports in Continuous Re-*
Gopalaratnam 1985, *Fracture and Impact Resistance of Steel Fiber Reinforced Concrete*
Gopalaratnam 1985a, *Softening of Plain of Concrete in Direct Tension*
Gopalaratnam 1985b, *Strength, Deformation and Fracture Toughness of Fiber Cement*
Gopalaratnam 1986, *Properties of Steel Fiber Reinforced Concrete Subjected to Impact*
Gopalaratnam 1987, *Experimental Investigation of Pull-Out Characteristics of Short Steel*
Gopalaratnam 1987a, *Failure Mechanisms and Fracture of Fiber Reinforced Concrete*
Gopalaratnam 1987b, *Tensile Failure of Steel Fiber Reinforced Mortar*
Gopalaratnam 1988, *On the Modeling of Inelastic Interfaces in Fibrous Composites*
Gopalaratnam 1990, *Axisymmetric Finite Element Study of Nonlinear Fiber Pull-Out*
Gopalaratnam 1990, *Fracture Toughness of Fiber Reinforced Concrete*
Guralnick, S. A., Singh, S., and Erber, T., 1987, *Plastic Collapse, Shakedown and Hysteresis*

Hillerborg 1980, *Analysis of Fracture by Means of the Fictitious Crack Model*
Hoff 1987, *Bibliography on Fiber Reinforced Concrete*

Japan Concrete Institute 1983, *Method of Test for Flexural Strength and Flexural Tough-*
Jenq 1986, *Crack Propagation in Fiber-Reinforced Concrete*
Johnston 1980, *Properties of Steel Fiber Reinforced Mortar and Concrete*
Johnston 1982a, *Definition and Measurements of Flexural Toughness Parameters of Fiber*
Johnston 1982b, *Steel Fiber Reinforced Concrete—Present and Future*

Kollegger 1987, *Material Model for Cracked Reinforced Concrete*
Kormeling 1980, *Static and Fatigue Properties of Concrete Beams Reinforced with Conti-*

Lankard 1975, *Fiber Concrete Applications*
Lawrence 1972, *Some Theoretical Considerations of Fiber Pull-Out from an Elastic Matrix*
Leslie 1976, *Flexural Behavior of High-Strength Concrete Beams*

Martinez 1982, *Spirally-Reinforced High-Strength Concrete Columns*
Mindess 1981, *Concrete*
Mindess 1983, *The Fracture of Fiber Reinforced and Polymer Impregnated Concretes*
Morrison 1988, *Analysis of the Debonding and Pull-Out Process in Fiber Composites*
Mphonde 1985, *Shear Test of High- and Low-Strength Concrete Beams with Stirrups*

Naaman 1974, *Probabilistic Analysis of Fiber Reinforced Concrete*
Naaman 1976, *Pull-Out Mechanism in Steel Fiber Reinforced Concrete*
Nawy 1983, *High-Strength Concrete*
Ngab 1980, *Behavior of High-Strength Concrete Under Sustained Compressive Stress*
Ngab 1981a, *Shrinkage and Creep of High Strength Concrete*
Ngab 1981b, *Microcracking and Time-Dependent Strains in High Strength Concrete*
Nilson 1985, *Design Implications of Current Research on High-Strength Concrete*

Pfeifer 1971, *Time Dependent Deformations in a 70 Story Structure*

Ramakrishnan 1980, *A Comparative Evaluation of Concrete Reinforced with Straight Steel*

Ramakrishnan 1987, *Performance Characteristics and Flexural Fatigue Strength on Con-*
Romualdi 1963, *Mechanics of Crack Arrest in Concrete*
Romualdi 1964, *Tensile Strength of Concrete Affected by Uniformly Distributed and Close-*
Russell 1986, *High-Rise Concrete Buildings: Shrinkage, Creep, and Temperature Effects*

Sargin 1971, *Stress-Strain Relationships for Concrete and Analysis of Structural Concrete*
Schickert 1977, *Results of Test Concerning Strength and Strain of Concrete Subjected to*
Schmidt 1975, *9000 psi Concrete - Why? Why Not?*
Shah 1971, *Fiber Reinforced Concrete Properties*
Shah 1974, *New Reinforcing Materials in Concrete*
Shah 1983, *Cyclic Loading of Spirally Reinforced Concrete*
Sheikh 1980, *Strength and Ductility of Tied Concrete Columns*
Stang 1986, *Failure of Fiber Reinforced Composites by Pull-Out Fracture*
Suaris 1983, *Properties of Concrete and Fiber Reinforced Concrete Subjected to Impact*
Swartz 1985, *Structural Bending Properties of High Strength Concrete*

Trost 1982, *The Calculation of Deflections of Reinforced Concrete Members*

Umoto 1981, *Shear Behavior of Reinforced Concrete Beams with Steel Fiber as Shear Re-*

van Mier 1986, *Fracture of Concrete Under Complex Stress*
Visalvanich 1982, *Fracture Model for Fiber Reinforced Concrete*

Wang 1978, *Stress-Strain Curves of Normal and Lightweight Concrete in Compression*
Warner 1975, *Axial Shortening in Reinforced Concrete Columns*
Wecharatana 1983, *A Model for Predicting Fracture Resistance of Fiber Reinforced*
Wei 1986, *Study of the Interface Strength in Steel Fiber-Reinforced Cement-Based Compo-*
Williamson 1978, *The Effect of Steel Fibers as Web Reinforcement in Reinforced Concrete*
Wittman 1982, *Fundamental Research on Creep and Shrinkage of Concrete*

Yu 1960, *Instantaneous and Long-Time Deflections of Reinforced Concrete Beams*

Zsutty 1968, *Beam Shear Strength Prediction by Analysis of Existing Data*

5

Alternate Design Methods

Design codes typically present and discuss in detail the proven and common design methods which are in use by the profession. Yet many codes refer to "other methods" as being acceptable as long as the conditions of equilibrium and compatibility are satisfied. The statement given in many codes is general and lacks specific examples.

Since the publication of the original Monograph, several unconventional methods have been developed for the design of reinforced concrete members. Some of these methods have been proven to correspond to the element behavior more realistically and can lead to a more economical design in many instances. Designers and researchers need to have a general understanding of these methods, and utilize them where they are appropriate. This chapter presents two such methods: the truss analogy and the triaxial stress state design. The former is gaining acceptance as an alternate design method, and is making its way into some textbooks on reinforced concrete design. The latter is a more recent development. Numerical examples are presented to illustrate the methods.

5.1 TRUSS MODELS

The idea of using truss models for following the flow of internal forces in reinforced concrete structures was introduced by Hennebique and advanced by Ritter (1899), and was further developed by Moersch (1908, 1922). Figure 5.1 summarizes a number of key steps in these early developments. Being based on careful observations of the behavior of actual and test structures as well as on a thorough understanding of basic principles, the clarity and the wide range of applicability of these concepts still deserve our admiration.

Truss models have always served a dual purpose. They allow the description of essential aspects of structural behavior, and they provide powerful tools for structural dimensioning. In the latter regard, Moersch's classical 45° truss model concept has been adopted by most codes of practice as the basis of their shear and torsion design provisions. Unfortunately, however, the originally simple and transparent truss model approach was obscured by many empirical modifications. As a result, rather than being simple, rational, and general, shear and torsion design procedures became complex, empirical, and restricted.

Despite the unfavorable code developments, practicing engineers have commonly applied truss models. However, as there was little if any official support, many engineers had some doubts about the justification of their methods. With the CEB-FIP *Model Code for Concrete Structures* (1978), the Canadian code, *Design of Concrete Structures for Buildings* (CSA, 1984), and similar documents, this situation has changed. The renewed interest in truss models has led to a universal acknowledgment of their potential and usefulness, but current code revisions have yet to avoid the danger of again introducing too many restrictions for their actual use.

This section provides an overview on recent advances in the area of truss model approaches and related theories. A number of example truss models for typical situations are presented, and hints for the development and practical application of truss models are given.

1 Recent advances

Over the past three decades significant progress was made in four main areas. First, limit analysis methods capable of predicting failure conditions were developed. Second, linear and nonlinear approaches such as the compression field theory were advanced to compute the load-deformation response. Third, in view of a unified design approach, covering dimensioning and detailing, the significance of geometric and static discontinuities in practical situations was emphasized and methods for their pragmatic treatment were proposed. Finally, along with the theoretical and practical developments, the supporting experimental evidence was increased substantially.

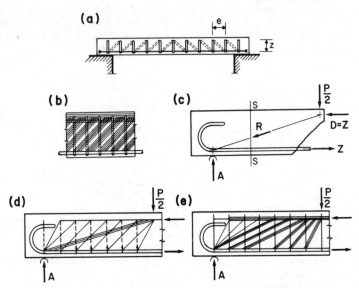

Fig. 5.1   Early developments. (*a*) Truss model adapted from Ritter (1899). (*b*) Truss model adapted from Moersch (1908). (*c*) Strut and tie action. (*d*) Combined strut and truss action. (*e*) Combined fan action. (*Parts* c, d, *and* e *adapted from Moersch, 1922.*)

There are many interrelations within and between the different areas. While the linear and nonlinear approaches as well as the kinematic limit analysis methods primarily address aspects of structural behavior, the static limit analysis procedures relate directly to dimensioning and detailing. A brief account of important developments is given in the following.

2 Methods of limit analysis

Limit analysis procedures have mainly been promoted by two schools, one around Thurlimann in Zurich and the other around Nielsen in Copenhagen. With a colloquium organized by IABSE (1979) in Copenhagen a first state-of-the-art report was produced, and later Thurlimann et al. (1983) and Nielsen (1984) presented comprehensive monographs on the subject.

The Zurich school has always been design-oriented and has relied heavily on the experience gained through large-scale experiments. Beginning with torsion studies, the school's later investigations turned to shear and more general problems. Using a variable-angle space truss approach, Lampert and Thurlimann (1971) treated beams subjected to torsion and flexure. Thurlimann et al. (1975) extended this work to cover warping torsion as well as combined flexure, shear, and torsion. Mueller (1976, 1978) supplemented the space truss theory by describing compatible failure mechanisms, and Marti (1980) provided a synthesis of the previous work and general limit analysis concepts.

The Copenhagen school has a strong applied mechanics background and continues the long-standing Danish tradition of applying limit analysis methods to structural concrete. Starting from yield criteria for reinforced concrete elements, Nielsen's school has produced a great number of contributions to the solution of shear problems. Nielsen (1971) gave a comprehensive treatment of members subjected to in-plane forces. Braestrup (1974) discussed shear in beams and introduced the so-called web crushing criterion. Nielsen et al. (1978) provided a summary of their work and treated a wide range of problems using mainly the kinematic method.

In an attempt to promote the application of limit analysis procedures in North America, Marti (1985a, 1985b) described the basic elements of truss models and demonstrated their use by means of various design examples. Marti (1986a, 1986b) also treated the so-called staggering concept of shear design.

3 Linear and nonlinear approaches

From tests on beams subjected to flexure and shear, Moersch (1922) knew that with decreasing amounts of transverse reinforcement diagonal cracks in the web become flatter, and that their inclination to the beam axis may be considerably less than 45°. However, he thought it would be practically impossible to compute the inclination of these cracks, and he recommended to continue using the simple and conservative 45° truss model approach.

By analyzing a truss model consisting of linearly elastic members and neglecting the concrete tensile strength, Kupfer (1964) solved Moersch's problem and found an equation for the inclination of the diagonal cracks.

Using the same assumptions, Baumann (1972) derived a similar equation for the crack direction in reinforced concrete panels subjected to plane stress states. For an orthogonal reinforcement in the x and z directions and applied stress components σ_x, σ_z, and τ_{xz} Baumann's equation can be written in the form

$$\tan^2\theta\,\rho_x(1 + \rho_z n) + \tan\theta\,\rho_x\frac{\sigma_z}{\tau_{xz}} = \frac{\sigma_x}{\tau_{xz}}\,\rho_z\,cot\,\theta + (1 + \rho_x n)\,\rho_z\,\cot^2\theta \quad (5.1)$$

where ρ_z and ρ_x are geometric reinforcement ratios, $n = E_s/E_c$ is the modular ratio, and θ is the inclination of the principal compressive stress direction to the x axis. It is noteworthy that Eq. 5.1 can be obtained from Kupfer's equation by substituting $(\sigma_x + \tau_{xz} \cot\theta)/\sigma_x E_s$ and $(\sigma_z + \tau_{xz}\tan\theta)/\rho_z E_s$ for the average axial strain at middepth of the web and the average stirrup strain, respectively.

Similar to Kupfer's analysis, Thurlimann and Luchinger (1973) considered a space truss model and derived expressions for the stiffness of cracked reinforced concrete girders subjected to torsion and flexure. Potucek (1977) treated girders subjected to flexure and shear by subdividing the webs into finite elements and applying Baumann's methods.

Mitchell and Collins (1974) abandoned the assumption of linear elasticity and introduced the so-called compression field theory for members subjected to torsion. Collins (1978) further developed the theory for reinforced concrete members in shear. Collins and Mitchell (1980) proposed an empirical expression for the degradation of concrete compressive strength due to diagonal cracking and provided a comprehensive treatment of the compression field approach for shear and torsion design of prestressed and nonprestressed concrete beams. Based on an extensive experimental investigation, Vecchio and Collins (1982) derived average stress-strain relationships for cracked reinforced panels. These experimentally verified stress-strain relationships, which—in contrast to the original compression field theory—account for tensile stresses in the concrete between the cracks, were used by Vecchio and Collins (1986) in their modified compression field theory. An overview of the 1984 Canadian code provisions for shear design, which combine compression field and limit analysis concepts, was given by Collins and Mitchell (1986). In particular, these provisions contain the relation

$$f_c = \frac{f'_c}{0.8 + 170\varepsilon_1} \quad (5.2)$$

for the maximum compressive stress that the diagonally cracked concrete can resist, where f'_c is the cylinder compressive strength of concrete and ε_1 the principal tensile strain in diagonally cracked concrete. A comprehensive treatment of the compression field approaches to shear and torsion problems can be found in Collins and Mitchell's (1987) book on prestressed concrete. Based on Collins' work, Hsu (1988) developed a variant of the compression field theory, the so-called softened truss model approach, with which he analyzed several problems.

It is natural that during the period of active and parallel development of limit analysis, linear approaches, and nonlinear approaches, the differences between the various methods were often overemphasized while the common features were not fully recognized. However, the different approaches supplement each other and, essentially, they differ only in the assumed stress-strain relationships for the cracked concrete. This was pointed out by Marti (1982), who discussed the basic assumptions of the different approaches in view of their application to members subjected to combined actions. From this point of view, Kupfer's and Baumann's works and related studies constitute a linear compression field theory which, together with an uncracked elastic response analysis and an estimate of the failure load based on limit analysis, permits the actual estimate of the failure load based on limit analysis. It permits also the actual load-deformation behavior to be similarly approximated by a more refined nonlinear compression field approach (Fig. 5.2). Collins' group deserves credit for the development and the effective implementation of a rational approach for shear and torsion design and, in particular, for the derivation of experimentally verified stress-strain relationships for cracked concrete. These empirical relationships can be utilized to estimate the effective concrete compressive strength needs in limit analysis considerations, and thus, they may be considered as the repayment of the loan obtained from the variable-angle space truss approach in the early stages of the development of the compression field theory.

4 Treatment of discontinuities

In the past, the conventional methods of dimensioning sections subjected to flexure and axial load were more and more refined and extended to include the effects of shear and torsion. However, since shear and torsion at a particular section are resisted by diagonal compressive stress fields in the concrete, they have an influence over a certain length on either side of that section. Therefore, when applying section-by-section design methods, it should be clear that one implicitly considers a region of a member around a particular section. Hence, all quantities determined on such a basis, in particular, the necessary amounts of reinforcement for shear and torsion, should be regarded as average values representative for a region around a section, rather than as sectional properties.

The preceding discussion reveals that section-by-section design methods can only work for regular conditions, or, in other words, if there is continuity of the relevant geometric, static, and material parameters. These parameters are assumed to change gradually between different sections and the methods break down for the case of discontinuities such as those shown in Fig. 5.3.

Considering any discontinuity, it is apparent that again a certain region around the section of the discontinuity rather than just that particular section should be

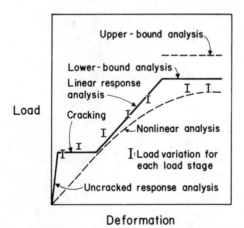

Deformation

Fig. 5.2 **Different load-deformation response predictions compared with test results.** (*Adapted from Marti and Kong, 1987.*)

treated. Schlaich and Weischede (1981) introduced the term *D-region* for such cases, and they suggested that the size of a D-region can be approximated by considering the influence region of the discontinuity using de Saint Venant's principle. Thus for linear members, D-regions extend over a distance on the order of the depth of the member on either side of the discontinuity (Fig. 5.4). For the regions between D-regions, where section-by-section design methods would apply, Schlaich and Weischede (1981) introduced the term *B-region*.

Schlaich's group has pointed to the anomaly that, whereas refined methods are available for treating B-regions, there is no equivalent for D-regions. Dimensioning and detailing of D-regions has often been regarded as an inferior task, while in fact it is of paramount importance for the quality of any reinforced concrete structure. In order to remedy this situation and to replace the hitherto applied collection of so-called detailing rules by a more rational approach, Schlaich's group proposed to consistently apply strut and tie models for B-regions as well as D-regions. As a guideline for the development of these models, they recommended visualizing the internal force flow according to a linearly elastic analysis and orienting the struts and ties such that they would roughly correspond to the resultants of the elastically determined stresses. Schlaich and Schaefer (1984) and Schlaich et al. (1987) illustrated their method by many examples.

There is no unique strut and tie model for a particular situation. Some subjective engineering judgment is needed in every case. However, this is not different from finding an appropriate static system when performing a structural analysis.

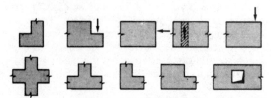

Fig. 5.3   Geometric, static, and combined geometric and static discontinuities.

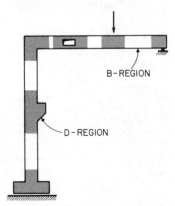

Fig. 5.4   B-regions and D-regions.

There are always many feasible solutions. Uniqueness of the solution is not required, as no extraordinary ingenuity is needed to arrive at a reasonable solution. Also, uniqueness of the solution is not desirable, as this would unnecessarily restrict the freedom to choose among several design options. What matters is consistency of the whole design process, starting from an appropriate structural analysis over an adequate dimensioning to a consequent detailing. In this regard, the views of Schlaich's group coincide with those of the promoters of limit analysis procedures. Minor differences of opinion exist only about the role of elastically determined stress fields for the development of truss models.

From a limit analysis point of view there is no essential difference between an elastic analysis and any other method leading to a statically admissible stress field. In fact, in every case there are certain residual or self-equilibrating stresses within a structure which cannot be determined reliably in practice and which are typically ignored in any structural analysis. Residual stresses do not affect the load-carrying capacity of a sufficiently ductile structure. They are influenced by restraints of imposed deformations due to shrinkage, creep, settlements, temperature, and other effects, and they are modified upon the occurrence of irreversible deformations owing to cracking, yielding, and bond slippage. To account for residual stresses and to make possible the necessary redistribution of the internal forces, it is recommended to provide a well-distributed minimum reinforcement in every part of a structure. Then a rather simple equilibrium solution is sufficient for determining the additional main reinforcement needed to transfer the applied loads. Consideration of elastically determined stresses is not necessary and not essentially superior compared with other equilibrium analyses. However, since linearly elastic analyses are readily available, it is quite reasonable to use them as some guide in developing truss models.

5 Supporting experimental evidence

It is beyond the scope of this brief review to compile a comprehensive list of experimental investigations supporting the application of truss models. Interested readers are referred to the monographs by Thurlimann et al. (1983), Nielsen (1984), and Collins and Mitchell (1987).

Recently a number of test series were conducted that were specifically planned to verify the applicability of truss model approaches. These include investigations concerning the staggering concept of shear design by Mailhot (1984) and Cerruti and Marti (1987); the deep beam studies by Rogowski et al. (1986); investigations on corbels, dapped ended beams, and beams containing openings by Cook and Mitchell (1988); and experiments on stepped beams by Dunstan (1987) and Goutama (1988).

6 Practical application

Truss models are discrete images of statically equivalent stress fields. The truss members correspond to uniaxially stressed struts and ties with finite dimensions, and the pin connections correspond to biaxially or triaxially stressed nodal zones.

Usually it is not necessary to develop complete stress fields. Truss models provide most of the information normally required. They allow the determination of size, position, distribution, and anchorage of the main reinforcement in a member.

When applying truss models, a trial and adjustment procedure is adopted in general. Starting from an assumed initial truss model, the truss member forces and the necessary strut widths can be obtained. The truss geometry may then have to be modified, for example, because the struts would not fit into the available space or because more space would be available to accommodate struts. Different constraints such as bend diameters of reinforcing bars or concrete cover dimensions may also influence the truss geometry. In any case, truss models should be drawn to scale to get a feel for the proportions and to avoid gross errors. Furthermore, development of the envisioned flow must be made possible through careful and consequent detailing. This is much more important than performing overly refined calculations. Simple but consistent equilibrium considerations, combined with some sound engineering judgment, suffice.

While truss models indicate the necessary amount, the correct position, and the required detailing of the main reinforcement, such models should only be applied in conjunction with a well-distributed minimum reinforcement in all those regions of a member where no main reinforcement is required. The minimum reinforcement accounts for residual stresses as well as the necessary redistribution of the internal forces in the cracked state. It enhances the ductility and it may contribute significantly to the ultimate resistance of a member.

The necessary minimum dimensions of the struts and nodal zones depend on the effective compressive strength of the cracked reinforced concrete f_c. While members with low reinforcement ratios are rather insensitive to the assessment of f_c, a more cautious approach is recommended for members with intermediate and high reinforcement ratios. As a first approximation, the value of $f_c = 0.6 f'_c$ suggested by Marti (1985a, 1985b) can be used, and for refined considerations, Eq. 5.2 may be applied. Further guidance was given by Collins and Mitchell (1986) and by Schlaich et al. (1987).

Apart from struts, ties, and nodal zones, general stress fields also contain fan-shaped and banded regions which correspond to a radial or parallel arrangement of elementary struts. Furthermore, consideration of arch-shaped stress fields is sometimes useful. However, as pointed out by Marti (1985a), fans, bands, and arches can always be replaced by statically equivalent struts or strut systems. Thus, struts, ties, and nodes are the basic tools for the development of truss models and stress fields. Their application is briefly illustrated in the following.

7 Isostatic beams

Consider the uniformly loaded, simply supported beam shown in Fig. 5.5a. Subdivide its span l into an even number of equal portions Δ; in other words, $l = 2n\Delta$. Replace the uniformly distributed load w by statically equivalent single forces $w\Delta$ and introduce the truss model shown in Fig. 5.5b to analyze the flow of the internal forces. Figure 5.5c represents the corresponding discontinuous stress field, and Fig. 5.5d and e gives the required vertical stirrup and bottom-chord reinforcements, while Fig. 5.5f shows the variation of the top-chord force. For the sake of simplicity, the lever arm of the top- and bottom-chord forces d_v has been assumed to be constant along the beam axis.

The parallelogram-shaped bands of web concrete shown in Fig. 5.5c are uniformly compressed, but there are jumps of the compressive stresses at the boundaries between adjoining bands. Near the support, the discontinuous stress field is terminated by a fan. The compressive stresses in the elementary struts forming this fan vary hyperbolically since the cross-sectional area of each strut varies linearly along its length. At the support, where the fan is centered, the stresses would be infinitely large. In reality, this is not possible and the stress field must be modified locally so that finite stresses result throughout the fan.

The truss posts correspond to uniformly distributed stirrups within the individual portions Δ (Fig. 5.5d). Near midspan, where theoretically no stirrups are required, a minimum stirrup reinforcement would be placed.

While the truss model results in a staggered diagram for the variation of the bottom-chord force, the discontinuous stress field yields a piecewise linear diagram (Fig. 5.5e). However, the truss model provides the correct amounts at the sections separating different portions Δ. In particular, it can be seen that a force of $wl\Delta/4d_v$ has to be anchored at the support.

The top-chord force variation is also piecewise linear, except near the support. There the variation is parabolic since the compressive stresses within the fan provide uniform stirrup forces along with linearly variable shear stresses acting on the top chord (Fig. 5.5f).

The weights of the necessary reinforcements are proportional to the areas of

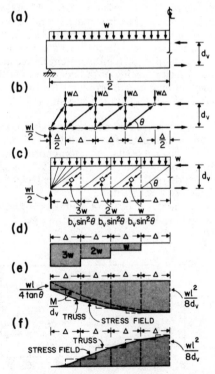

Fig. 5.5　Simply supported beam. (a) Geometry and loading. (b) Truss model. (c) Discontinuous stress field. (d) Required stirrup resistance per unit length of beam. (e) Bottom-chord force variation. (f) Top-chord force variation.

the diagrams in Fig. 5.5d and e. Flexure requires a longitudinal reinforcement with a weight of

$$W_{lM} = \frac{wl^3 \gamma_s}{12df} \tag{5.3}$$

where γ_s is the specific weight and f_y is the yield strength of the reinforcement. From Fig. 5.5d we find a necessary stirrup reinforcement with a weight of

$$W_{tV} = 6m(n - 1)\left(\frac{d_v}{l}\right)^2 W_{lM} \tag{5.4}$$

where the factor $m > 1$ accounts for development lengths, while Fig. 5.5e indicates a weight of

$$W_{1V} = \frac{3_n - 1}{4n^2} W_{lM} \tag{5.5}$$

for the additional longitudinal reinforcement required for shear. Figure 5.6 represents the ratio $(W_{lV} + W_{tV})/W_{lM}$ as a function of the span-to-depth ratio l/d_v. Note that development lengths have been ignored for this figure. It can be seen that the reinforcement required for shear is only a small fraction of the reinforcement required for flexure, particularly for slender beams. Furthermore, the sum $W_{lV} + W_{tV}$ appears to be rather insensitive to the choice of tan $\theta = d_v/\Delta$. Thus the choice of θ is not of primary economic concern and should be based on practical considerations. The reduction of reinforcement congestion due to a larger stirrup spacing will enable easier placing of the concrete. On the other hand, selection of a very low angle θ may create problems for the anchorage of the longitudinal reinforcement at the support. Practical values of θ range from about 25 to 45°.

If the beam is indirectly supported by another member, as shown in Fig. 5.7, the fan near the support may be replaced by a half-band of uniformly compressed web concrete. However, this necessitates a top-chord reinforcement over a length of $\Delta/2$ from the support. While Eqs. 5.3 and 5.4 remain unchanged, the fraction of the right-hand side of Eq. 5.5 has to be replaced by $(6n + 1)/(8n^2)$ to account for this additional reinforcement.

For a uniformly loaded cantilever beam of span $l = n\Delta$ and a fan terminating the discontinuous stress field near the clamped end, we get expressions similar to

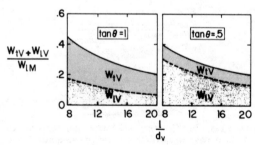

Fig. 5.6 Comparison of weights of transverse and longitudinal reinforcements required for shear with weight of longitudinal reinforcement required for flexure.

Eqs. 5.3 through 5.5, that is, $W_{lM2} = wl^3\gamma_s/(6d_vf_y)$, $W_{tV} = 12\ m(n - 1)(d_v/l)^2$, W_{lM} and $W_{lV} = (3n - 1)W_{lM}/2n^2$. For an indirect support, with a uniform diagonal compressive stress field instead of a fan near the clamped end, the latter expression has to be replaced by $W_{lV} = (3n + 1)W_{lM}/2n^2$ (Fig. 5.8).

The longitudinal reinforcement can be curtailed according to the tension-chord force variation. In determining cutoff locations it may be assumed that the resistance provided by a reinforcing bar increases linearly over its development length. However, as demonstrated by Marti (1986b) the bars must be extended beyond the theoretical cutoff points by a distance of at least one-half of the stirrup spacing to account for the discrete distribution of the stirrups. Additional extensions are necessary for longitudinal bars placed in the outer portions of flanges. This requirement, which is due to the so-called shear-lag effect, can also be explained by using truss models (Marti, 1985a, 1985b).

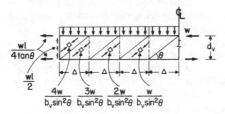

Fig. 5.7   Discontinuous stress field for indirectly supported beam.

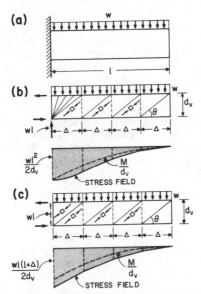

Fig. 5.8   Cantilever beam. (*a*) Geometry and loading. (*b*) Discontinuous stress field and top-chord force variation. (*c*) Discontinuous stress field and top-chord force variation for indirect support condition.

8   Continuous members and general loading

The truss model approach can easily be generalized for continuous members and arbitrary loading, as demonstrated by Marti (1986a, 1986b). Once the support reactions have been determined, the member can be subdivided into segments bounded by sections of zero shear force, and the different segments can be treated individually. Considering the segments as free bodies with known applied forces and moments, the internal force paths in each segment can be visualized by means of truss models, and the reinforcement can be dimensioned and detailed accordingly.

Statically indeterminate support reactions are commonly determined from a linearly elastic analysis of the uncracked system. For variable loads such analyses result in moment and shear force envelopes. The sections of zero shear force can shift within certain regions along the member axis. Depending on the sign of the shear force, the truss diagonals within such regions may be inclined to the left or the right, while there is only one possibility in regions where the shear force does not change its sign. In applying any structural analysis, it should be remembered that because of restraint actions and irreversible deformations, there are always certain residual stresses which depend on the entire loading and restraining history and which cannot reliably be determined in practice. From a purely analytical point of view this may be deplored, but from a design point of view matters are quite different. In fact, based on the observation that the necessary redistribution of the internal forces indeed takes place in a sufficiently ductile structure, any reasonable equilibrium solution can be used for the structural dimensioning and detailing. Complicated analyses are not necessary in general.

As a practical procedure it is suggested to apply an elastic analysis to find moment and shear force envelopes and to adjust these by superimposing a freely selected residual stress state. This corresponds to the procedure applied in shakedown analysis of elastic-plastic systems, and it is somewhat simpler, more transparent, and inherently more conservative than the usual approach which allows moment redistribution within certain limits for each individual loading case. If deemed necessary, an estimate of the residual stress state to be added to the elastically determined stresses can be made by considering cracked member stiffnesses. An interesting possibility to perform such an investigation is to utilize the truss model used for proportioning the member by assigning proper stiffness values to the individual truss members.

In conclusion, it is interesting to extend the preceding analysis of the necessary weights of reinforcement to uniformly loaded spans of continuous beams. Setting the distances from the point of contraflexure to the clamped end and to the section of maximum positive moment equal to $\eta_1\Delta$, and $\eta_2\Delta$, respectively, we get the following weights of reinforcement for the length $(\eta_1 + \eta_2)\Delta$:

$$W_{lM} = \frac{w\Delta^3\gamma_s}{6d_vf_y}(\eta_1^3 + 3\eta_1^2\eta_2 + 2\eta_2^3) \tag{5.6}$$

$$W_{tV} = \frac{wm\Delta d_v\gamma_s}{2f_y}(\eta_1 + \eta_2)(\eta_1 + \eta_2 - 1) \tag{5.7}$$

$$W_{lV} = \frac{w\Delta^3\gamma_s}{12d_vf_y}[3(\eta_1 + \eta_2)^2 - \eta_1] \tag{5.8}$$

Equation 5.8 is valid for a fan-shaped termination of the stress field near the clamped end. For a uniform diagonal compressive stress field instead of a fan, the expression within brackets on the right-hand side of Eq. 5.8 has to be replaced by $[3(\eta_1 + \eta_2)^2 + \eta_1 + 2\eta_2]$. Incidentally, Eq. 5.6 reveals that W_{lM} becomes a minimum if $\eta_1 = \eta_2$. In that case, with $\eta_1\Delta = \eta_2\Delta = \frac{1}{4}$, we get a value of $wl^3\gamma_s/32d_vf_y$ for the weight of the necessary flexural reinforcement for a span of length l, in other words, three-eighths of the value given by Eq. 5.3 for a similar beam on simple supports.

9 Section-by-section design procedures

While the truss model approach is applicable to general geometric and loading configurations such as to B- and D-regions according to Schlaich's terminology (Fig. 5.4), a simple section-by-section design procedure can be developed for B-regions.

Assuming that the shear force V at a section is resisted by a uniform diagonal compressive stress field in the web concrete, the internal forces presented in Fig. 5.9 are obtained. From equilibrium we derive the relations

$$V \le A_v f_y \frac{d_v \cot \theta}{s} \tag{5.9}$$

$$\frac{M}{d_v} + \frac{N}{2} + \frac{V}{2} \cot \theta \le A_{lb} f_y \tag{5.10a}$$

$$-\frac{M}{d_v} + \frac{N}{2} + \frac{V}{2} \cot \theta \le A_{lt} f_y \tag{5.10b}$$

$$V \le f_c b_v d_v \sin \theta \cos \theta \tag{5.11}$$

where M, N, and V are the applied moment, axial force, and shear force, respectively; b_v is the effective web width; A_{lb} and A_{lt} are the cross-sectional areas of bottom- and top-chord reinforcements, respectively; and A_v and s are the cross-sectional area and the spacing of stirrups, respectively. Note that similar to Eqs. 5.3 through 5.8, appropriate load and resistance factors should be taken into account when applying Eqs. 5.9 through 5.11. Also, all quantities determined based on a section-by-section design approach should be regarded as average values for

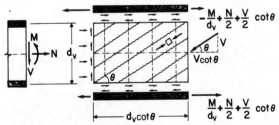

Fig. 5.9   Forces acting on web and stringer elements according to section-by-section design procedure.

a region with a length on the order of d_v cot θ on either side of a section rather than as sectional properties.

Comparison with Fig. 5.5 reveals that the section-by-section design procedure provides the same results as a truss model or a discontinuous stress field approach at sections where the stirrup reinforcement is staggered, such as at the sections separating different portions Δ, because at such sections the discontinuous stress field is uniform over d_v. Thus, if such a section is used for subdividing a member into B- and D-regions, there will be no special problems regarding the continuity of the force flow between the different regions.

It is easy to extend these considerations to variable-depth members and to prestressed members with inclined tendons. For such cases, components of the effective prestressing force and components of flexural compression and tension in the direction of the applied shear have to be taken into account when determining the effective shear force in the web.

A member subjected to combined actions can be idealized as an assemblage of interconnected web and stringer elements, and the sectional forces and moments can be replaced by an equivalent system of axial and shear forces acting on these elements. The individual web elements may then be treated similarly as that shown in Fig. 5.9. Details on this approach were given by Marti (1982) and Thurlimann et al. (1983). Marti (1989) also extended the section-by-section approach to plates subjected to combined moments, in-plane forces, and transverse shear forces.

10   Nodal zones and fans

Introducing a finite compressive stress f_c and therefore finite strut widths, a truss joint becomes a nodal zone with finite dimensions. Consider the forced D, D_1, and D_2 given in Fig. 5.10a and assume that the associated struts are compressed to f_c. The intersection points of the strut edges define the triangular nodal zone ABC. This zone can be interpreted as a wedge which is uniformly compressed in all directions. Since the strut widths are proportional to the strut forces, and the side faces of the nodal zone are perpendicular to the struts, the nodal zone can be viewed as the force triangle. However, the intersection point G of the three forces lies outside of the nodal zone.

Rather than using one strut for D, we can introduce two struts for its compo-

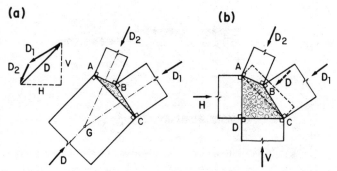

Fig. 5.10   Nodal zones. (a) Connection of three struts. (b) Strut force D split into components H and V.

nents V and H (Fig. 5.10b). The nodal zone ABC obtained in Fig. 5.10a is complemented by the nodal zone ACD corresponding to forces D, V, and H, and this results in the quadrilateral nodal zone $ABCD$.

Knowing how to split a strut into two equivalent struts and how to connect struts at nodal zones, we may now reverse the procedure and replace two struts by one equivalent strut. Thus we may consider the resultant D of the two forces D_1 and D_2 in Fig. 5.10b. The associated strut would bear on the side AC of the nodal zone ACD. Introducing D_1 and D_2 instead of D results in the addition of the small triangle ABC to the nodal zone, but the important observation is that points A and C are determined correctly by considering the equivalent single strut for D. This observation is fundamental for the development of fan-shaped stress fields for arbitrary loading.

Arbitrarily distributed loads can be replaced by equivalent single loads, and these can be transferred by single struts. Similar to points A and C in Fig. 5.10b, the endpoints of the side of the nodal zone on which the single strut bears remain valid when we return to the original problem and replace the single strut by a series of struts radiating from the nodal zone to take the distributed load. However, the side face of the nodal zone on which the struts bear will be curved rather than straight. Further details were given by Marti (1985a), who also described procedures for nodal zones connecting struts with unequal stresses.

11   Typical D-regions

A node connecting three struts or ties may be classified as CCC, CTC, TCT, or TTT, where C and T indicate a compression strut and a tension tie, respectively (Fig. 5.11a). Considering a strut with a node at either end, there are six different combinations of node types. Of these, the four configurations shown in Fig. 5.11b are particularly useful. As demonstrated in Fig. 5.11c, configurations 2 and 3 provide truss models for closing and opening joints of frames, respectively. Combining the basic configurations of Fig. 5.11b, one arrives at the drawings of Fig. 5.11d, which can be utilized to solve the typical D-region problems represented in Fig. 5.11e.

12   Conclusion

Truss models are simple, transparent, adaptable, and sufficiently accurate tools for the dimensioning and detailing of structural concrete. The classical approach has been substantially supplemented and generalized by significant theoretical, experimental, and practical work over the past three decades. This section has reviewed these developments and has summarized recommendations, which are hoped to assist practicing engineers in developing and applying truss models.

5.2   DESIGN UTILIZING MULTIAXIAL STRESS STATES

In recent years there has been increasing evidence, both analytical and experimental, linking the strength and behavior of reinforced concrete structural members with triaxial stress conditions which invariably develop within structural concrete at its ultimate limit state. This suggests that ignoring these triaxial stress conditions, as most current design concepts do, cannot lead to an improvement of our understanding of structural behavior. In fact, it is such an understanding that is generally deemed essential for the development of safe and efficient design procedures.

In this section this evidence is summarized and presented in a unified form. Although the conclusions drawn are of general applicability, only their application to common cases such as those of beams in pure flexure or combined flexure and shear is discussed. It is considered that a demonstration of successful application in these cases will provide incentive for application in more complex situations where design procedures are currently inadequate or even lacking.

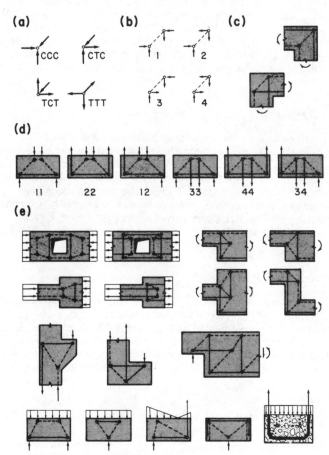

Fig. 5.11   Methodical approach for treatment of D-regions. (a) Classification of node types. (b) Basic configuration of single strut. (c) Application to frame corners. (d) Combining basic configurations. (e) Typical applications.

1 Beams in flexure

At present, the flexural capacity of beams is assessed on the basis of the *plane-sections* theory. This theory describes analytically the relationship between flexural capacity and geometric characteristics by considering the equilibrium conditions at critical cross sections. Compatibility of deformation is satisfied by assuming that plane cross sections remain plane, and the longitudinal concrete and steel stresses are evaluated by the material stress-strain characteristics. Transverse stresses are not considered to affect flexural capacity and, therefore, are ignored.

It is well known, however, that concrete is weak in tension and strong in compression. Therefore its primary purpose in a reinforced concrete structural member is to sustain compressive forces, while steel reinforcement is used to sustain tensile forces, with concrete providing protection to it. Since concrete is used to sustain compressive forces, it is essential that its strength and deformational response under such conditions be known.

The stress-strain characteristics of concrete in compression are considered to be adequately described by the deformational response of concrete specimens such as prisms or cylinders under uniaxial compression. Typical stress-strain curves providing a full description of the behavior of such specimens are shown in Fig. 5.12, which indicates that a characteristic feature of the curves is that they comprise an ascending and a gradually descending branch. (It will be seen later, however, that perhaps the most significant feature of concrete behavior is the abrupt increase of the rate of lateral expansion that the specimen undergoes when the load exceeds a level close to, but not beyond, the peak level. This level is the *minimum-volume* level, marking the beginning of a dramatic volume dilation,

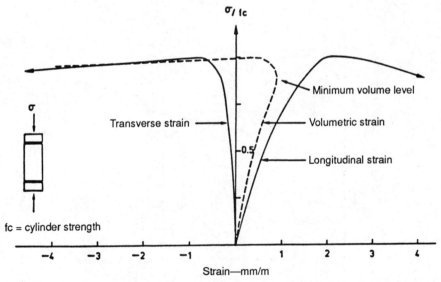

Fig. 5.12   Typical stress-strain curves obtained from tests on concrete cylinders under uniaxial compression.

which follows the continuous reduction of the volume of the specimen that has occurred up to this load level. The variation of the volume of the specimen under increasing uniaxial compressive stress is also shown in Fig. 5.12. It is important to note that although the curves in Fig. 5.12 describe the deformational response of concrete both in the direction of loading and at right angles to this direction, it is only the former which is considered essential by the plane-sections theory for the description of the longitudinal stress distribution within the compressive zone of the beam cross section.

The axial stress–axial strain and the axial stress–lateral strain curves of Fig. 5.12 may be combined to form the axial strain–lateral strain curve shown in Fig. 5.13. It is interesting to note that the curve of Fig. 5.13 also comprises two portions, each corresponding, respectively, to the ascending and the descending branches of the stress-strain curves of Fig. 5.12, with the transition between these portions corresponding to the portion of the stress-strain curves between the minimum-volume and peak stress levels. If uniaxial stress-strain data do indeed describe the deformational behavior of the compressive zone of the beam, then an axial strain–lateral strain relationship (such as that shown in Fig. 5.13) should provide a realistic description of the deformational behavior of an element of concrete in this zone. The deformational response of the compressive zone can be established by testing a reinforced concrete beam (such as that shown in Fig. 5.14) under two-point loading and measuring longitudinal and transverse strains at the top face of the beam within the middle zone. Such tests have already been carried out (Kotsovos, 1982), and the strains measured in the region of the deepest flexural cracks have been used to plot the longitudinal strain–transverse strain curve shown in Fig. 5.15. The figure also includes the curve (shown in Fig. 5.13) established from tests on cylinders under uniaxial compression, and it is apparent that only the portion of the latter to the minimum-volume level can provide a re-

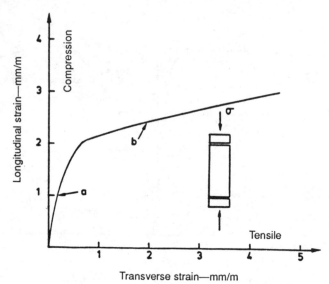

Fig. 5.13   Typical axial strain–lateral strain curve constructed from stress-strain curves in Fig. 5.12. *a*, *b*—ascending, descending branches.

alistic description of the beam behavior. Beyond this level, the cylinder curve deviates dramatically from the beam curve.

The preceding results clearly demonstrate that in spite of the prominence given to them in flexural design, the postyield uniaxial stress-strain characteristics *cannot* describe the behavior of an element of concrete in the compressive zone of a reinforced concrete beam in flexure. Such a conclusion should come as no surprise since it has been found by experiment that, unlike the ascending

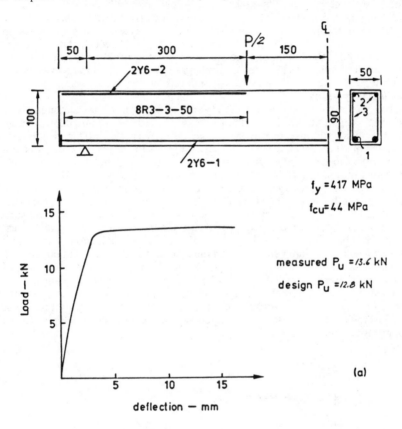

Fig. 5.14   (a) Design details and measured response of typical reinforced concrete beam. (b) Assessment of average stress in compressive zone based on measured values.

branch, the descending branch does not necessarily represent material behavior; it may merely describe secondary testing effects due to the interaction between test machine and specimen (Kotsovos, 1983a). On the other hand, the ascending branch is insufficient to fully describe the behavior of the compressive zone.

Additional evidence in support of these arguments can be obtained easily by assessing the average longitudinal stress in the compressive zone of the reinforced concrete beam shown in Fig. 5.14. The figure also provides design details of the beam together with its experimentally obtained load-deflection relationship. Using the measured value of the load-carrying capacity of the beam and the strength of the tensile reinforcement, the average stress in the compressive zone at failure can be calculated as indicated in the figure. The calculated average stress in the compressive zone is found to be 67 MPa (9700 psi), which is 75% higher than the uniaxial compressive strength of concrete f_c. Such a large stress can only be sustained if the stress conditions in the compressive zone are *triaxially* compressive.

It has been argued that even in the absence of stirrups, a triaxial compressive state of stress can be developed due to the occurrence of volume dilation in localized regions within the compressive zone (Kotsovos, 1982). This view is supported by the experimentally established shape of the transverse deformation profile of the top face of the beam, as shown in Fig. 5.16. The characteristic feature of this profile is the large transverse expansion (indicative of volume dilation) that occurs in the region of cross sections coinciding with a deep flexural crack when the load-carrying capacity of the beam is approached. This localized transverse expansion is restrained by concrete in the adjacent regions, and such a restraint may be considered equivalent to the application of a confining pressure that has been assessed to be at least 10% of f_c. An indication of the effect that such a small confining stress has on the load-carrying capacity of concrete in the longitudinal direction is given in Fig. 5.17, which describes the variation of the peak axial compressive stress sustained by cylinders with increasing confining pressure. The figure indicates that a confining pressure of 10% of f_c is sufficient to increase the load-carrying capacity of the specimen by more than 50%, and this should be the cause of the large compressive stresses developing in the compressive zone.

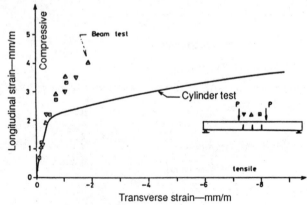

Fig. 5.15   Typical relationships between longitudinal and transverse strains measured on top face of reinforced concrete beams at critical sections.

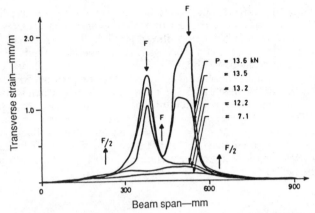

Fig. 5.16   Typical variation of transverse deformation profile of compressive top face of reinforced concrete beam in Fig. 5.19, with increasing load, indicating the development of internal actions F for compatibility purposes.

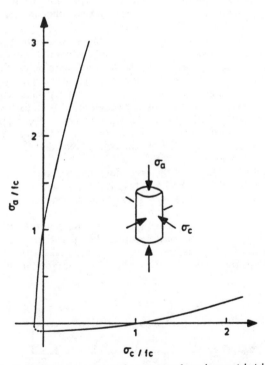

Fig. 5.17   Typical failure envelope of concrete under axisymmetric triaxial stress.

Concurrently, the expanding concrete induces tensile stresses in adjacent regions, and this gives rise to a compression-tension-tension state of stress. Such a state of stress reduces the strength of the concrete in the longitudinal direction. (In fact, Fig. 5.17 indicates that a tensile stress of about 5% of f_c is sufficient to reduce the cylinder strength by about 50%.) It has been shown (Kotsovos, 1984) that collapse occurs due to horizontal splitting of the compressive zone in regions between deep flexural cracks (Fig. 5.18). Concrete crushing, which is widely considered to be the cause of flexural failure, appears to be a postfailure phenomenon, which occurs in the compressive zone of cross sections coinciding with a deep flexural crack due to the loss of the restraint provided by the adjacent concrete. It is important to emphasize that the development of triaxial stress conditions is a key feature of structural behavior *only* at the late stages of the loading history of the beam.

2 Shear capacity

Shear capacity of a reinforced concrete beam is defined as the maximum shear force that can be sustained by a critical cross section. When deemed necessary, shear reinforcement is provided in order to carry that portion of the shear force which cannot be sustained by concrete alone. The amount of reinforcement required for this purpose is assessed by using one of a number of available methods invariably developed on the basis of the truss analogy concept (Ritter, 1899; Moersch, 1909), stipulating that a reinforced concrete beam with shear reinforcement may be considered to behave as a truss once inclined cracking occurs.

A prerequisite for the application of the concept of *shear capacity of critical sections* in design appears to be the widely accepted view that the main contributor to shear resistance is *aggregate interlock* (Fenwick and Paulay, 1968; Taylor, 1968; Regan, 1969), for only through aggregate interlock can the "cracked" web be the sole contributor to the shear resistance of a reinforced concrete beam, as specified by current code provisions such as BS 8110 (British Standards Institution, 1985). Furthermore, the concept of shear capacity of critical sections is itself a prerequisite for the application of the truss analogy, since it is the loss of the shear capacity below the neutral axis that the shear reinforcement is considered to offset.

It would therefore appear from the preceding discussion that the aggregate interlock concept, although not explicitly referred to, forms the backbone of current concepts describing the causes of shear failure. Yet this concept is incompatible with fundamental concrete properties—a crack propagates in the direction of the maximum principal compressive stress and opens in the orthogonal direction (Kotsovos, 1979; Kotsovos and Newman, 1981). If there were a significant shearing movement of the crack faces (which is essential for the mobilization of aggregate interlock), then this movement should cause crack branching in all lo-

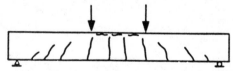

Fig. 5.18 Typical failure mode of reinforced concrete beam in flexure.

calized regions where aggregate interlock is affected. The occurrence of such crack branching has not been reported to date.

The inadequacy of the concepts currently used to describe the causes of shear failure has been demonstrated in a recently completed experimental program (Kotsovos, 1987a, 1987b). The program was based on an investigation of the behavior of reinforced concrete beams with various arrangements of shear reinforcement (Fig. 5.19) and subjected to two-point loading with various ratios of

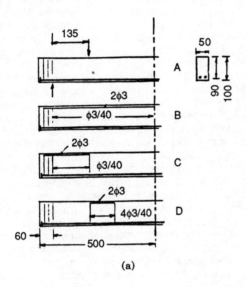

(a)

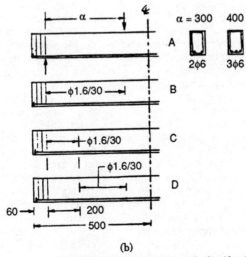

(b)

Fig. 5.19   Design details of beams. (a) $a/d = 1.5$. (b) $a/d > 2.5$.

shear span to depth a/d. The main results of this program are given in Fig. 5.20, which shows the load-deflection curves of the beams tested.

On the basis of the concept of shear capacity of critical sections, all beams having shear spans without shear reinforcement, either throughout or over large portions of their lengths, should have similar load-carrying capacities. Yet beams C and D were found to have significantly higher load-carrying capacities than beams A, which had no shear reinforcement throughout their spans. In fact, beams D in all cases exhibited a ductile behavior, which is indicative of a flexural mode of failure, and their load-carrying capacities were higher than those of beams A by an amount varying from 40 to 100%, depending on a/d. These results clearly indicate that such behavior *cannot* be explained in terms of the concept of shear capacity of critical sections, and thus the failure of the beams cannot be described as a "shear" failure as defined by this concept.

The evidence presented in Fig. 5.20 also contrasts the view that aggregate interlock makes a significant contribution to shear resistance. This is because the large deflections exhibited by beams D in all cases and beams C in most cases led to a large increase in the inclined crack width and thus considerably reduced, if not eliminated, aggregate interlock. In fact, near peak load the inclined crack of beams D had a width in excess of 2 mm (0.08 in.) which is by an order of magnitude larger than that found by Fenwick and Paulay (1968), and which would reduce aggregate interlock by more than half. It can only be concluded, therefore, that in the absence of shear reinforcement, the main contributor to the shear resistance of a reinforced concrete beam at its ultimate limit state is the *compressive zone,* with the region of the beam below the neutral axis making an insignificant contribution, if any.

In view of the negligible contribution of aggregate interlock to the shear resistance of a reinforced concrete beam without shear reinforcement, shear resistance should be associated with the strength of the concrete within the region of the beam *above* the neutral axis. The validity of this view has been verified by testing reinforced concrete T-beams with a web width significantly smaller than that generally considered to provide adequate shear resistance (Kotsovos et al., 1987). Design details of a typical beam with 2.6-m (8.5-ft) span tested under six-point loading are shown in Fig. 5.21, while Fig. 5.22 shows a typical mode of failure.

The tests indicated that the load-carrying capacity of the beams was up to three times higher than that predicted on the basis of the currently accepted concepts. It was also found that failure usually occurred in regions *not* regarded by current code provisions as the most critical. As the web width of these beams was inadequate to provide shear resistance, these results support the view that the region of the beam above the neutral axis (the flange in the present case) is the main, if not the sole, contributor to shear resistance.

It is also interesting to note in Fig. 5.22 that the inclined crack, which eventually caused failure, penetrated very deeply into the compressive zone. In fact, it locally reduced the depth of the neutral axis to less than 5% of the beam depth. In view of such a small depth of the compressive zone, it may be argued that concrete is unlikely to be able to sustain the high tensile stresses caused by the presence of the shear force. Such an argument is usually based on the erroneous assumption that concrete behavior within the compressive zone of a beam at its ultimate limit state is described realistically by using uniaxial stress-strain characteristics. This assumption is in conflict with the failure mechanism discussed in the preceding section in the case of flexural capacity.

In the case of the compressive zone in the region of a section coinciding with a flexural crack, concrete in the region of a section through the tip of a deep inclined crack is also subjected to a wholly compressive state of stress. This is because concrete (due to the small neutral axis depth) will reach its minimum-

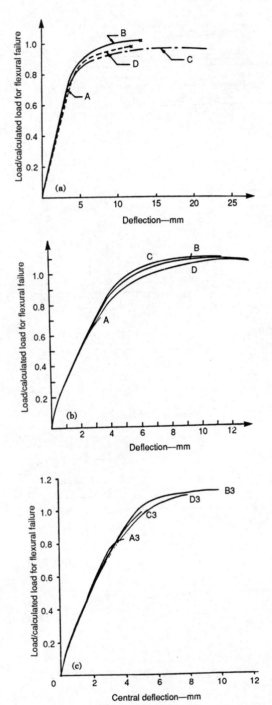

Fig. 5.20 Load-deflection curves of beams. (a) a/d = 1.5. (b) a/d = 3.3. (c) a/d = 4.4.

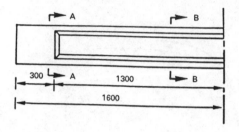

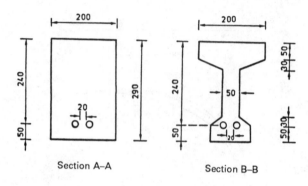

Section A–A   Section B–B

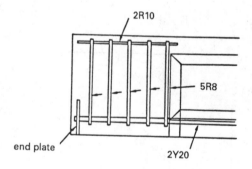

2R10

5R8

end plate

2Y20

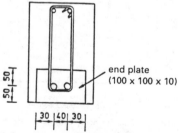

end plate
(100 × 100 × 10)

30 | 40 | 30

Fig. 5.21 Design details of typical reinforced concrete T-beam tested under six-point loading.

volume level before this level is reached anywhere else within the compressive zone. As discussed earlier, this compressive state of stress represents the restraining effect of the surrounding concrete. It is considered that a part of the vertical component of this compressive state of stress counteracts the tensile stresses developing in the presence of shear force. Hence in spite of the presence of such a force, the state of stress remains compressive, and this causes a significant enhancement of the local strength. A schematic representation of the mechanism providing shear resistance is shown in Fig. 5.23.

3 Compressive force path concept

A recent attempt to summarize the experimental information discussed in the preceding sections and present it in a unified and rational form has led to the formulation of the concept of the *compressive force path* (Kotsovos, 1988a). On the basis of this concept, the load-carrying capacity of a reinforced concrete structural member is associated with the strength of the concrete in the region of the paths along which compressive forces are transmitted to the supports. The path of a compressive force may be visualized as a "flow" of compressive stresses with varying sections perpendicular to the path direction and with the compressive force representing the stress resultant at each section (Fig. 5.24). It is considered that failure is related to the development of tensile stresses in the region of the path, and such stresses may develop due to a number of causes, the main ones being the following:

1. *Changes in path direction.* A tensile stress resultant (T in Fig. 5.24) develops for equilibrium purposes at locations where the path changes direction.

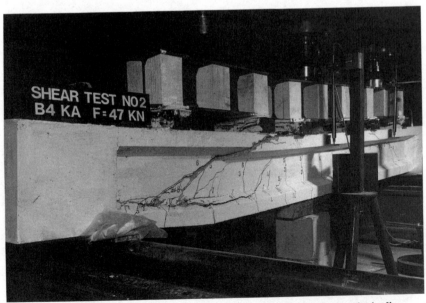

Fig. 5.22   Typical mode of failure of reinforced concrete T-beam under six-point loading.

2. *Varying intensity of compressive stress field along path.* The compressive stress will reach a critical level at the smallest cross section of the path, where the stress intensity is the highest before this level is reached in adjacent cross sections. As was seen in Subsections 1 and 2, this level marks the start of an abrupt and large material dilation, which will induce tensile stresses (t_1 in Fig. 5.24) in the surrounding concrete.

3. *Tip of inclined crack.* It is well known from fracture mechanics that large tensile stresses (t_2 in Fig. 5.24) develop perpendicular to the direction of the maximum principal compressive stress in the region of the crack tip (Kotsovos, 1979; Kotsovos and Newman, 1981).

4. *Bond failure (Kotsovos, 1986).* Bond failure at the level of the tension reinforcement between two consecutive flexural cracks changes the stress conditions in the compressive zone of the beam element between these cracks, as indicated in Fig. 5.25. From the figure it can be seen that the loss of the bond force results in an extension of the right-hand-side flexural crack, which is sufficient to cause an increase dz of the lever arm z, such that $C \cdot dz = V \cdot a$. The extension

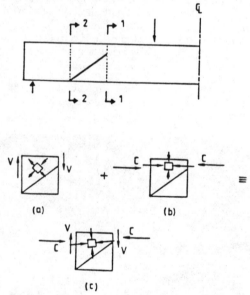

Fig. 5.23   Schematic representation of mechanism providing shear resistance.

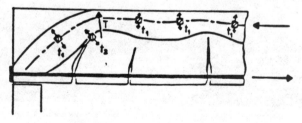

Fig. 5.24   Compressive force path.

of the flexural crack reduces the depth of the neutral axis and thus increases locally the intensity of the compressive stress block. This change in the stress intensity should give rise to tensile stresses in the manner described in item 2.

In order to use the preceding concept as the basis for describing the causes of failure of structural concrete members, it is essential to visualize the shape of the path along which a compressive force is transmitted to the supports. This is not necessarily a difficult task, and it has been shown that, for a simply supported reinforced concrete beam at its ultimate limit state, the compressive force at the cross section in midspan is transmitted to the support by following a path which, for any practical purpose, may be considered to be bilinear (Kotsovos, 1983b, 1988). The change in the path direction appears to occur at a distance of approximately twice the effective depth d for two-point loading with a shear-span-to-depth ratio a/d greater than approximately 2.0, and for uniformly distributed loading (UDL) with a span-to-depth ratio L/d greater than approximately 6.0 (Fig. 5.26a). For smaller ratios it is considered to occur at the cross

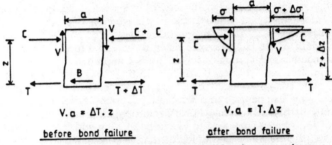

Fig. 5.25   Effect of bond failure on stress conditions in compressive zone.

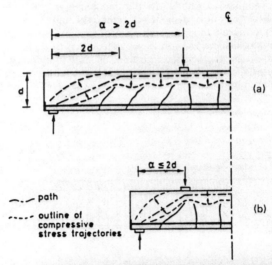

Fig. 5.26   Schematic representation of path of compressive force and corresponding outline of compressive stress trajectories for reinforced concrete beams with various a/d ratios.

section coinciding with the load point, assuming that UDL can be replaced by an equivalent two-point loading at the third point (Fig. 5.26b).

4 Modeling

The compressive force path concept may be introduced in design by developing physical models capable of providing a realistic description of the features of structural concrete behavior described. For example, a reinforced concrete beam (without transverse reinforcement) subjected to two-point loading may be modeled as a "comblike" structure tied by the tension reinforcement, as shown in Fig. 5.27 [Kotsovos, to be published (a)]. It can be seen in the figure that the "comb" comprises a frame with inclined legs, providing a simplified but realistic description of the shape of the compressive force path, and a number of "teeth" representing the concrete cantilevers which form between consecutive flexural or inclined cracks occurring within the beam web under increasing load. The shape of the cross section of the model is that of the actual beam.

Using the compressive force path (see Fig. 5.26) as a guide, the horizontal projection of the inclined legs of the frame may be given a value equal to either the shear span (for $a/d < 2$) or twice the beam depth (for $a/d > 2$). On the other hand, the width of the teeth may be taken to be equal to half the depth of the horizontal member of the frame, since there is comprehensive experimental evidence (Leonhardt and Walther, 1961/62) indicating that crack spacing at the ultimate limit state is approximately equal to half the depth of the neutral axis. The same model may also be used to represent a reinforced concrete beam subjected to uniformly distributed loading. For a beam of span greater than $6d$ it may be modeled as for a beam subjected to two-point loading with $a/d > 2$. For smaller beam spans, the uniformly distributed loading is considered to be equivalent to concentrated loading applied at the third point.

In compliance with the compressive force path concept, strength is considered to be predominantly provided by the tied frame with the concrete "teeth" making a small contribution to shear resistance through bond forces which develop between concrete and tension reinforcement. Although, contrary to Kani's (1964) hypothesis, these forces are considered to be insufficient to cause flexural failure of the teeth, their presence is essential for the overall beam strength since, as discussed in Subsection 3, bond failure causes a significant stress distribution within the compressive zone (see Fig. 5.25), and this may lead to collapse.

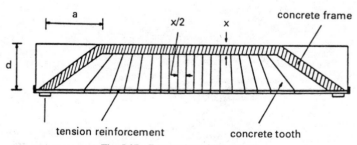

Fig. 5.27   Proposed comblike model.

5 Failure criteria

To implement the model just described in design, it is essential to complement it with a failure criterion. Such a criterion cannot be unique since failure may occur due to a number of causes. It is well known that these can be classified into four categories (Kani, 1964; Kotsovos, 1988a), as indicated in Fig. 5.28.

Type I behavior is characterized by a flexural mode of failure which occurs when the flexural capacity is attained. In view of the complex triaxial stress conditions which develop within the compressive zone at the ultimate limit state, it is considered sufficient for practical purposes to assess the flexural capacity on the basis of a rectangular stress block. Therefore, for an underreinforced concrete beam with a rectangular cross section, the flexural capacity of the model may be assessed as indicated in Appendix 1 of Section 5.3 of this chapter. Equation 5.12 in Appendix 1 can be used to determine the load-carrying capacity of the beam by considering the equilibrium conditions between internal and external actions.

Type II behavior characterizes beams in which the horizontal projection of the inclined leg of the frame of the proposed model (inclined portion of compressive force path) is greater than, or equal to, twice the beam depth ($a/d \geq 2$). Such beams, under the combined action of a bending moment and a shear force, may fail due to a number of causes (described in Subsection 3) before flexural capacity is attained. An analytical expression of the combination of these internal actions causing failure has already been derived empirically (Bobrowski and Bardham-Roy, 1969) and, with a slight modification, is as shown in Appendix 2 of this chapter. The approach used for the implementation of this expression in design is also outlined in Appendix 2.

Type III behavior characterizes beams in which the horizontal projection of the inclined leg of the frame of the model is equal to the shear span a, the latter attaining values between d and $2d$. As indicated in Fig. 5.28, $a = 2d$ is taken to correspond to the lowest point of Kani's valley, whereas $a = d$ corresponds to flexural capacity, provided type IV failure (to be discussed) is prevented. The combination of internal actions causing failure for $a = d$ and $a = 2d$ can be obtained easily from Eqs. 5.12 and 5.13, respectively (see Appendices 1 and 2). For intermediate values of the shear span (that is, $d < a < 2d$ it is considered sufficient for design purposes to establish the combination of internal actions by linear interpolation. The resulting combination of internal actions may be used in design, as indicated in Appendix 2 for type II behavior.

Type IV behavior characterizes beams in which the horizontal projection of the inclined legs of the frame of the model is smaller than the beam depth. Collapse may occur due to splitting of either the horizontal portion (flexural failure) or the inclined portion of the path. Such beams can be designed as discussed elsewhere (Kotsovos, 1988b) by using the simple design procedure indicated in Fig. 5.29. It should be noted, however, that if the load-carrying capacity of a type IV beam is exceeded, the excess load is unlikely to be sustained by using conventional web reinforcement (Kotsovos, 1988b). It has been suggested that an improvement of the load-carrying capacity can be achieved by increasing the cross-sectional area of the beam while using nominal reinforcement (as specified in current code provisions) in order to reduce the likelihood of instability caused by out-of-plane sections developing due to the heterogeneous nature of concrete.

6 Provision of transverse reinforcement

As discussed in the preceding subsection and in Appendix 2 of this chapter, beam behavior types II and III (characterized by modes of failure occurring before flexural capacity is reached), one of the ways in which flexural capacity may be attained involves the provision of transverse reinforcement. Such reinforcement is provided in order to sustain that portion of the internal tensile actions (developing in the region of the compressive force path) which cannot be sustained by concrete alone.

For type II behavior, significant internal tensile actions may develop for equilibrium purposes within both the region where the compressive force path changes direction and, for the case of point loading, the horizontal portions of the path in the region of point loads. In the former case, the transverse reinforcement required to sustain such action will slightly modify the comblike model (shown in Fig. 5.27), as indicated in Fig. 5.30. Figure 5.30 shows the region where inclined and horizontal members of the model join, and indicates that the transverse reinforcement not only sustains the action of the vertical component V of the inclined compression, but also subjects the shaded concrete block of the beam web, where it is anchored, to a compressive force D. This force balances the shear force V acting on the right-hand side of this block. It should be noted, how-

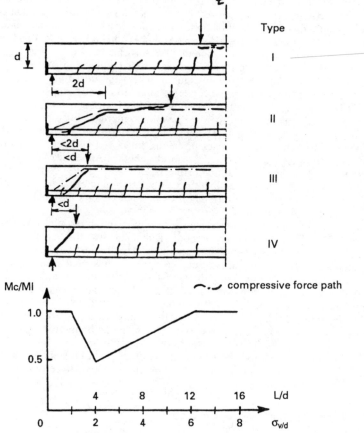

Fig. 5.28   Types of behavior exhibited by reinforced concrete beams without shear reinforcement subjected to two-point loading.

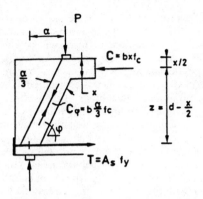

(a) Moment   equilibrium $Cz = P\alpha$ yields x

(b) Horizontal force equilibrium $T = C$ yields A_s

(c) Check whether $\alpha/3$ satisfies vertical force
     equilibrium $C_\varphi \sin\varphi = P$

     If not, adjust b and repeat

Fig. 5.29   Design method for type IV behavior proposed by Kotsovos (1988b).

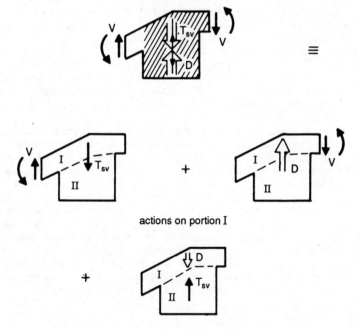

actions on portion I

actions on portion II

Fig. 5.30   Effect of transverse reinforcement on internal actions in region where path changes direction.

ever, that the transverse reinforcement will be activated only when the capacity of the concrete to sustain the action of the internal tensile force alone is exceeded. When this occurs, the excess tensile force will be sustained by the reinforcement, which may be assessed as described in Appendix 3 of this chapter. Following current practice, the spacing of the transverse reinforcement should be smaller than the beam effective depth d, which is considered to be equal to the width (in the longitudinal direction) of the shaded block of the web (see Fig. 5.30).

On the other hand, in the case of point loading, although the horizontal portion of the path is capable of sustaining a significantly larger shear force than that presently considered, shear capacity may be lost when bond failure occurs between two consecutive flexural or inclined cracks. Bond failure will increase the depth of the right-hand crack, thus causing stress redistribution, as indicated in Fig. 5.25. Considering a rectangular cross section (for purposes of simplicity), the resulting transverse tensile stresses with the corresponding stress resultant and the amount of reinforcement required to sustain it may easily be assessed as described in Appendix 3 of this chapter. Such reinforcement should be placed beyond the region where the compressive force path changes direction within the shear span.

As discussed in Subsection 5 for type III behavior, failure is associated with a large reduction in the neutral axis depth in the region of the tip of the main inclined crack. Such a reduction in depth will lead to the development of tensile stresses within the compressive zone for the reasons described in item 2 of Subsection 3. Failure, therefore, will occur when the strength of the compressive zone under the combined action of compressive and tensile stresses is exceeded. This type of failure may be prevented either by providing reinforcement that would sustain the tensile stresses that cannot be sustained by concrete alone, or by reducing the compressive stresses. While the amount of reinforcement required to sustain the tensile stresses is difficult to assess, since the tensile stresses are difficult to calculate, the compressive stresses can be reduced easily by providing stirrups throughout the length of the horizontal projection of the inclined crack (which in the case of two-point loading equals the shear span a). The stirrups may be designed as indicated in Appendix 4 of this chapter, where it can be seen that their contribution to the flexural capacity of the critical section equals $M_f - M_c$, where M_f is the flexural capacity of the beam and M_c is calculated as described in Appendix 2 of this chapter.

The presence of stirrups beyond the critical section is deemed essential, since it has been shown experimentally that reinforcing with stirrups to the critical section only does not safeguard against brittle failure (Kotsovos, 1987a), as the inclined crack is likely to extend deeply into the compressive zone. Although the presence of stirrups within this region only inhibits crack opening and therefore may prevent further crack extension, the section through the tip of the inclined crack has the smallest neutral axis depth, and thus concrete in the compressive zone of this section will be the first to reach the minimum-volume level. As discussed in Subsections 1 and 2, the volumetric expansion that follows will induce tensile stresses in adjacent sections, and these may lead to splitting of the compressive zone and collapse before flexural capacity is attained. This type of failure may be prevented by extending the transverse reinforcement beyond the crack tip to a distance approximately equal to the neutral axis depth.

7 Experimental verification

The proposed model has already been used to predict the load-carrying capacity of deep beams (type IV behavior) (Kotsovos, 1988b), and Figs. 5.31 to 5.33 indicate a close correlation between predicted and experimental values. No distinction has been made between beams with and without web reinforcement since, as discussed in Subsection 5, the effect of such reinforcement on the load-carrying capacity has not been found to date to be significant (Kotsovos, 1988b).

For the case of reinforced concrete beams in shear, the proposed model has been used to design beams *A, B,* and *C* (shown in Figs. 5.21 and 5.34), which were subsequently tested under two-point (beams *A* and *B*) and four-point (beams *C*) loading, as indicated in Fig. 5.35 [Kotsovos, to be published (b)]. These beams were chosen not only to provide evidence in support of the proposed model, but also to demonstrate the inefficiency of current shear design procedures. The main results of the tests are presented in Table 5.1 and Figs. 5.36 to 5.38, while a typical example of design calculations is given in Appendix 5 of this chapter. Table

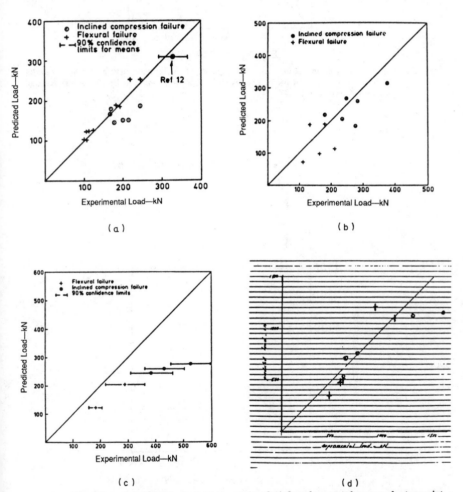

Fig. 5.31 Correlation of predicted load-carrying capacity of reinforced concrete beams under two-point loading with experimental values reported by various authors. (*a*) Rawdon de Paiva and Siess (1965) and Smith and Vantsiotis (1982). (*b*) Ramakrishnan and Ananthanarayana (1968). (*c*) Kong et al. (1970). (*d*) Subedi (1988).

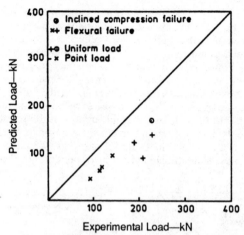

Fig. 5.32   Correlation of predicted load-carrying capacity of reinforced concrete deep beams under single-point loading and uniformly distributed loading reported by Ramakrishnan and Ananthanarayana (1968).

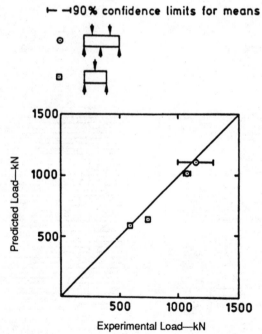

Fig. 5.33   Correlation of predicted load-carrying capacity of continuous and simply supported reinforced concrete deep beams under single-point loading with experimental values reported by Rogowski et al. (1986).

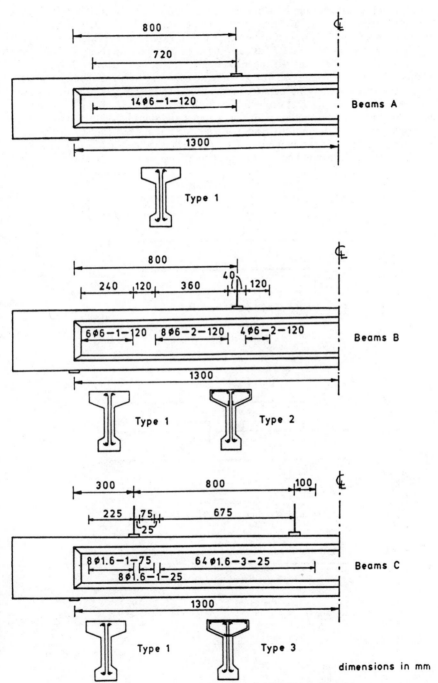

Fig. 5.34   Transverse reinforcement details of beams tested.

5.1 also includes the strength values predicted by BS 8110 (British Standards Institution, 1985) and ACI 318 (1989) and indicates that while the design strengths of the beams were only slightly smaller than the experimental values, the code predictions underestimate the load-carrying capacities considerably.

Table 5.1 indicates that the mean strength value obtained from the tests on beams A is slightly smaller than the strength value for beams B. Such a small difference in load-carrying capacity indicates that flange reinforcement does not have a significant effect on beam strength. It can be seen in Fig. 5.36, however, that the deformational response of beams A and B is characterized by a considerable difference in ductility. The figure shows that unlike beams A, which exhibit brittle behavior, the behavior of beams B is ductile. Such a difference in behavior can be attributed to the effect of the flange reinforcement since in all

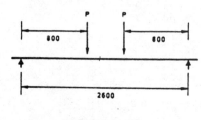

(a) Beams A and B

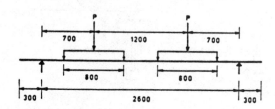

(b) Beams C

Fig. 5.35   Loading configuration used for tests.

Table 5.1   Predicted and measured load-carrying capacity of beams tested

Beam	Load type	Predicted total sustained load, kN			Measured total sustained load, kN
		British code	ACI code	Proposed method	
(1)	(2)	(3)	(4)	(5)	(6)
A	Two-point	120.0	112.2	—	191.0
B	Two-point	120.0	112.2	180.8	192.2
C	Four-point	45.6	32.2	223.6	240.1

other aspects beams *A* and *B* are the same. Flange reinforcement, therefore, is essential if a reinforced concrete beam is to behave in a ductile manner that, in compliance with current design philosophy, will enable it to give ample warning in the event of impending collapse. Beams *C*, which also contain web reinforcement, exhibit ductile behavior as well.

Typical stages of the cracking process of the beams tested are shown in Figs. 5.37 and 5.38. From the figures it can be seen that in all cases, inclined cracking extended from the bottom face of the beam to the bottom face of the flange as the load increased to a level as low as 20% of the failure load. The number of web cracks increased with increasing load, and in the case of beams *A*, inclined cracking penetrated into the flange at a load level of approximately 50% of the failure load. It should be noted, however, that up to and perhaps a little beyond this level, the cracks were hardly visible since crack widths were smaller than about 0.1 mm (0.004 in.).

The rate of crack extension decreased significantly as the load increased beyond a load level of approximately half the failure load. However, one of the inclined cracks of beams *A* propagated toward the point load, thus reducing the depth of the neutral axis to a very small value (see Fig. 5.37*a*). Such a reduction should cause a significant increase in the intensity of the compressive stresses in the cross section through the crack tip, and as discussed in Subsection 2, concrete in this region will be the first to undergo a considerable dilation, which will induce tensile stresses to the concrete in adjacent regions. Under the combined action of compressive and tensile stresses, it is the concrete in these adjacent regions that will fail due to longitudinal splitting, leading to structural collapse. Such longitudinal splitting has, in fact, been the cause of collapse of beams *A*, as indicated in Fig. 5.38*a*. It should also be noted that although beams *A* did not

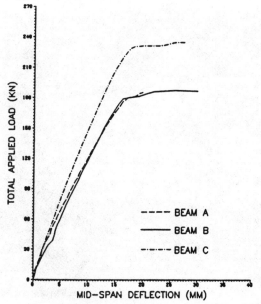

Fig. 5.36   Load-deflection curves of beams in Figs. 5.21 and 5.34.

attain their flexural capacity, the transverse web reinforcement (which was provided in order to sustain the tensile internal action that develops due to the change in the direction of the path of the compressive force) did, in fact, sustain a force that was higher than the design value.

For beams *B,* the presence of the transverse flange reinforcement prevented

total load = 50 kN

total load = 90 kN

Fig. 5.37(*a*)   **Significant stages of cracking process, Beams *A*.**

the extension of inclined cracking into the flange, and failure eventually occurred due to failure of the compressive zone within the middle zone of the beam close to one of the point loads (see Fig. 5.37b). It is interesting to note that the failure mode of beams *B* is characterized by vertical splitting of the compressive zone along the longitudinal axis of the beams. Such a mode of failure is also compatible

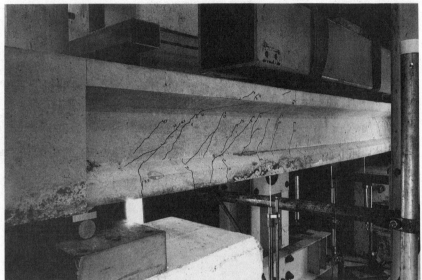

total load = 130 kN

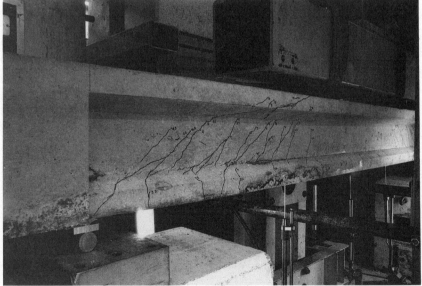

total load =190 kN

Fig. 5.37(*a*)   (*Continued*) Significant stages of cracking process, Beams *A*.

with the view expressed earlier, namely, that failure of the compressive zone occurs due to the development of tensile stresses, which causes splitting in the longitudinal direction. While horizontal splitting is prevented by the vertical legs of the flange reinforcement, vertical splitting is possible since the horizontal legs of the flange reinforcement are not continuous throughout the flange width.

total load = 50 kN

total load = 90 kN

Fig. 5.37(b) Significant stages of cracking process, Beams B.

The cracking process of beams C under four-point loading was similar to that of beams B, that is, the web cracks propagated to the underside of the flange at early load stages and then multiplied as the load increased to a level approximately 15% higher than that corresponding to the calculated flexural capacity (see Fig. 5.37c). At this level, the beam had reached its "true" flexural capacity

total load =160 kN

total load = 192.2 kN

Fig. 5.37(b)   (*Continued*) **Significant stages of cracking process, Beams B.**

since, as indicated in Fig. 5.36, it exhibited a stable increase in deflection under near-constant load. However, as the flexural cracks were increasing in both depth and width and flexural failure seemed to be imminent, a large inclined web crack suddenly appeared. Eventually failure occurred as the inclined crack pen-

total load = 60 kN

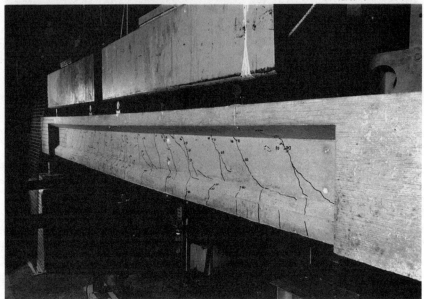

total load = 170 kN

Fig. 5.37(c)   Significant stages of cracking process, Beams *C*.

ctrated into the flange in the region of the point load near the middle zone of the beam.

As can be seen in Fig. 5.38c, the cause of failure appears to have been the "snapping" of the flange reinforcement, which was designed to sustain a tensile

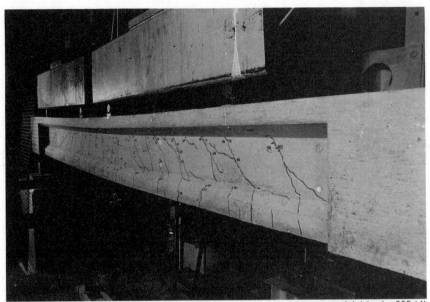

total load = 235 kN

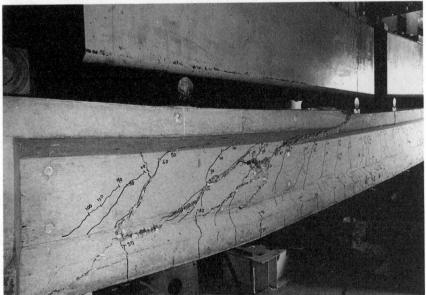

total load = 240.1 kN

Fig. 5.37(c)   (Continued) Significant stages of cracking process, Beams C.

force corresponding to a load level approximately 10% lower than the actual failure load. Although in the present case the beams exhibited ductile behavior, it would appear that underestimating the flexural capacity may lead to types of failures other than flexural, which may be brittle in nature and thus not give ade-

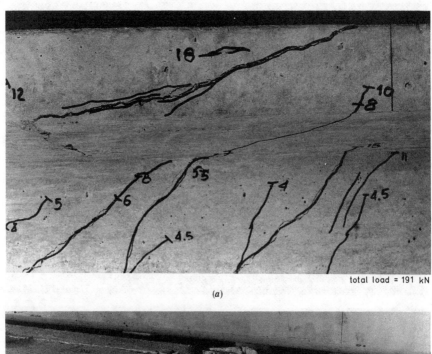

total load = 191 kN

(a)

total load = 192.2 kN

Fig. 5.38   Crack pattern in region where failure occurred. (a) Beam A. (b) Beam B. (c) Beam C.

quate warning of the impending collapse. A safety factor for flexural failure smaller than those specified for other modes of failure may eliminate the possibility of brittle failure.

It is also interesting to note that failure occurred in a region not considered critical by current design methods since it is not subjected to the maximum shear force.

8 Conclusions

Designing in compliance with the compressive force path has been found to lead to both safe and efficient design solutions since the beams tested sustained comfortably the design load with transverse reinforcement of between 30 and 70% less than that specified by current code provisions.

Current design methods appear to be not only inefficient, but also unsafe, since some of the beams tested have been found to fail in regions not considered critical by current code provisions.

For modes of failure other than flexural, it is recommended to specify safety factors larger than that specified for flexural failure since it was found that underestimating the flexural capacity may lead to failure of the brittle type.

5.3 APPENDICES

1 Assessment of Flexural Capacity

$$M_f = T \cdot z = C \cdot z \tag{5.12}$$

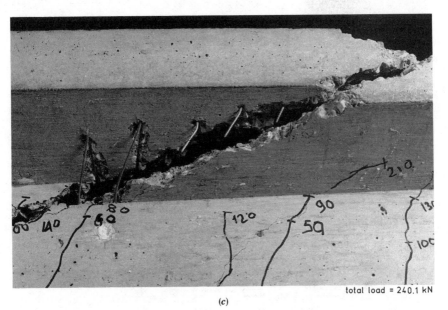

(c)

Fig. 5.38 (*Continued*) **Crack pattern in region where failure occurred.** (*a*) **Beam** *A*. (*b*) **Beam** *B*. (*c*) **Beam** *C*.

where $C = b \cdot x \cdot \sigma_c$
$\quad\quad T = A_s f_y$
$\quad\quad \sigma_c = 0.8 f_{cyl} = 0.64 f_{cu}$
$\quad\quad f_{cyl}$ = cylinder concrete strength
$\quad\quad f_{cu}$ = cube concrete (characteristic) strength
$\quad\quad f_y$ = characteristic strength of tension steel

See Fig. 5.39.

2 Failure Criterion for Type II Behavior

$$M_c = 0.875sd\left(0.342b_1 + 0.3\frac{M_f}{d^2}\sqrt[4]{\frac{z}{s}}\right)\sqrt{\frac{16.66}{\rho_w f_y}} \tag{5.13}$$

where M_c = moment corresponding to shear failure, N · mm
$\quad\quad M_f$ = flexural capacity, N · mm
$\quad\quad s$ = distance of cross section from support, mm (For two-point loading,
$\quad\quad\quad s$ = shear span; for uniformly distributed loading, $s = 2d$.)
$\quad\quad d$ = effective depth, mm
$\quad\quad z$ = lever arm of horizontal internal actions, mm

$\quad\quad \rho_w = \dfrac{\text{area of tension steel}}{\text{web area of concrete to effective depth}}$

$\quad\quad f_y$ = characteristic strength of tension steel, N/mm^2
$\quad\quad b_1$ = effective width, mm

b_1 given by the lesser of $b_0 + 2b_s$ or $b_0 + 2d_s$, with b_0, b_s, and d_s shown in Fig. 5.40.
Equation 5.13 may be used in design as follows:

1. Select cross section s.
2. Find moment M_a, applied moment, at cross section s due to applied loading.
3. Design cross section s to sustain a given M_f.
4. Determine M_c from Eq. 5.13.

If $M_c > M_a$, only nominal stirrups would be needed. If $M_c < M_a$, either increase the area of tensile steel (thus increasing M_c to a level greater than, or equal to,

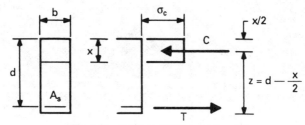

Fig. 5.39　Assessment of flexural capacity.

M_a), or increase the cross section. The alternative is to provide stirrups in accordance with the requirements described in Appendices 3 and 4.

3   Assessment of Transverse Reinforcement for Type II Behavior

Region Where Path Changes Direction.   For the situation depicted in Fig. 5.26a the excess tensile force is calculated as follows:

$$T_{sv} = V = V_a - V_c \tag{5.14}$$

$$V_c = \frac{M_c}{s}$$

where V_a = applied shear force
    V_c = portion of V_a sustained by concrete alone
    M_c = moment calculated from Eq. 5.13

The transverse reinforcement over a length d to sustain T_{sv} is given by

$$A_{sv} = \frac{T_{sv}}{f_{yv}}$$

where f_{yv} is the characteristic strength of the transverse reinforcement.

Horizontal Portion of Path.   Using the information given in Fig. 5.41, the following steps are followed:

1. $$\Delta z = \frac{Vx}{2T} \tag{5.15}$$

    where $V = V_a - V_c$.

2. $$x' = 2(d - z - \Delta z) > 0$$

    If $x' < 0$, increase the cross section.

3. Assess the nominal triaxial compressive stress σ_c':

$$\sigma_c' = \frac{C}{bx'}$$

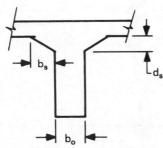

Fig. 5.40   Definition of b_o, b_s and d_s in Eq. 5.13.

4. Assuming $0.8f_{cyl}$ describes a uniaxial condition, assess the confining pressure σ_{conf} required for $0.8f_{cyl}$ to increase to σ_c' using the expression

$$\sigma_c' = 0.8f_{cyl} + 5\sigma_{conf}$$

$$\sigma_{conf} = \frac{\sigma_c' - 0.8f_{cyl}}{5}$$

5. Assume transverse tensile stress,

$$\sigma_t = -\sigma_{conf}$$

(Compression is positive.)

6. The tensile force over length d is given by

$$T_{sv} = \sigma_t \cdot b \cdot d$$

7. The amount of reinforcement required over length d in order to sustain the tension T_{sv} will thus be

$$A_{sv} = \frac{T_{sv}}{f_{yv}}$$

4   Assessment of Transverse Reinforcement for Type III Behavior

The moment equilibrium condition of the free body, shown in Fig. 5.42, can be expressed as follows:

$$M_f = M_c + T_{sv}\left(\frac{a}{2}\right)$$

where $M_f = R \cdot a$. From this expression the total force sustained by stirrups is

$$T_{sv} = \frac{2(M_f - M_c)}{a}$$

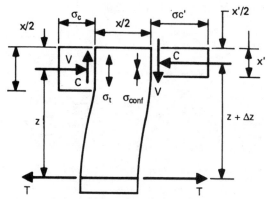

Fig. 5.41   Assessment of transverse reinforcement for type II behavior.

Thus the amount of reinforcement required is

$$A_{sv} = \frac{T_{sv}}{f_{yv}}$$

Excess Tension Due to Change in Path Direction.   Following Subsection 1 in Appendix 3, Eq. 5.14,

$$T_{sv} = 52{,}000 - 37{,}500 = 14{,}500 \text{ N}$$

$$A_{sv} = \frac{14{,}500}{360} = 40 \text{ mm}^2$$

Provide two $\phi 1.6$–1–25 ($= 39 \text{ mm}^2$).

Excess Tension Due to Bond Failure.   Following Appendix 3, Eq. 5.15,

$$\Delta z = \frac{14{,}500 \times 76}{2 \times 351{,}680} = 2 \text{ mm}$$

$$x' = 33 - 2 = 31 \text{ mm (shown in Fig. 5.41)}$$

$$A'_c = 12{,}400 \text{ mm}^2 \text{ (area of compressive concrete)}$$

$$\sigma'_c = 28.4 \text{ N/mm}^2$$

$$\sigma_{\text{conf}} = \frac{28.4 - 26}{5} = 0.5 \text{ N/mm}^2$$

The tensile stress resultant over a length of 240 mm is

$$T_{sv} = 0.5 \times 200 \times 240 = 24{,}000 \text{ N}$$

The reinforcement required is

$$A_{sv} = \frac{24{,}000}{360} = 67 \text{ mm}^2$$

The additional flange reinforcement is $\phi 1.6$–3–25 (see Fig. 5.34).

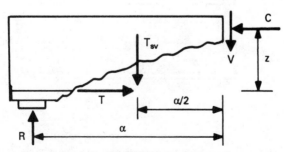

Fig. 5.42   Equilibrium near the support.

5   Design Calculations for Beams C in Figs. 5.21 and 5.34

Flexural Capacity

$$A_s = 628 \text{ mm}^2$$

$$f_y = 560 \text{ N/mm}^2$$

Hence,

$$T = 351,680 \text{ N}$$

$$f_{\text{cyl}} = 32.6 \text{ N/mm}^2$$

$$\sigma_c = 0.8 \times 32.6 = 26 \text{ N/mm}^2$$

Since $C = T$,

$$A_c = \frac{351,680}{26} = 13,526 \text{ mm}^2$$

Thus, $x = 76$ mm and $x_g = 33$ mm. The lever arm is

$$z = 240 - 33 = 207 \text{ mm}$$

Hence the flexural capacity is

$$M_f = 351,680 \times 207 = 72,797,760 \text{ N} \cdot \text{mm}$$

The maximum sustained four-point load as indicated in Fig. 5.20 is thus $4 \times 52,000$ N.

Shear Force Sustained by Concrete.   There are two possible shapes of path, as indicated in Fig. 5.43.
    Path 1.   The shear span is $a = 300$ mm ($< 2d = 480$ mm and $> d = 240$ mm), as shown in Fig. 5.43a. By assessing M_c for $a = 480$ mm and $a = 240$ mm,

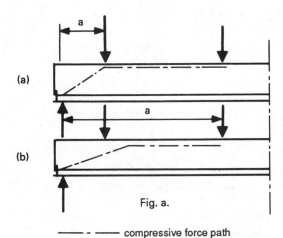

Fig. a.

——— - ——— compressive force path

Fig. 5.43   Compressive force path for different shear spans.

we obtain M_c for s = 300 mm by linear interpolation as follows. For s = 480 mm, from the design equation in Appendix 2 (Eq. 5.13),

$$M_c = 25,500,000 \text{ N} \cdot \text{mm}$$

For s = 240 mm,

$$M_c = M_f = 72,797,760 \text{ N} \cdot \text{mm}$$

Thus for s = 300 mm,

$$M_c = 72,797,760 - \frac{(72,797,760 - 25,500,000)60}{240} = 60,973,320 \text{ N} \cdot \text{mm}$$

However, the applied bending moment at s = 300 mm is M_a = 31,020,000 N · mm $\ll$ 60,973,320 N · mm. Thus for this path transverse reinforcement is not required.

Path 2. The shear span is a = 1100 mm, as shown in Fig. 5.43*b*. From the design equation in Appendix 2 (Eq. 5.13),

$$M_c = 41,220,000 \text{ N} \cdot \text{mm}$$

$$V_c = \frac{41,220,000}{1100} = 37,500 \text{ N}$$

The applied shear force is V_a = 52,000 N > 37,500 N. Thus the path is more critical and transverse reinforcement is required.

5.4 CONDENSED REFERENCES / BIBLIOGRAPHY

ACI 318 1989, *Building Code Requirements for Reinforced Concrete*

Baumann 1972, *On the Problem of Net Reinforcement of Surface Structures*
Bobrowski 1969, *A Method of Calculating the Ultimate Strength of Reinforced and Pre-*
Braestrup 1974, *Plastic Analysis of Shear in Reinforced Concrete*
BSI 1985, *Code of Practice for Design and Construction (BS 8110)*

CEB-FIP 1978, *Model Code for Concrete Structures*
Cerruti 1987, *Staggered Shear Design of Concrete Beams: Large Scale Tests*
Collins 1978, *Towards a Rational Theory for Reinforced Concrete Members in Shear*
Collins 1980, *Shear and Torsion Design of Prestressed and Non-Prestressed Concrete*
Collins 1986, *A Rational Approach to Shear Design—The 1984 Canadian Code Provi-*
Collins 1987, *Prestressed Concrete Basics*
Cook 1988, *Studies of Disturbed Regions Near Discontinuities in Reinforced Concrete*
CSA 1984, *Design of Concrete Structures for Buildings (CAN3-A23.3-M84)*

Dunstan 1987, *Joint Performance of RC Stepped Beams Subjected to Pure Moment*

Fenwick 1968, *Mechanisms of Shear Resistance of Concrete Beams*

Goutama 1988, *Tests on Reinforced Concrete Stepped Beams*

Hsu 1988, *Softened Truss Model Theory for Shear and Torsion*

IABSE 1979, *Colloquium on Plasticity in Reinforced Concrete*

Kani 1964, *The Riddle of Shear and Its Solution*
Kong 1970, *Web Reinforcement Effects on Deep Beams*
Kotsovos 1979, *Fracture Processes of Concrete under Generalized Stress States*
Kotsovos 1981, *Fracture Mechanics and Concrete Behaviour*
Kotsovos 1982, *A Fundamental Explanation of the Behaviour of RC Beams in Flexure*
Kotsovos 1983a, *Effect of Testing Techniques on the Post-Ultimate Behaviour of Concrete*
Kotsovos 1983b, *Mechanisms of "Shear" Failure*
Kotsovos 1984, *Deformation and Failure of Concrete in a Structure*
Kotsovos 1986, *Behaviour of Reinforced Concrete Beams with a Shear Span to Depth Ra-*
Kotsovos 1987, *Behaviour of RC T-Beams in Shear*
Kotsovos 1987a, *Shear Failure of Reinforced Concrete Beams*
Kotsovos 1987b, *Shear Failure of RC Beams: A Reappraisal of Current Concepts*
Kotsovos 1988a, *Compressive Force Path Concept: Basis for Ultimate Limit State*
Kotsovos 1988b, *Design of Reinforced Concrete Deep Beams*
Kotsovos to be published (a), *Designing RC Beams in Compliance with the Concept of the*
Kotsovos to be published (b), *Behaviour of RC Beams Designed in Compliance with the*
Kupfer 1964, *Generalization of Moersch's Truss Analogy Using the Principle of Mini-*

Lampert 1971, *Ultimate Strength and Design of Reinforced Concrete Beams in Torsion*
Leonhardt 1961/62, *The Stuttgart Shear Tests*

Mailhot 1984, *Experiments on the Staggering Concept for Shear Design*
Marti 1980, *On Plastic Analysis of Reinforced Concrete*
Marti 1982, *Strength and Deformations of Reinforced Concrete Members under Torsion*
Marti 1985a, *Basic Tools of Reinforced Concrete Beam Design*
Marti 1985b, *Truss Models in Detailing*
Marti 1986a, *Staggered Shear Design of Simply Supported Concrete Beams*
Marti 1986b, *Staggered Shear Design of Concrete Bridge Girders*
Marti 1987, *Response of Reinforced Concrete Slab Elements to Torsion*
Marti 1989, *Design of Concrete Slabs for Transverse Shear*
Mitchell 1974, *Diagonal Compression Field Theory—A Rational Model for Structural Con-*
Moersch 1908, 1922, *Reinforced Concrete Construction—Theory and Application*
Moersch 1909, *Concrete Steel Construction*
Mueller 1976, *Failure Mechanisms for Reinforced Concrete Beams in Torsion and Bend-*
Mueller 1978, *Plastic Analysis of Reinforced Concrete Walls and Beams*

Nielsen 1971, *On the Strength of Reinforced Concrete Discs*
Nielsen 1978, *Concrete Plasticity*
Nielsen 1984, *Limit Analysis and Concrete Plasticity*

Potucek 1977, *Stresses in Webs of Reinforced Concrete T-Beams Subjected to Flexure*

Ramakrishnan 1968, *Ultimate Strength of Deep Beams in Shear*
Rawdon de Paiva 1965, *Strength and Behaviour of Deep Beams in Shear*
Regan 1969, *Shear in RC Beams*
Ritter 1899, *Hennebique's Construction Method*
Rogowski 1986, *Tests of Reinforced Concrete Deep Beams*

Schlaich 1981, *Detailing Reinforced Concrete Structures*
Schlaich 1984, *Detailing in Reinforced Concrete Design*
Schlaich 1987, *Toward a Consistent Design of Structural Concrete*
Smith 1982, *Shear Strength of Deep Beams*
Subedi 1988, *Reinforced Concrete Deep Beams: A Method for Analysis*

Taylor 1968, *Shear Stresses in RC Beams without Shear Reinforcement*
Thurlimann 1973, *Stiffness of Cracked Reinforced Concrete Beams Subjected to Torsion*
Thurlimann 1975, *Torsion, Flexure and Shear in Reinforced Concrete Girders*
Thurlimann 1983, *Application of the Theory of Plasticity to Reinforced Concrete*

Vecchio 1982, *The Response of Reinforced Concrete to In-Plane Shear and Normal Stress-*
Vecchio 1986, *The Modified Compression Field Theory for Reinforced Concrete Elements*

6

Horizontal Members

This chapter presents a rather comprehensive coverage of horizontal members encountered in tall reinforced concrete buildings. Written by a number of experienced designers from around the world, the chapter is rich in that it presents a design-oriented discussion of such topics as posttensioned slabs, deep beams, stairs, and short foundation beams.

The reader may find some repetition of the material on shear presented in Section 5.2 of this Monograph. This was found necessary as the section on shear in this chapter is a specific example of the multiaxial stress design concept.

Section 6.6 on stairs is practically the same as that presented in the Committee's previous publications, for no major new research data on stairs could be found since the publication of the Council's original Monographs.

6.1 CONCRETE FLOOR SYSTEMS

Concrete floors in concrete buildings can be categorized as follows (see Fig. 6.1):

1. Two-way construction: flat-plate, flat-slab, waffle-slab, and two-way slab construction
2. One-way construction: solid-slab, pan-joist, and beam and slab construction

The various systems serve different functional purposes. Flat-plate and solid-slab construction is commonly used for spans up to 10 m (35 ft) in apartment buildings, hotels, and short-span office buildings. Pan-joist, beam and slab, and waffle construction is prevalent for spans in the range of 6 to 20 m (20 to 65 ft). The most common use of pan-joist construction is in buildings requiring longer spans, such as office buildings, hospitals, and garages. Two-way beam and slab construction is less prevalent in countries with high cost of labor and formwork. Precast concrete units are sometimes used to reduce the cost of formwork and labor. These precast units take on various shapes and sizes, the most common being the precast, pretensioned double-tee system and the pretensioned hollow-core slab system. Concrete topping slabs are generally cast over these precast units to obtain a monolithic floor and to level out any out-of-plane unevenness of the precast units.

When selecting an appropriate floor system for the design of concrete buildings, a key consideration in making an economic choice lies in the repetition of formwork and the speed with which the structure can be completed. One of the considerations in this regard is whether a system such as the *flying-form* system of formwork can be used. The flying-form system is very advantageous with flat-plate construction in hotels and apartment buildings, and has been adopted for use with pan-joist construction for office buildings. To make the flying-form system work in the latter case, it is important that the spandrel beams, if needed, be as close as possible to the depth of the pan-joist floor system. This imposes a

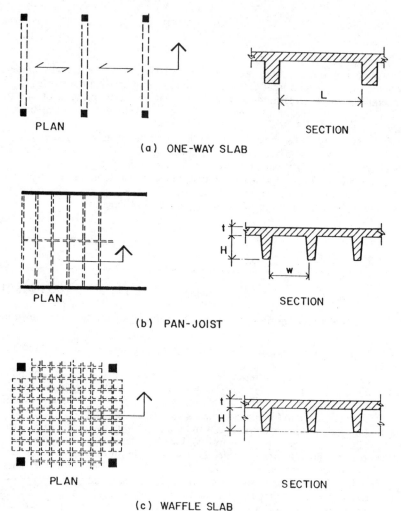

Fig. 6.1 Types of cast-in-place concrete floors.

penalty on the primary frame that is used to resist the lateral forces acting on the building.

1 Design criteria

Stiffness, strength, and ductility.   An inherent advantage of the concrete floor system is its stiffness, which results in lower deflection under static loads as well as producing less floor vibration under moving loads. Concrete floors consequently are not susceptible to floor vibrations unless unusual conditions are encountered. With increased research, the desired strength and ductility characteristics can be obtained by careful detailing (ACI 318, 1989). The recommendations of ACI 318-89 take into account both strength and ductility requirements, which become all the more important in seismic areas. Openings in concrete floor beams for the passage of mechanical ducts also have to be designed (Lorensten, 1965; Nasser et al., 1967).

Since the Ronan Point disaster in London in 1968, much thought has been given to the problems involved in the design of high-rise buildings against progressive collapse. The problem is of particular importance with large-panel precast construction. It has been suggested that structures will have to be designed either to withstand a prescribed pressure that might be caused by gas explosion, or to remain stable after the forcible removal of a major structural component. If a wall panel is removed, the floor system will be required to bridge over the resulting gap. In that situation, large deflections would be permissible, and a yield line analysis would be most suitable for design.

Deformations.   In the design of concrete floors, both short-term and long-term deflections have to be considered (ACI 318, 1989). Another factor requiring consideration is crack width under service load conditions. The ACI code recommendation for crack widths has proved to be satisfactory in practice.

Fire rating.   Most major building codes require a minimum 2-hour rating on floors for hotels, apartments, and office buildings. Concrete floors have an inherently higher fire rating capability, which obviates the necessity for fireproofing material, except in some types of pan-joist construction. Tests conducted at the Underwriters Laboratories (1971) indicate the minimum thickness of concrete slabs required to obtain a given fire rating. In this respect, the use of lightweight concrete proves beneficial.

Ceiling construction.   In apartment and hotel buildings, flat-plate construction has an economic advantage in that it produces a finished floor and ceiling, thereby eliminating the need for suspended ceiling construction. This results in the additional advantage of lower floor-to-floor heights.

Dead loads and live loads.   Concrete floor construction in general has a higher dead load than comparable construction using other materials. This imposes a penalty on the vertical supporting elements and the foundation system. However, the penalty for additional dead weight can be minimized through the use of lightweight concrete. With regard to live loads, in general, the heavier the live load, the more economical concrete construction becomes. Flat-plate, flat-slab, and pan-joist construction have proved economical in supporting higher live loads since the cost of the formwork is almost unchanged. Under heavy live loads, moreover, the floor-to-floor heights or the depth of the structure are much lower in concrete construction than in any other type of construction.

Acoustical ratings. In general, concrete construction provides good acoustical ratings as it reflects only surface noise. It is ranked much superior to most other types of construction in this regard.

Diaphragm action. In the design of tall structures, the transmission of lateral loads to the vertical resisting elements is an important criterion. Concrete construction in general gives excellent diaphragm action.

Diaphragm action comes into play in a floor system when transverse loads at the floor level are transmitted into the columns and into the laterally stiff and torsionally stiff shear core of the building. If the transverse load system is nonsymmetric because of a lack of symmetry in the building or because of asymmetry of load, the diaphragm action transmits torsion as well as shear into the core. Provided the floor system is monolithic in construction, diaphragm action will usually not prove to be critical for design purposes. A simple and convenient method of accounting for diaphragm action is to find any suitable statically admissible force field which serves the purpose of transmitting the transverse load system to the reactive core. This force field can consist of tension and compression struts which form a frame or truss in the plane of the floor system. When necessary, additional steel reinforcement is then positioned to act as tension struts, while a check on concrete strength capacity is made in the regions of the compression struts.

Resistance to thermal movements, column shrinkage and creep, and differential settlement. In the design of concrete structures, thermal movements, column shrinkage and creep, and differential settlements become very important. Due to the monolithic action of reinforced concrete construction, there is a greater resistance to these movements due to structural stiffness. The movements are resisted by the floors primarily in bending. These bending moments have to be considered in the design of the concrete floor construction. The inherent monolithic action of concrete construction significantly reduces the free movements due to temperature and inelastic column shortening (Fintel and Khan, 1965, 1969).

2 Analysis and design

The analysis of floor framing systems is generally done using elastic analysis based on ultimate loads and capacity reduction factors, in accord with ACI 318 (ACI, 1989). The analysis is expedited through the use of computer programming, which enables the engineer to analyze and design floor elements for shear, bending, and for torsional forces. The effect of axial forces is generally disregarded in the design of floors unless unusual conditions exist. The floor members must have adequate strength to resist all the forces to which they are subjected, including dead and live loads, lateral loads, temperature loads (Fintel and Khan, 1965), shrinkage and creep effects (Fintel and Khan, 1969), and torsional loads (Colaco, 1970). At the present time, most of the building codes as well as the ACI code generally treat only dead, live, and lateral loads; very little specific provision is made for the effects of the other forces mentioned.

It is important to note that most ultimate strength design codes allow for some redistribution between positive and negative moments. Typical is the draft British code, which allows up to 30% redistribution in buildings of up to three floors and 10% in buildings of four or more floors. Such figures, although in some codes quite small, do give tacit recognition to the inelastic behavior of concrete frames at overload. The careful application of such moment redistributions can in some cases lead to important savings in design.

Although some minor differences occur from country to country in the formulation of the flexural strength equations, practical differences are not significant. Thus the concrete compressive stress block is assumed in most European countries to be parabolic straight, whereas an equivalent rectangular stress block is used in many English-speaking countries. Differences are, in most practical situations, insignificant.

More divergence has been observed in ultimate strength design methods for shear. According to the ACI code, the shear capacity of a section in combined bending and shear is obtained by adding to the shear cracking load a quantity representing the contribution of the shear reinforcement. European practice follows more closely the truss analogy theory (see Chapter 5). Nevertheless, no purely rational theory has yet been proposed, let alone accepted, and the semi-empirical nature of all design procedures for shear reinforcement ensures that divergence, both qualitative and quantitative, is not great.

Upper-bound methods are, strictly speaking, not design methods at all, but rather methods of analysis. This is certainly true of the yield line theory, which, although well documented in the literature, has not found wide acceptance as a practical design tool. Criticisms of the yield line approach have centered on possible serviceability problems in slabs designed on the basis of yield line analysis, and on the inability of the method to provide a clear-cut estimate of, or bounds to, the strength of the member. On the other hand, use of the method has been advocated on the grounds that it provides a simple, useful technique of analysis in the many cases where no clear-cut alternative is available.

Other considerations that enter into the selection of the floor framing system primarily relate to the interaction of the floor with the primary system resisting lateral loads. In hotel and apartment buildings, part of the slab acts in conjunction with the columns to form the frame that resists lateral loads. The width of the slab to be used in this connection is not clearly defined. Values less than the full width, equal to the full width, and sometimes greater than the full width have all been shown to be valid in different circumstances. In-plane action of the floor slab is required primarily to distribute lateral load to the various structural elements in the building which resist the lateral forces. The actual in-plane deformation of the floors has no significant effect on the distribution of this load, and the assumption that the floors are fully rigid in plane is commonly used. The out-of-place bending of floor slabs is important. A very small resistance to bending for a slab connecting two vertical elements can have a significant effect on the behavior of the whole system. It is therefore most important to ensure that the connecting members possess the necessary flexural strength, and also that the joints between the slab and the columns be given careful consideration. Floor elements are also called upon to resist the torsional effects due to asymmetry of the structure or of the lateral forces. In the design of interacting systems where shear walls are coupled by the floor framing system, the stiffness of the beam that connects the shear walls is very important in the overall behavior of the shear wall system. In this connection, the effect of nonprismatic beams on the stiffness should be considered. In the case of systems that use pan-joist construction for floors, the frame is generally considered to be formed by that joist or beam that falls directly on the column line. In some instances, the joists on either side of the centerline of the column could be considered as part of the lateral load-resisting system of the building if the torsional stiffness of the spandrel beam into which they are framed is large. It is obvious that as the torsional stiffness of the spandrel beam increases, the effectiveness of those joists outside the centerline of the frame increases also. In a primary system consisting of closely spaced columns on the exterior face, deformations of the floor will occur due to shear lag effects in the columns. In some instances, the stiffness of the beams becomes important as part of the bracing of the vertical supporting elements. This aspect of the problem deals primarily with the effective length of columns as they are affected by the stiffness of the floor members.

3   Office buildings

Cast-in-place concrete floor systems

Pan-joist system.   In the United States the pan-joist system is one of the most commonly used systems for concrete buildings. The construction is based on the use of standardized pans generally available in 760-mm (30-in.) widths and with depths ranging from 250 to 500 mm (10 to 20 in.). The conventional pan-joist layout for an office building is shown in Fig. 6.2. It is well known that the thickness of the slab is controlled not by structural requirements but by fire-rating requirements, as mentioned earlier. In the case of a 2-hour fire-rating requirement, the slab thickness is 120 mm (4.5 in.) for normal-weight concrete and 100 mm (4 in.) for lightweight concrete. These requirements resulted in the so-called skip-joist

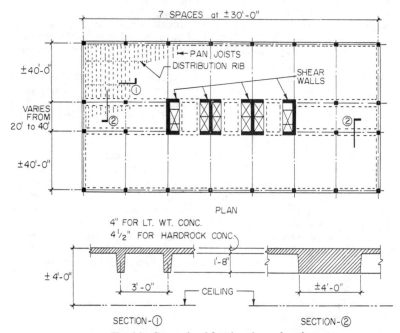

Fig. 6.2 Conventional framing plan and sections.

system, where the center-to-center distance of the pan-joist ribs has been increased from approximately 1 m (3 ft) to a maximum of 3 m (10 ft).

The floor system can be built with either lightweight concrete or conventional normal-weight concrete. Figure 6.3 shows the reinforcing quantities in a one-way slab and Fig. 6.4 gives the reinforcing quantities in pounds per square foot and kilograms per square meter for different span lengths for continuous pan-joist construction.

Haunched-girder system. In the pan-joist system described, the joists are carried by a girder that spans between columns. The girders have traditionally had the same depth as the pans for ease of formwork. Unfortunately this method results in an excessive quantity of concrete and, consequently, a high dead weight of the structure. In 1975 Colaco recommended the use of the *haunched-girder* system in conjunction with pan-joist construction, as shown in Fig. 6.5. The haunched-girder system has the advantage of having the largest depth at the column location where the shears and moments are maximum. The system uses less concrete and reinforcing bars and has the secondary benefit of using the haunched girder as part of the lateral load-resisting system in the building.

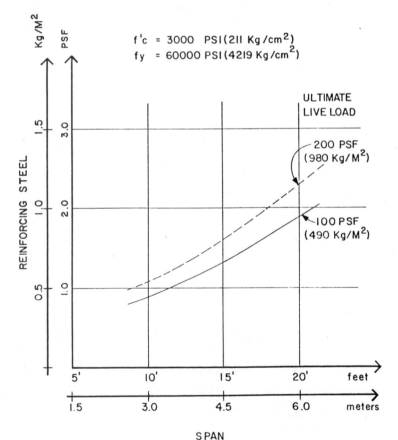

Fig. 6.3 One-way solid slab, interior span.

Flat-slab construction. Flat-slab construction consists of a reinforced concrete slab with or without a thickened portion at the column locations. The thickened portion, called a *drop panel,* is utilized to take care of punching shear and flexural problems at the column. This construction is generally used for spans of 9 to 10 m (30 to 35 ft). Reinforcing quantities for a mild steel reinforced flat slab are shown in Figs. 6.6 and 6.7. A variation of this approach is to taper the drop panel at the columns, thereby giving more flexibility for mechanical work in areas where headroom and floor-to-floor height are extremely tight, such as in areas next to airports. In some cases, flat slabs are posttensioned. The conventional way to posttension slabs in the United States is a one-way-banded posttensioning system, where strands are concentrated in the column strip in one direction (typically the short span direction) and the strands in the other direction are spaced uniformly across the entire bay. This type of system is very seldom seen in office buildings due to considerations of future flexibility to cut holes and increase live loads. A variation of this system has just been introduced in the United States. The system has been prevalent in Europe, primarily in Switzerland, for many years and was called *support-strip* method. In the United States, it is called *two-way-banded posttensioning* system. It has been used recently on the five-story Barton Oaks project in Austin, Tex. The technique consists of concentrating the

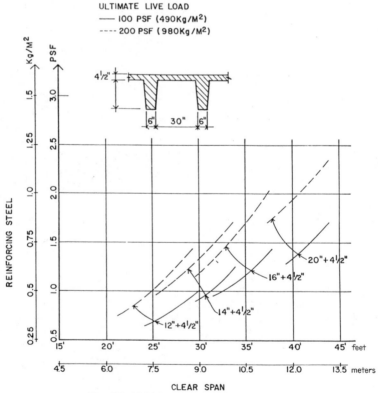

CLEAR SPAN

Fig. 6.4 Multiple-span pan joists, interior spans.

posttensioning in the column strips in both directions and leaving the center part of the slab (the middle-strip regions) with mild steel reinforcement only. This has the distinct advantage of concentrating the posttensioning in narrow bands, leaving the center part open for cutting holes in the future. Concentrated posttensioning also enables larger strands to be used and results in a more direct transmission of load to the columns than the one-way-banded system.

Waffle system. A waffle system is a two-way slab system using dome pans typically 750 by 750 mm (30 by 30 in.). The height of the domes will range from 250 to 500 mm (10 to 20 in.). Reinforcing quantities for mild steel reinforced waffle systems are also shown in Figs. 6.6 and 6.7. This type of construction is expensive because of the high cost of formwork and labor, and it therefore generally is used where the waffle system can be exposed for its aesthetic appeal.

Precast concrete floors

Double tees. Pretensioned precast double tees are very seldom used in office construction. Typical widths of the double tees are 2.4 m (8.0 ft), and the total depth varies from 400 to 750 mm (16 to 30 in.). These double tees usually span from the exterior face of the building to the core. They are laid down side by side and are carried by a precast inverted T-beam, which in turn rests on the columns. The whole assembly is completed by the placement of a topping slab over the double tees to get diaphragm action and level out any unevenness in the floor construction. The major drawback of precast concrete construction is its lack of redundancy, the inability of the precast floor system to participate with the primary lateral load-resisting system, and the difficulty of making horizontal penetrations through the stems of the double tees.

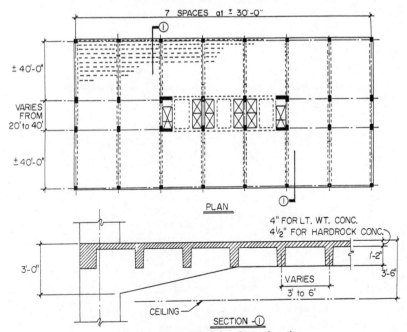

Fig. 6.5 Haunched-girder plan and section.

Hollow-cored planks.   Hollow-cored planks are prestressed pretensioned units that range in thickness from 100 mm (4.0 in.) to approximately 300 mm (12 in.). These members vary in width from 600 mm (24 in.) to 3 m (10 ft). Hollow-cored planks are typically used for short-span construction up to approximately 9 m (30 ft). They need to be carried on bearing walls or on inverted double-tee beams, which in turn rest on the columns. The system is completed by the placement of topping slab to get diaphragm action and to level out any unevenness in the pre-cast construction. Sometimes if tight tolerances can be maintained, the topping slab can be eliminated and the grouting between hollow-cored planks has to be designed to carry the diaphragm shears across the floor.

4 Hotels and apartment buildings

Cast-in-place construction

Flat-plate system.   Flat-plate construction is the most prevalent method of building hotels and apartment buildings in the United States. The use of flying forms enables this kind of construction to be built extremely rapidly, with the construction time ranging from 3 to 4 days per floor. Spans up to about 8 m (25 ft)

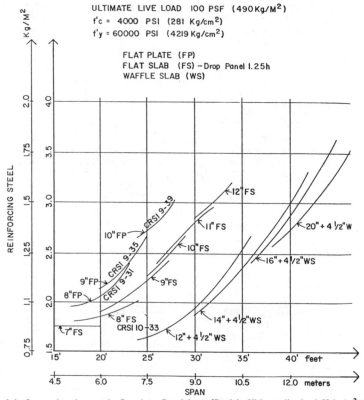

Fig. 6.6   Square interior panels: flat plate, flat slab, waffle slab. Ultimate live load 50 kg/m² (100 psf).

are generally mild steel reinforced and the quantities of reinforcements as a function of span are shown in Fig. 6.7. The openings that have to be provided in the
flat-plate slab for plumbing and mechanical purposes have to be coordinated very
carefully to ensure the shear capacity of the slab at the column locations. Where
spans increase, posttensioning in the form of one-way-banded posttensioned construction is generally used to minimize the thickness of the concrete slab. The
one other advantage of this system is that posttensioning enables columns to be
placed at every other room module so that spans in the range of 9 m (30 ft) can be
achieved on the floor. A significant advantage of this type of construction is that
it minimizes or eliminates the requirement for transfer girders, which would otherwise be needed if columns were placed at every room module, or approximately 4.5 m (15 ft).

Precast.   Several alternative systems are in use. The hollow-cored plank system described previously is fairly common. Another system in use is the *filigree*
system, which consists of a precast slab with reinforcing trusses embedded in the
slab and extending above the precast slab. The precast slab rests on load-bearing
walls or on a cast-in-place column strip slab band.

5 Detailing and construction

The detailing of cast-in-place concrete structures generally follows the requirements shown in the detailing manuals and is based on different design codes (ACI

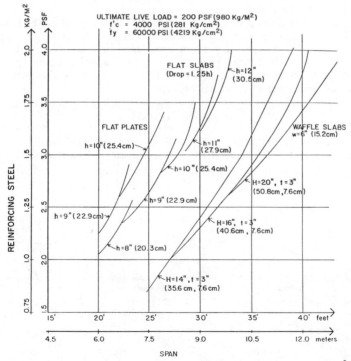

Fig. 6.7   Square interior panels: flat plate, flat slab, waffle slab. Ultimate live load 980 kg/m² (200 psf).

318, 1989). Very careful attention should be paid to the sequencing of the reinforcing bars. For example, in flat-plate and flat-slab construction, at the column locations the column strip bars from each direction need to be indicated to show which bars are on top. The same is true in the middle strip, where the bottom bars in the two directions need to be specified to show which bars are at the bottom. In pan-joist construction it is typical to provide for the top bars of the pan joist to be set and the temperature reinforcing, usually in the form of a welded wire fabric, to be placed on top of the top bars of the joist. U.S. practice generally does not use bent bars for shear, and all the shear forces not carried by the concrete are typically carried by stirrups. In girders, the U-type stirrups are generally split with adequate lap lengths to develop the vertical leg of the stirrups.

In girder construction, and especially in haunched-girder-type work, prefabricating the reinforcing bar cages is becoming more prevalent. This requires close coordination of the detail at the columns, where the column bar locations have to be coordinated with the prefabricated cage of reinforcement bars for the girders (see Fig. 6.8). Some of the stirrups through the beam-column joint are typically placed on site. In seismic areas, where the stirrup and main reinforcing requirements are extremely heavy, most of the stirrups, especially through the joint, are placed on site. Special consideration is required for the embedment of the top bars at the beam-column joints to make sure that straight embedment lengths and hooks are properly coordinated with the column cage. Problems arise when the congestion of the reinforcing is so large that it makes the placement of concrete extremely difficult. The only remedy for this type of design is to increase member sizes wherever possible and to use superplasticizers in the concrete mix to facilitate the flow of concrete.

For precast concrete details, the Prestressed Concrete Institute (PCI) *Design Handbook* (1980) has recommendations for the detailing of not only the precast members themselves but also the connections. Due regard should be given to the bearing points, and the bearing pad details are extremely important. In precast construction, the tolerance problem for the lengths of members, the camber, and erection tolerances become especially critical.

In the construction planning for a particular project, a careful study is generally required of all aspects of concrete constructibility. Mix designs, methods of concrete transportation and placement, the use of admixtures, hot and cold weather concreting, flying forms, slip-forming techniques, and details of placing reinforcements have to be coordinated carefully. Another important aspect of the

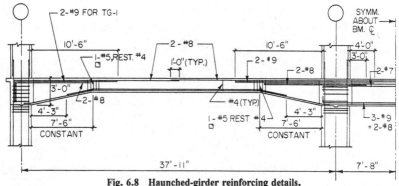

Fig. 6.8 Haunched-girder reinforcing details.

constructibility is the stripping times for formwork. Engineers generally specify the following concrete strength requirements for stripping times:

1. Column and wall sides $40\% f'_c$
2. Beam sides $70\% f'_c$
3. Beam bottoms $85\% f'_c$

These strength values have to be studied with both the shoring and the reshoring requirements to maintain a cycle of construction that suits the project schedule. In case of difficulty, special techniques, such as the use of high-early-strength cements, increased concrete strengths above those specified, or additional floors of shoring, can be used to expedite construction. A great deal of research has been done on shoring sequences and shoring loads so that the load-carrying capacity of the green concrete slabs is not exceeded (which would result in a progressive collapse of the structure under construction). Special care is required to ensure that for large floor areas the shoring is not removed all at one time. Reshoring should commence almost immediately behind the removal of the shores. A typical construction sequence in the United States is to have two complete floors of shores and one complete floor of reshoring based on a normal 5-day cycle per floor. In some cases, construction has proceeded at the rate of 3 days per floor. Special precautions are required to ensure the distribution of loads on the lower floors according to their ability to carry the wet weight of the concrete above. Construction tolerances, both vertical and horizontal, have proved to be achievable goals within the tolerance requirements of the ACI code.

6.2 POSTTENSIONED SLABS AND BEAMS

1 Posttensioned floor systems

Posttensioned concrete floor construction may consist of slabs with or without beams. Slabs of constant thickness are referred to as flat plates. Flat plates may incorporate small capitals, not extending more than $l/6$ in any one direction. Slabs utilizing larger capitals (drop panels) are classified as flat slabs. Flat plates are practical for spans of up to about 9 m (30 ft), flat slabs cover the range of spans between about 8 and 12 m (26 and 39 ft), while slab beam systems are used for still larger spans.

In comparison with reinforced concrete floor construction, posttensioned floor systems permit larger spans with reduced floor thickness and deflection. Flying forms may be used with flat plates. Forms are usually removed after 3 days, immediately after the posttensioning of the tendons. If the floor system is free to shorten under the action of prestress, no cracking will occur under service loads. Compared to pretensioned precast construction, a posttensioned system takes full advantage of span continuity. An irregular column layout is easily accommodated in a flat-slab or a flat-plate system.

The design of continuous posttensioned floor construction requires specialized training; the labor can be reduced significantly using computer programs.

2 Basic design criteria

The design of concrete beams and T-beams in reinforced and posttensioned construction is basically the same except for the consideration of prestress forces.

Flat plates and flat slabs can be designed using the method described next, noting that the amount of labor for the flat slab is larger because of the varying stiffnesses. The change in stiffness due to the presence of a small capital in a flat-plate system is generally ignored. The beneficial effect for shear is, however, taken into consideration.

The method most often used to analyze flat plates, and upon which present code provisions are based, is the beam strip method in conjunction with the equivalent-frame and the balanced-load concept (Lyn, 1963; PIT, 1977). The balanced-load concept permits the computation of moments for specified loads and the calculation of secondary moments which have to be added to the factored moments for strength design. The balanced-load concept simplifies design and helps in visualizing. Nevertheless, the amount of computational effort to design a posttensioned slab is enormous. Thus, computer programs based on the equivalent-frame and the balanced-load concept have been developed.

Tendons are generally uniformly distributed in one direction and banded in the other direction (Fig. 6.9). Banding of tendons in one direction offers several advantages:

1. It provides an insider view of how the loads are picked up by the primary system of uniformly distributed strands, transferred to the secondary system of strands (banded strands), and finally dumped onto the support.

2. It increases shear strength by placing a larger portion of the balanced load over the support area.

3. It provides a postfailure reserve strength due to catenary action (CSA, 1984).

4. It permits irregular column layout in one direction.

5. It reduces chances of cutting a strand when holes have to be drilled through the slab at a later date.

6. It eliminates or reduces weaving of strands and hence labor cost.

Tests and applications have demonstrated that a posttensioned flat plate behaves as a flat plate regardless of tendon placement.

3 Design example

Frame 1 of a flat-plate parking slab (Fig. 6.10) built in Calgary, Alta., in 1981 is analyzed to demonstrate the various design steps.

Step 1 Stiffnesses based on the geometry of the frame and material properties are computed using the approximation proposed by Rice and Hoffman (1985).

Step 2 Moment distribution is carried out for balanced, net, and factored loads.

Step 3 Shear and moment diagrams are plotted to determine flexural stresses in accordance with CAN3-A23.3-M84 (CSA, 1984; A23.3 for short). The Canadian code distributes net moments to column and middle strips, resulting in higher stress in the column strips, particularly adjacent to the column. Computed stresses are compared with allowable stresses, and minimum bonded reinforcement is determined.

Step 4 Shear and moment diagrams are plotted for factored loads. $V_c/3$ and $V_c/6$ corrections and secondary moments are added. Balanced, primary, and secondary moments are computed (Fig. 6.11).

Step 5 The flexural resistance is calculated using improved values of f_{ps} (A23.3, sec. 18.7.2) and compared with the factored moment.

Step 6 The moment redistribution factor is computed and moments are redistributed as permitted and required.

4   Two-way shear

The factored shear resistance of two-way slabs is computed using A23.3 (eq.11-33 or eq. 11-34). The shear resistance can be increased significantly if control over the extent of the reversed curvature of the tendons is exercised. Otherwise V_p should be taken conservatively as zero.

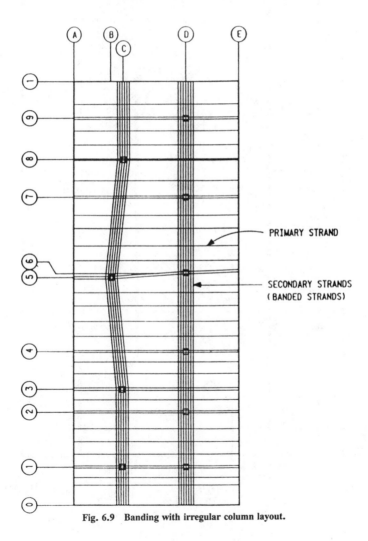

Fig. 6.9   Banding with irregular column layout.

If the factored shear stress resistance is exceeded, shear capitals could be considered which generally do not need to be larger than 1200 by 1200 mm (4 by 4 ft), the size of half a sheet of plywood. If the thickness of the capitals is taken equal to the thickness of the slab, shear stresses will seldom cause a problem. Where shear capitals are not acceptable (as in apartment buildings), shear studs can be

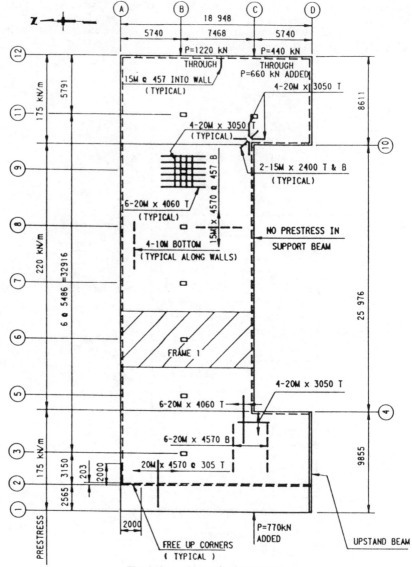

Fig. 6.10   parking slab of case study.

conveniently introduced (Mokhtar et al., 1982). These shear studs will soon be available for the U.S. market.

Two-way shear must consider moment transfer partially by flexure and partially by eccentricity of shear (Fig. 6.12).

5 Design details

Structural restraint.   Engineers designing posttensioned slabs normally experience no difficulty computing moments, shears, and stresses for specified and fac-

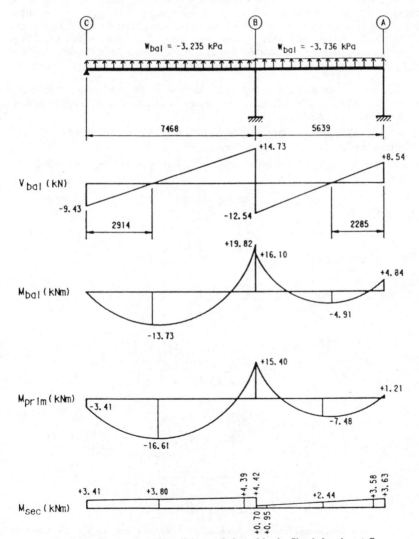

Fig. 6.11   Shear and moment diagrams, balanced loads. Simple bearing at C.

tored loads correctly. Structural restraints, however, are often not clearly understood or not properly considered. Structural constraints are due either to walls in the direction of prestress, to elevator and stairwells, or to stiff columns. Restraint prevents the posttensioned member from shortening. The average compression P/A_g is partially or fully absent in the prestressed member (Fig. 6.13). Net stresses may exceed the allowable stresses and the modulus of rupture. The balanced load is unchanged, the beneficial effect of reduced deflection is still applicable, and the design for strength is unaffected.

The missing P/A_g term can, however, cause serious cracking if shrinkage, creep, and temperature stresses are not resisted by additional mild reinforcement. The floor slab in the case study (Fig. 6.14) cracked severely perpendicular to the direction where structural restraints existed. No prestress was supplied in the banded direction at grid A (if supplied, most of this force would have been diverted to compress the stiff wall element), and little prestress was supplied at grid C, where the slab is supported on a ledge of a reinforced concrete beam that does not shorten.

Restraints can be overcome by following these rules:

1. Free up corners and close as late as possible to prevent diagonal cracking across corners. Walls will bend over away from corners, allowing compression of slab by prestress.

2. Provide mild reinforcement of at least 0.2% of gross area parallel to walls and other areas of slab that cannot shorten.

3. Insert pour strips in large floor areas, to be left open as long as possible.

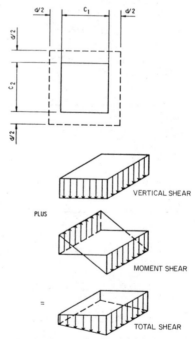

Fig. 6.12 Shear and moment interaction relationship for interior column moment about one axis only.

Structural restraint due to stiff columns was investigated in a case study (Fig. 6.15; Fintel and Ghosh, 1978). It was demonstrated that the final prestress force of the individual floors was close to 100% of the prestress force applied, with the exception of level 3, since for architectural reasons, extremely stiff columns were used up to level 3. Hence, in general, the restraint caused by stiff columns does not change the prestress level in the floor slabs significantly. Prestress forces can be adjusted to ensure that each floor receives the design prestress.

Corrosion. Corrosion of reinforcement should not be a problem if the crack width at the surface is limited to 0.4 mm (0.02 in.) with a concrete cover of at least 25 mm (0.98 in.) and bar diameters less than 20 mm (0.8 in.) (Kriz and Raths, 1965). Properly designed posttensioned floor structures will not crack under specified loads with stresses calculated as outlined in Step 3 of Subsection 3 and structural restraints prevented or properly accounted for.

(a) NO RESTRAINT

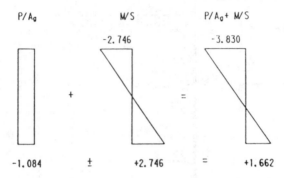

(b) FULL RESTRAINT

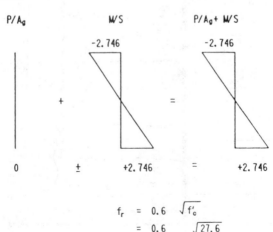

$$f_r = 0.6 \sqrt{f'_o}$$
$$= 0.6 \sqrt{27.6}$$
$$= 3.152 \text{ MPa}$$

Fig. 6.13 Stresses due to net loads with and without restraints.

Stressing boxes. If a building is to be erected between two existing structures, the space required for stressing the tendons is not always available. In that case stressing boxes permitting anchor plates some small distance away from the actual support may be required. This reduces the extent over which uplift is produced and introduces a concentrated downward force at the face of the stressing box, causing a change in the balancing-load moment diagram, which can often be ignored.

The design of the stressing boxes involves the tension on both sides of the box (Fig. 6.16) due to the prestress applied at the front, beam shear and flexure at the front of the boxes because of the concentrated downward forces of the tendons, and stress concentrations at the reentrant corners. Thus, in general, there will be a top and bottom layer of reinforcing bars on either side and in front of the stressing boxes.

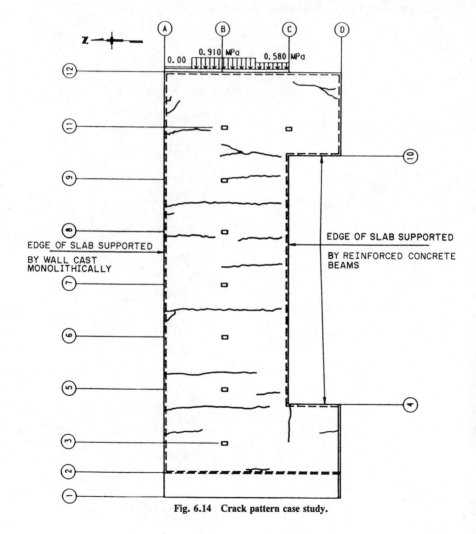

Fig. 6.14 Crack pattern case study.

Raising of anchors. The question has often been asked whether some benefit could be gained from raising the anchors at the end supports, since it would increase the balancing load. In the case of a simple span it is easily shown that the additional negative span moment due to the increased sag is exactly offset by an opposing positive span moment introduced by the anchor eccentricity. It follows that no benefit is gained by introducing eccentricity at a simple span end. When the balancing moment diagrams for single or multiple spans fixed to end supports using concentric and eccentric anchors are compared, it is seen that anchor eccentricity increases the opposing moment, which is beneficial.

Slab kinks. Kinks in slabs between supports may occur in parking ramps or in the outside portion of the main floor of a building to accommodate stairs or landscaping. At first glance one may think that a moment is introduced due to the

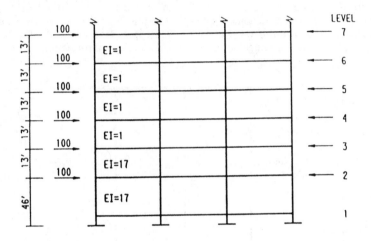

LEVEL	2	3	4	5	6	7
7	0.1	-0.4	-2.9	-4.1	18.3	88.9
6	-0.8	-2.7	-3.8	18.4	88.9	
5	-2.9	-3.1	18.2	88.7		
4	0.6	18.4	84.9			
3	29.8	71.0				
2	75.0					
ACCUMULATED PRESTRESS (6 FLOORS)	101.8	83.4	96.7	99.8	99.9	99.9

Fig. 6.15 Retention of prestressed forces in floors as successive floors are posttensioned.

kink of the prestress forces. It can be easily demonstrated that such a force does not exist. The draped tendon in the kinked slab (Fig. 6.17) can be thought of as the superposition of a draped tendon in a straight slab plus a straight concentric tendon in a kinked slab. The free-body diagram does not reveal any upward force.

Depending on the diameter of the tendon, a perfect kink cannot be produced. This results in local moment changes, which for a 13-mm (0.5-in.) cable can probably be ignored. Problems can arise if no chair is placed at the location of the kink K since the cable tries to straighten out from A to B (position of first chairs adjacent to K) before casting. This could cause a local failure of the slab at K.

Failure of anchorage zones.   Anchorage zones of posttensioned slabs are generally reinforced with two 10-mm (0.4-in.) or 15-mm (0.6-in.) bars to control bursting stresses. Bursting reinforcement for beams is usually designed on an individual basis. Anchorage zones may still fail if curing was not adequate or if honeycombing occurred. Unless special precautions are taken, curing near slab edges is generally not as good as away from edges. It is advisable to place test cylinders next to anchorage zones for reliable strength information.

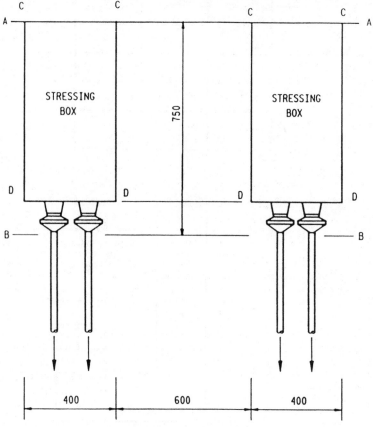

Fig. 6.16 Plan view of stressing boxes.

Fire endurance.   Codes specify covers for reinforcing bars and prestress tendons according to the specified fire rating and type of restraint. Restraints are produced in multiple spans due to a tendency of the floor member to curl up when the underside is heated, or due to the compression produced by the bending resistance of columns or walls in the lower portion of the floor member (negative moment) (Fig. 6.18). Restraints thus increase fire endurance. Fire endurance can

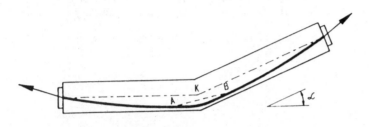

a) DRAPED TENDON IN KINKED SLAB

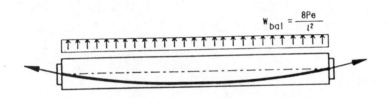

$$W_{bal} = \frac{8Pe}{l^2}$$

b) DRAPED TENDON IN STRAIGHT SLAB

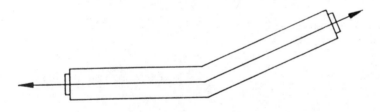

c) STRAIGHT, CONCENTRIC TENDON IN KINKED SLAB

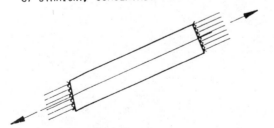

d) FREE BODY DIAGRAM FOR ONE HALF OF MEMBER

Fig. 6.17 Treatment of kinked posttensioned members.

also be increased by increasing the amount of mild reinforcement provided (Gustaferro, 1972).

6.3 SHEAR CONSIDERATIONS

Current code provisions for shear design are generally considered to be too empirical and complex, and considerable efforts are being made to revise them. The objective of these efforts is the development of *rational* design methods similar, if possible, in clarity to the method used to design structural members in flexure.

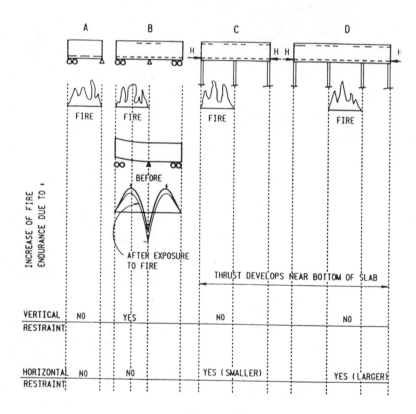

FIRE ENDURANCE IS THE TIME AT WHICH THE
CRITICAL TEMPERATURE IS REACHED

NOTE:
FOR RESTRAINED CONDITION FIRE ENDURANCE
INCREASES SIGNIFICANTLY.
HENCE FIRE COVER APPROXIMATELY ½
OF THOSE FOR UNRESTRAINED CONDITION

Fig. 6.18   Effect of restraint on fire endurance.

However, such an objective is difficult to achieve without the existence of a theory which could provide a realistic description of the underlying causes of shear failure.

In view of this it is considered that the concepts forming the basis of current shear design methods should be reappraised and a suitable theory developed before a revision of the code provisions for shear design is attempted. In the following, evidence in support of this argument is presented, and a concept that may serve as the basis for the development of such a theory is introduced. The implications of using this concept in design are discussed, and it is argued that its use should yield rational and simple design methods.

1 Basis of code provisions

Shear capacity of critical section. The shear capacity of a cross section is defined in codes of practice in terms of the nominal shear stress $v = V/bd$, where V is the shear force and b and d are the width and depth of the cross section, respectively. A structural member without shear reinforcement is considered to fail in shear when v at a *critical section* exceeds a *critical value* before the flexural capacity of the member is attained. This value is provided by the code and is dependent on the strength of the concrete, the yield stress, and the percentage of the tension reinforcement (Kong and Evans, 1980).

For a structural member to be able to attain its flexural capacity when v at a critical section exceeds the code value, shear reinforcement should be provided so as to prevent shear failure. Thus the objective of a shear design procedure is to realistically assess the amount of shear reinforcement required to carry that portion of the shear force that cannot be sustained by concrete alone.

According to the preceding reasoning a reinforced concrete beam without shear reinforcement subjected to two-point loading will fail in shear when the shear capacity of the *shear span* is exceeded before the flexural capacity of the beam is attained. Shear failure, therefore, can *only* be prevented by placing shear reinforcement *throughout* the shear span.

Yet it has been predicted by finite-element analysis (Kotsovos, 1983) and subsequently verified by experiment (Kotsovos, 1984a) that placing shear reinforcement within the *middle,* and *not* the shear span of beams having a rectangular cross section and a shear-span-to-depth ratio a_v/d of approximately 2.0 (beam D in Fig. 6.19) results in a load-carrying capacity significantly larger than that of beams without shear reinforcement (beam A in Fig. 6.19). In fact, the load-carrying capacity of the former beams has been found to be similar to that of beams reinforced in compliance with the code (BSI, 1985) provisions for shear design (beams B and C in Fig. 6.19).

These results clearly indicate that such behavior cannot be explained in terms of the concept of the *shear capacity of a critical section,* and thus the failure of the beams cannot be described as a shear failure, as defined by this concept.

It is also interesting to note that the results of Fig. 6.19 contradict the view that significant transfer of shear forces occurs across the surfaces of inclined cracks. This transfer of shear forces, generally termed *aggregate interlock,* is widely considered to be the main contributor to shear resistance in the absence of shear reinforcement (Taylor, 1968; Fenwick and Paulay, 1968; Regan, 1969).

However, the greater load-carrying capacity and ductility exhibited by the beams with shear reinforcement within the middle span cause larger crack widths, which should *reduce* aggregate interlock (Reinhardt and Walraven, 1982).

Therefore if aggregate interlock were indeed one of the main contributors to shear resistance, then the reduction in aggregate interlock should *reduce,* and *not* increase, the load-carrying capacity of the beams.

It appears from this behavior that in beams without shear reinforcement, the shear force is mainly resisted by the compressive zone, with the zone below the neutral axis making an insignificant contribution, if any.

Truss analogy. Truss analogy forms the basis for the assessment of the amount of shear reinforcement sufficient to prevent shear failure. (See Section 5.1 for more details.) Shear reinforcement, such as links, is thought to become effective once inclined cracking (with respect to the direction of the tension reinforcement) occurs. Then it is generally considered that shear is resisted by the structural member acting as a truss, the shear reinforcement forming the tensile members (ties) of the truss and the concrete between the inclined cracks forming the compression members (struts), which are parallel to the crack direction (Fig. 6.20). The truss is designed such that it does not fail before flexural failure occurs.

The shear reinforcement forming the ties of the truss is thought to sustain the load which cannot be sustained by concrete across an inclined crack, and thus to restore the shear capacity of the cross section through the inclined crack tip (Fig. 6.21). This implies that if the location of the inclined crack causing failure were

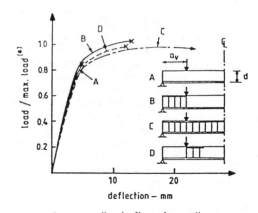

• corresponding to flexural capacity

Fig. 6.19　Typical load-deflection relationships of beams with $a_v/d \approx 2.0$.

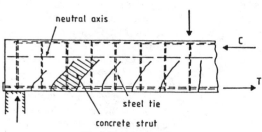

Fig. 6.20　Truss analogy.

known, then shear failure due to an extension of this crack could *only* be prevented by placing shear reinforcement *across* the crack faces.

However, it has been found by experiment (Leonhardt and Walther, 1961/62) that for a beam subjected to two-point loading with a value of a_v/d between approximately 3.0 and 4.0, the inclined crack causing failure occurs within the region of the shear span extending to a distance of approximately 2.0d from the support (Fig. 6.22). Following the reasoning of the preceding paragraph, shear failure due to extension of the *preceding* inclined crack could *only* be prevented by placing shear reinforcement within this region.

Yet it has been shown recently by means of finite-element analysis (Kotsovos, 1983) that reinforcing only this region is ineffective since the load-carrying capacity of such a beam (beam *B* in Fig. 6.23) has been found *not* to be significantly larger than that of the same beam without shear reinforcement (beam *A* in Fig. 6.23). Such behavior could only be explained by the concept of shear capacity of a critical section, but this concept, as discussed in the preceding section, cannot provide a realistic description of the causes of shear failure.

It has also been found that placing shear reinforcement beyond a distance of 2.0d from the support not only prevents shear failure but also allows the beam to attain its flexural capacity (beam *D* in Fig. 6.23) (Kotsovos, 1984a). The absence of shear reinforcement across the faces of the inclined crack is considered to indicate that, as for the case of beams without shear reinforcement within the shear span (discussed in the preceding section), shear is resisted by the compressive zone and *not* by the region of the beam below its neutral axis.

The first results obtained from an ongoing experimental program (Kotsovos, 1984a) appear to confirm this behavior. Such behavior is considered to indicate that, although the shear reinforcement is assessed so as to restore the shear capacity of the cross section through the tip of an inclined crack, it is the reinforce-

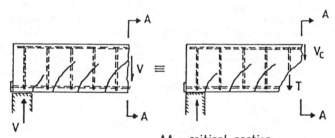

AA = critical section

Fig. 6.21   Function of steel ties in truss analogy.

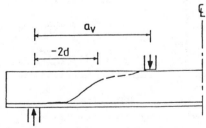

Fig. 6.22   Typical mode of failure of beams with a_v/d between 3.0 and 4.0.

ment *beyond* this section that prevents shear failure. Therefore, it appears that the truss analogy, although found in practice to yield safe design solutions, cannot provide a satisfactory description of the mechanism of shear resistance of reinforced concrete structural members with shear reinforcement.

2 Causes of shear failure

The shear resistance of reinforced concrete beams without shear reinforcement is usually associated with the *beam* and the *arch and tie* actions. It may be considered, therefore, that shear failure occurs when these actions are "overcome." The arch and tie action may be "overcome" either by compression failure of the arch, or by yielding of the tie. Anchorage failure may also occur, but this should always be prevented by proper anchoring of the tension steel. Failure mechanisms leading to the destruction of the beam action are more difficult to visualize.

Concrete cantilever.   Perhaps the most widely known concept proposed to date describing a mechanism for the destruction of the beam action is that of the *concrete cantilever* (Kani, 1964). This is the concrete between two consecutive flexural cracks which, under the action of bond forces developing between tension reinforcement and concrete due to beam action, reacts as a cantilever fixed to the compressive zone. The concept postulates that the beam action is destroyed, and thus shear failure occurs when the cantilever fails in flexure.

Although this prompted a number of detailed investigations of the stress conditions at the boundaries of a concrete cantilever (Taylor, 1968; Fenwick and Paulay, 1968), and these have led to the development of design equations (Regan, 1969), the concept appears to suffer from the serious drawback that it is incompatible with the observed modes of shear failure of reinforced concrete beams. These are characterized by the formation of an inclined crack within the compressive zone, which is indicative of failure of the support (compressive zone) rather than the cantilever itself (see Fig. 6.25). It is therefore considered that the causes of shear failure should be sought in the region of the path along which the compressive force is transmitted to the supports since it is the failure of the compressive zone that always appears to lead to the collapse of a beam. It is interesting to note that failure in the region of this path can cause shear failure, irre-

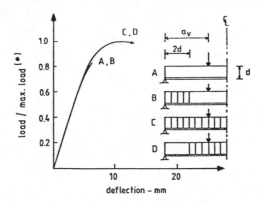

corresponding to flexural capacity

Fig. 6.23   Typical load-deflection relationships of beams with a_v/d between 3.0 and 4.0.

spective of whether this is due to the destruction of the beam or to arch and tie action.

Compressive force path. It has recently been postulated (Kotsovos, 1983) that shear failure is associated with the presence of tensile stresses developing in the region of the path along which the compressive force is transmitted to the supports. The path of the compressive force may be visualized as a "flow" of compressive stresses with varying sections perpendicular to the path direction and with the compressive force representing the stress resultant at each section (Fig. 6.24). Tensile stresses may develop perpendicular to the path due to a number of causes, the main ones being the following.

1. *Changes in path direction.* A tensile stress resultant (T in Fig. 6.24) develops for equilibrium purposes at locations where the path changes direction.

2. *Varying intensity of compressive stress field along path.* The compressive stress will reach a critical level at the smallest cross section of the path, where the stress intensity is the highest before this level is reached in adjacent cross sections. As will be seen in a following section, this level marks the start of an abrupt and large material dilation which will induce tensile stresses (t_1 in Fig. 6.24) in the surrounding concrete (Kotsovos, 1984b).

3. *Tip of inclined cracks.* It is well known from fracture mechanics that large tensile stresses (t_2 in Fig. 6.24) develop perpendicular to the direction of the maximum principal compressive stress in the region of the crack tip (Kotsovos, 1979; Kotsovos and Newman, 1981a).

3 Evidence supporting concept of compressive force path

An indication of the validity of the concept of the compressive force path may be provided by considering the behavior of reinforced concrete beams without shear reinforcement subjected to two-point loading. It is well known that the observed behavior of such beams with rectangular cross section may be divided into four types, depending on a_v/d (see Fig. 6.25; Kani, 1964). The underlying causes of the observed behavior may be described by the concept of the compressive force path as follows.

Type I, characterized by flexural failure of the middle span, which allows the beam to attain its flexural capacity. It has been predicted by analysis (Kotsovos, 1981) and verified by experiment (Kotsovos, 1982) that the beam *does not* collapse due to material failure at cross sections where the compressive strains are

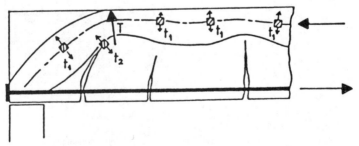

Fig. 6.24 Path of compressive force indicating locations of tensile stresses.

the largest, as suggested by classical flexural theory. Instead, it occurs in regions adjacent to these cross sections, which are subjected to a compression-tension state of stress, the tensile stress developing within the compressive zone, as described by item 2 in the preceding subsection.

Type II, characterized by a mode of failure caused by an inclined crack, which initiates near the tip of one of the flexural cracks closest to the support and propagates near horizontally toward the load point. It may also propagate toward the support along the tension reinforcement, but anchorage failure can be avoided by correctly anchoring the steel.

The crack pattern just before failure indicates that it is realistic to consider that the compressive force is transmitted to the support by following a path consisting of two near linear portions intersecting at a point lying at a distance between approximately $2.0d$ and $2.5d$ from the support (Fig. 6.25). As described in item 1 of the preceding subsection, this change in the path direction gives rise to a tensile stress resultant which should cause failure when the capacity of the region to sustain the combined compression-tension state of stress is exceeded.

Alternatively, tensile stresses may develop within the portion of the compressive force path closest to the load point due to bond failure at the level of the tension reinforcement between two consecutive flexural cracks (Kotsovos, 1984b). Bond failure changes the stress conditions of the beam element between these cracks, as indicated in Fig. 6.26. From the figure it can be seen that the loss of the bond force results in an extension of the right-hand flexural crack, sufficient to cause an increase Δz of the lever arm z, such that $C \cdot \Delta z = V \cdot a$. The extension of the flexural crack reduces the depth of the neutral axis and thus increases locally the intensity of the compressive stress block. This change in the stress intensity should give rise to tensile stresses at right angles to the path, in the manner described in item 2 of the preceding subsection.

Figure 6.26 also indicates that the concrete enclosed by the neutral axis and the two consecutive flexural cracks is not stressed once bond failure occurs. As

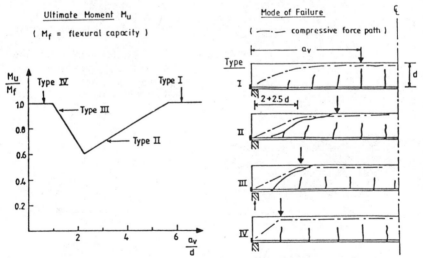

Fig. 6.25   Types of behavior exhibited by reinforced concrete beams without shear reinforcement subjected to two-point loading.

a result, failure as described by the concept of the concrete cantilever cannot occur.

It appears therefore from the preceding that failure occurs due to tensile stresses developing within the compressive zone in the direction perpendicular to the longitudinal axis of the beam *beyond* a distance of between approximately $2.0d$ and $2.5d$ from the support. This is thought to indicate that when reinforcing with links, only the portion of the shear span beyond this distance should be sufficient to prevent shear failure. As discussed in a previous section, such behavior has in fact been predicted by finite-element analysis (Kotsovos, 1983), and the first results of an ongoing experimental work appear to confirm the predictions (Kotsovos).

Type III, characterized by a mode of failure caused by an inclined crack which forms independently of the flexural cracks. As for type II behavior, the crack pattern indicates that it is realistic to consider that once the inclined crack forms, the path of the compressive force within the shear span is linear and joins the reaction at the level of the tension reinforcement, with the load at the level of the compressive stress resultant (Fig. 6.25). The varying intensity of the compressive stresses (C_a and C_b in Fig. 6.27) along the linear path is unlikely to give rise to tensile stresses (t_b in Fig. 6.27) in the orthogonal direction which are large enough to cause failure of a beam with a rectangular cross section. Since therefore the upthrust due to the change in direction of the compressive force is balanced by

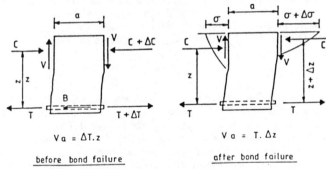

Fig. 6.26   Effect of bond failure on stress conditions in compressive zone.

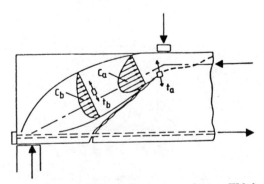

Fig. 6.27   Stress conditions within shear span for type III behavior.

the applied load, it can only be the tip of the inclined crack that may induce tensile stresses (t_a in Fig. 6.27) in the region of the path which are sufficiently large to cause failure.

However, the inclined crack is unlikely to penetrate into the region under the load point since the triaxial compressive stress conditions which exist there increase considerably the strength of the concrete. Instead, it propagates near horizontally toward the compressive zone of the middle span in order to bypass this high-strength region (Kotsovos, 1983). As a result, the tensile stresses which exist near the crack tip, at right angles to the direction of crack extension (Kotsovos, 1979; Kotsovos and Newman, 1981a), combined with the longitudinal compressive stresses due to the bending action, create a compression-tension state of stress within the region of the middle span adjacent to the load point, which eventually causes failure.

The preceding reasoning provides a realistic description of the causes that lead to the observed mode of failure of reinforced concrete beams exhibiting type III behavior (Fig. 6.25) and is compatible with the results shown in Fig. 6.19, which indicate that the presence of links *only* within the *middle* span of such beams can prevent shear failure.

Type IV, similar to type III behavior, is characterized by a linear path of compressive force. However, in contrast with type III behavior, the tensile stresses (t in Fig. 6.28) due to the varying intensity of the compressive stresses (C_a and C_b in Fig. 6.28) along the path cause "splitting" in the direction of the path. Collapse may occur due either to failure of the middle span in flexure for a long beam, or to extension of the "splitting" toward the load point or the support for a short beam. In the latter case, the type of failure is similar to that of plain concrete subjected to a concentrated load (Kotsovos and Newman, 1981b).

4 Design implications

Perhaps the main characteristic of the proposed concept is that shear resistance is predominantly provided by the *compressive zone* of a reinforced concrete structural member and *not,* as widely considered, the region of the structural member below its neutral axis. Consequently a shear design procedure safeguards against shear failure when the compressive zone has adequate shear capacity, which increases with the size of the compressive zone. When the shear capacity is exceeded, shear failure may be prevented in one of the following ways:

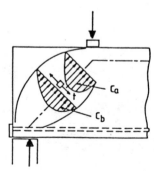

Fig. 6.28   Stress conditions within shear span for type IV behavior.

1. By increasing the cross section of the structural member, thus increasing the size of the compressive zone.

2. By providing additional tension reinforcement within the region likely to fail in shear, with the reinforcement having adequate anchoring length into the adjacent regions. This increases the depth of the neutral axis, thus also resulting in a larger compressive zone.

3. By providing shear reinforcement so as to sustain the tensile stresses which cannot be sustained by concrete at right angles to the path of the compressive force.

In order to implement this procedure in practical design it is essential to have available an analytical description of the stress conditions that cause shear failure. This analytical description should be used not only as a criterion for failure, but also as a basis for the calculation of the tensile force to be sustained by the shear reinforcement, should approach 3 be adopted. Such an analytical description, in which the stress conditions leading to failure are expressed in terms of the internal actions (bending moment and shear force) that cause them, has already been derived empirically for beams (Bobrowski and Bardhan-Roy, 1969). It is as follows:

$$M_{cx} = 0.875\, a_{vx}d\left(0.342b_1 + 0.3\frac{M_{fx}}{d^2}\sqrt{\frac{z}{a_{vx}}}\right)^4\sqrt{\frac{16.66}{pf_y}} \qquad (6.1)$$

in which the subscript x denotes a given cross section at a distance x from the support and

where M_{cx} = moment corresponding to shear failure, N · mm
$\quad M_{fx}$ = flexural capacity, N · mm
$\quad a_{vx} = M_{ax}/V_{ax}$,
$\quad M_{ax}$ = applied bending moment at a given section x, N · mm
$\quad V_{ax}$ = shear force at a given section x, newtons
$\quad z$ = level arm, mm
$\quad d$ = effective depth, mm
$\quad p$ = the ratio (area of tension steel)/(area of concrete to effective depth)
$\quad f_y$ = characteristic strength of steel, N/mm^2
$\quad b_1$ = effective width, mm

b_1 is given by the lesser of $b_0 + 2b_s$ or $b_0 + 2d_s$, with b_0, b_s, and d_s shown in Fig. 6.29.

Equation 6.1, which has been found to give close predictions of the load causing shear failure (Bobrowski, 1982), may be used in practice as follows:

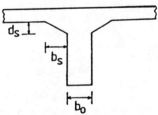

Fig. 6.29   Definition of b_0, b_s, and d_s in Eq. 6.1.

1. Find M_{ax} and V_{ax} at section x due to applied loading.

2. Determine $a_{vx} = M_{ax}/V_{ax}$.

3. Determine M_{cx} at section x by using Eq. 6.1.

If $M_{cx} \geq M_{ax}$, only nominal stirrups would be needed in beams and ribs of anisotropic slabs, and no shear reinforcement would be required in solid slabs.

If $M_{cx} > M_{fx}$, then M_{fcx} is to be used as the critical maximum value instead of M_{cx}. In such a case an increase in flexural, and not shear, reinforcement can enhance the ultimate capacity of the cross section.

If $M_{fx} > M_{cx} < M_{ax}$, then in order to avoid failure, either increase the area of the effective tensile steel, or increase the cross section. The other alternative, provided that $M_{ax} < M_{fx}$, is to provide links in accordance with the following requirements:

$$\frac{A_{sv}}{s_v} \geq \frac{V_{ax} - \dfrac{M_{cx}}{a_{vx}}}{\gamma_{ms}\gamma_f\gamma_c\, f_y d} \tag{6.2}$$

where A_{sv} = cross-sectional area of two legs of a link
  s_v = spacing of links
  γ_{ms} = material factor for reinforcement
  γ_f = appropriate load factor
  γ_c = factor covering mode and consequences of failure
  f_y = characteristic strength of link reinforcement

Providing links as specified by Eq. 6.2 is compatible with the concept of the compressive force path, and *not* with truss analogy, since the presence of the links is considered to restore the capacity of the structural member to sustain tensile stresses at right angles to the path, thus enabling concrete to carry the compressive force.

5 Wide implications

The underlying basis of the proposed concept is the view that an element of concrete in a structure *always* fails in *tension*. This view is supported by both analysis predictions (Kotsovos, 1981) and experimental evidence (Kotsovos, 1982), which indicate that a concrete structure collapses before the strength of the concrete in compression is attained anywhere within the structure.

The reason for this behavior appears to lie in the *large* and *abrupt dilation* which concrete undergoes once a level close to, but *not beyond,* the ultimate compressive strength is exceeded. This level, which marks the transition from the consolidation to the dilation stage, is the *minimum-volume* level, which has also been termed *onset of unstable fracture propagation* (OUFP) (Kotsovos, 1979; Kotsovos and Newman 1981a).

Since there is always within a structure a localized region in compression where the onset of unstable fracture propagation is exceeded before this level is reached in the surrounding regions, also in compression, concrete dilation in this region induces tensile stresses in the surrounding concrete. At the same time, for equilibrium purposes, the surrounding concrete restrains dilation. While this restraint increases the strength of the dilating region, the tensile stresses eventually turn the state of stress in the surrounding concrete into a state of stress with at least one of the principal stress components tensile, and thus reduce strength (Kotsovos, 1982). Therefore it is always the surrounding concrete under combined compression-tension that fails first.

This mechanism is one of many which may give rise to tensile stresses leading to the collapse of a structure before the compressive strength of concrete is attained. The concept of the compressive force path not only identifies as the most critical tensile stress fields those existing in the region of the path along which the compressive force is transmitted to the supports, but also indicates possible mechanisms which may give rise to such stress fields. It should be recognized, however, that although tensile failure in other regions may not be the primary cause of structural collapse, it may also eventually lead to collapse by causing instability of a structure.

It is interesting to note that the concept of the compressive force path is in compliance with the properties of concrete as a material (such as stress-strain relationships, failure criteria, failure mechanism), since by using an analytical model of these properties in numerical methods of analysis (for example, the finite-element method), the mechanisms of failure indicated by the concept are also predicted by the analysis (Kotsovos, 1984b; Kotsovos, 1983).

It would therefore appear that if this concept could be applied successfully in design, then the properties of concrete as a material could form a *common* basis for both analysis and design. Such a common basis is desirable since it can be used to simplify current design procedures by revising those of the design assumptions which are in conflict with fundamental material properties. It is the incompatibility between design assumptions and material properties that is considered to have led to the complexity of current code provisions for design.

6 Conclusions

1. The concepts that form the basis of current provisions for shear design are found to be incapable of providing a realistic description of the causes of various modes of shear failure exhibited by reinforced concrete beams.

2. Furthermore, the evidence provided indicates that, in contrast with widely held views, shear resistance is mainly provided by the compressive zone, with the region of a beam below its neutral axis making an insignificant contribution, if any.

3. It is postulated that the underlying causes of shear failure are associated with the development of tensile stresses in the region of the path along which the compressive force is transmitted to the supports and shown that the concept is compatible with characteristic features of the behavior of reinforced concrete beams.

4. The proposed concept is also in compliance with fundamental properties of concrete as a material and it is argued that design procedures can only be simplified by revising those design assumptions which are in conflict with these material properties.

6.4 DEEP BEAMS

Deep beams behave differently from shallow beams, and hence require different design procedures. In a deep beam, plane sections before loading do not remain plane after loads are applied to the member; this relates primarily to flexure. Important differences occur after cracking when deep beams develop a tied arch or truss action; this relates primarily to shear. In this case, significant postcracking shear strength is possible because a large portion of the load can be transmitted directly to the supports through diagonal compression in the web, provided that the flexural reinforcement is adequately anchored into the supports.

1   Background

Kong (1990) has edited a text dealing solely with deep beams, which provides current information on many aspects of deep beam design. This section provides a general overview of the more important aspects and attempts to present conclusions and recommendations for the practical design of deep beams.

Examples.   Deep beams often occur as transfer girders in high-rise structures. Foundation walls supported more or less continuously from below and loaded by point loads (columns) from above are another common example of deep beams. Deep beams are also encountered in the design of rectangular suspended containers, such as storage tanks or swimming pools. In this case, the weight to be supported may be suspended from the bottom edge of the walls, creating an adverse stress pattern in a deep beam, calling for additional "hanger" reinforcement (stirrups).

What is a deep beam?   There is no universally accepted definition of a deep beam, as some authors focus on the flexural behavior while others focus on the shear behavior. The definition also depends on whether the beam is uncracked (elastic) or cracked. In general European references focus on flexural behavior, whereas North American references focus primarily on shear behavior. For example, CEB-FIP (1978) suggests that simply supported beams of a span-to-depth ratio L/D less than 2, and continuous beams of L/D less than 2.5, be designed as deep beams. L is the beam span and is the smaller of the center-to-center span or 1.15 times the clear span, and D is the overall beam depth, both in meters. ACI 318 (1989) suggests that beams with clear-span-to-depth ratios of less than 5, which are loaded on one face and supported on the opposite face so that compression struts can develop between the loads and the supports, should be treated as deep beams. In reality, the deep beam problem is a coupled problem, which requires a solution that treats shear and flexure in a consistent manner.

Distinguishing behavior of deep beams.   In the initial elastic uncracked condition, Bernoulli's hypothesis that plane sections before bending remain plane after bending is not valid for deep beams. Figure 6.30 illustrates this for a simple-span beam. In the deep beam case, the distance between the centroid of the flexural tension and the compression zones is less than if plane sections had remained plane. Since the internal lever arm is smaller, the flexural tension and compression resultants must be larger than predicted by straight-line theory. The problem is even more acute for continuous beams, where the internal lever arm over interior supports is even smaller than in the case of simple-span beams. The net result is that deep beams require more flexural reinforcement (in total) distributed over a larger tension zone than predicted by usual shallow beam theory.

   After cracking and at the ultimate load, deep beams transfer a significant portion of the load directly to the support by *direct compression struts* going from the load to the support. A portion of the load may be transferred to the supports through stirrups, as shown in Fig. 6.31. Typical crack patterns for shallow and deep beams are compared in Fig. 6.31a and b. Large-scale tests on deep beams have been reported by Leonhardt and Walther (1966) and by Rogowsky et al. (1986). From the crack pattern and strain measurements one can deduce idealized

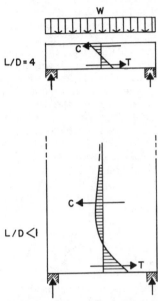

Fig. 6.30   Comparison of elastic stress distributions for shallow and deep beams.

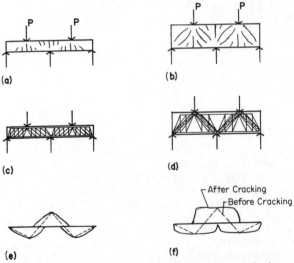

Fig. 6.31   Comparison of shallow and deep beam behavior.

truss models, as shown in Fig. 6.31*c* and *d*. From these models (or the strain measurements) one can determine the forces acting in the top and bottom flexural reinforcements, as shown in Fig. 6.31*e* and *f*. In a deep beam it is apparent that the anchorage of the flexural reinforcement is critical. The direct compression struts require large chord forces at the supports. The net result is that flexural reinforcement should be well-anchored into the supports, and must not be cut off or curtailed in accordance with the bending moment diagram.

Deep beams, being very stiff, are sensitive to differential support "settlements" as well as to shear deformations. Such settlements may be due to creep, shrinkage, or thermal movement of supporting members, as well as to geotechnical considerations. From the tests of two-span continuous beams of Rogowsky et al. (1986), it was found that even without support settlements, negative support moments were considerably less than predicted by shallow beam theory. This is presumably due to shear deformations and nonlinear material behavior (such as cracking). As a result, for the design of continuous beams two distributions of bending moments should be considered. The first should be based on an elastic analysis that includes support settlements but ignores shear deformation effects. The second distribution should be based on the first, with the negative moments reduced 40% and the positive moments and support reactions adjusted accordingly. (This is based on experimental observations.) The net result is that design envelopes should allow for the effects of differential support settlements, shear deflections, and nonlinear material behavior.

The addition of stirrups without additional flexural reinforcement does little to increase the shear capacity until the direct compression strut is completely suppressed. Stirrups "use" horizontal force, which could otherwise equilibrate direct compression struts. The addition of stirrups thus reduces the force carried by the direct compression struts while at the same time it increases the force carried by the stirrups.

Tests with low web reinforcement ratios produce highly variable results, which no reasonable design method can predict. The strength is influenced by residual stresses, concrete tensile strength, and limited concrete ductility, which are all difficult to predict. Deep beams should be provided with a reasonable amount of web reinforcement (say, 0.4% vertical and horizontal) in order to improve their reliability. In practice, one should provide stirrups for at least 30% of the direct strut capacity.

2 Design approaches

Several different design methods for deep beams exist around the world. A few of the more important methods are discussed here.

Classical elastic analysis.   It has long been recognized that the Bernoulli hypothesis is not valid for deep beams. Much of the early work on deep beams emphasized elastic analysis, and many elastic solutions can be found in the literature. The Portland Cement Association (PCA, 1980) still provides information on the elastic stress distribution in simple-span and continuous deep beams. Leonhardt and Walther (1966) found that after cracking, the stresses deviate significantly from the elastic distribution. Beam capacity cannot be predicted by elastic analysis.

If reinforcement is proportioned solely in accordance with an elastic stress distribution, main reinforcement would be curtailed in regions of low bending moment. In real beams which demonstrate marked strut-and-tie action, the curtailed reinforcement is inadequate as a tie, and much of the potential postcracking strength is lost.

A useful insight, which can be drawn from the elastic solutions, is the estimation of the internal lever arm for flexure and the depth of the tension zone. The design force for the flexural tension reinforcement can be determined by dividing the applied moment by the internal lever arm. The resulting main flexural reinforcement should be distributed over most of the tension zone to control cracks. The CEB-FIP (1978) and CIRIA (1977) recommendations recognize this in their reinforcement detailing requirements. These documents also highlight the need for adequate anchorage of the main flexural reinforcement. Shear strength analysis was largely ignored because the beams of interest at the time (in other words, beams deep enough to have nonlinear but elastic behavior) were generally deep enough that shear strength was not critical.

Finite-element analysis. The finite-element method may be applied to the analysis of deep beams. Linearly elastic finite elements can produce solutions which can be utilized as discussed. Nonlinear finite-element models can predict the capacity of reinforced concrete deep beams with reasonable accuracy. Cook and Mitchell (1988) report a nonlinear finite-element analysis of continuous deep beams which had heavy vertical stirrup reinforcement. The analysis predicted deformations, principal stresses, principal strains, and ultimate loads. The predicted strengths were within 4% of actual measured strengths for the four tests analyzed. In the tests, failure resulted from yielding of the stirrups followed by crushing of the concrete after gross deformation of the member. As in all well-designed beams, yielding of the reinforcement governed the ultimate load, while crushing of the concrete governed the ultimate deformation.

The accuracy of every finite-element program is likely to be different. To predict ultimate capacity, it is considered essential that the model incorporate nonlinear constitutive relationships for the steel and concrete. In the case of the concrete, the model should account for strain softening. The accuracy of the program should be verified by comparison with test results. It will be better when the ultimate load is governed by yielding of the reinforcement rather than by the concrete strength.

Currently nonlinear finite-element analysis is still not used for routine design, but for special critical problems it offers an alternative to physical testing. Unless one has unlimited time and money, to use nonlinear analysis effectively one must start with a "reasonable design" (concrete dimensions and reinforcement) to be analyzed. The "reasonable design" must be developed by some other method.

ACI 318. The 1977 edition of ACI 318 provided empirically derived equations for the shear strength of deep beams. These equations, while safe for simple-span beams, are unsafe for continuous beams. For the sample of continuous beams reported by Rogowsky et al. (1986), the ratio of test to calculated strength ranged from 0.48 to 1.38. Over half of the tests had measured strengths less than the strength predicted by the ACI code. The empirical equations in ACI 318 are based on simple-span test data. The current version of ACI 318 (1989) indicates that the equations should not be used for continuous beams. One is directed to design continuous beams for shear as though they were shallow beams or to design them on the basis of appropriate truss models.

Kong, Robins, and Sharp. The method of Kong et al. (1975) was used to analyze the data of Rogowsky et al. (1986). The ratios of test to calculated strength ranged from 0.53 to 1.31. For beams with heavy stirrup reinforcement (vertical web reinforcement ratio approximately 0.6%), the predictions were more reasonable. For this group of tests, the ratio of average test to predicted values was 1.17. For the remainder of the tests, the ratio of test to predicted values was highly variable and generally quite unsafe.

The method was originally developed for simple-span deep beams, which were generally deeper than those of the test series in question. The formulation is essentially a kinematic failure mechanism calculation on a critical surface, running from the face of the support to the face of the load. As such, it should be valid for continuous deep beams, provided that there is sufficient web reinforcement to reduce variability and improve ductility.

Truss models.   Truss models can be used readily for the design of deep beams. Truss models themselves are the subject of a separate section of this Monograph (see Chapter 5), which should be referred to for the general application of the method. Rogowsky and MacGregor (1986) presented a detailed description of how truss models may be used for the design of deep beams, along with a design example.

Truss models were used to analyze the test data of Rogowsky et al. (1986). For the beams with heavy stirrup reinforcement (assuming the effective concrete strength equal to the specified strength), the ratios of test to calculated strength ranged from 0.94 to 1.02 (mean 1.00, standard deviation 0.03). For other beams, the prediction accuracy depends on the truss model used because the beams are not always ductile enough to fully redistribute forces in accordance with the truss model. If the model assumed full yield of the top reinforcement over the support when in fact it did not yield (due to lower than expected negative moments), unconservative predictions resulted. In practice, these problems can readily be overcome by providing enough web reinforcement to ensure ductility along with considering various moment distributions.

Truss models are sufficiently accurate for design if reasonable minimum web reinforcement is provided (say, 0.4% vertical and horizontal, well anchored and distributed) and if a range of support reactions is considered (various moment distributions to account for support settlement and shear deformation effects).

Posttensioning.   For applications such as transfer girders, posttensioning can be used to an advantage. When a significant portion of the load is permanent, a harped tendon profile is often used to balance all or a portion of the permanent load, as shown in Fig. 6.32a. Staged stressing can be used to prevent overstressing the girder before all of the permanent load is present (in other words, staged stressing to match construction progress). With this approach the posttensioning tendon carries a significant portion of the load to the support, thus reducing the load that must be carried by the ordinary nonprestressed reinforcement and concrete.

Occasionally the loading and girder geometry will be such that the minimum permissible tendon profile radius is so large that a harped tendon profile is not very efficient. For such cases Marti (1990) has proposed a method of posttensioning with straight tendons to improve the stress state in the web of the girder, as shown in Fig. 6.32b. Without prestressing, the concrete in the web is in a state of more or less pure shear, which implies a principal tension stress in the concrete equal to half the maximum shear stress. By adding uniform vertical and horizontal stresses of suitable magnitude with posttensioning, the maximum principal tensile stress can be reduced significantly or eliminated, as shown in Fig. 6.32c. By reducing the tension stresses and strains in the concrete, web cracking can be controlled. When developing appropriate truss models, the forces from posttensioning should be treated as loads on the concrete. After grouting, that portion of the strand stress-strain curve not used during posttensioning operation can be used by the strand so that it can also assist the structure by acting as bonded reinforcement.

3 Summary

This section has presented an overview of the design of deep beams. The bias here is toward the use of equilibrium truss models, which give reasonable strength predictions when beams have sufficient web reinforcement to ensure ductile behavior. For the design of deep beams the following is recommended:

1. Proportion and detail the reinforcement in accordance with an equilibrium truss model. The consequent and consistent detailing of the reinforcement is essential.

2. Consider the effects of differential support settlements (and the experimentally observed shift of moment from support to midspan regions) and include them in the resulting design envelopes for shear and moment.

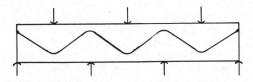

(a) Harped tendon profile balances column loads.

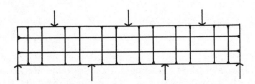

(b) Straight vertical and horizontal tendons improve stress state in web.

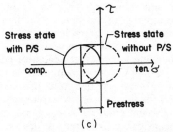

(c)

Fig. 6.32 Posttensioning of deep beams.

3. Use sufficient "minimum" reinforcement to ensure ductile behavior. In shear spans where a major diagonal direct compression strut exists, the stirrups crossing the strut should have a shear capacity of not less than 30% of the applied shear force.
4. Consider the use of posttensioning to balance a significant portion of the load, and to improve the stress state in the beam web.

4   Research needs for deep beams

Further work is necessary in the area of serviceability considerations for deep beams. The current recommendations for minimum reinforcement to control cracking are crude and perhaps occasionally unconservative. Franz and Breen (1980) have investigated the problem for statically determinate beams, but most real deep beams are statically *in*determinate. Column restraint, beam shortening due to drying shrinkage, heat of hydration and subsequent thermal contraction, differential support settlements, and stress redistribution due to creep, all have an influence on the reinforcement required to control cracking. Field observations and well-documented case histories would be useful in confirming how much reinforcement is actually required to control cracks successfully.

The use of posttensioning to improve the stress state in the webs of deep beams is currently underutilized. Further work is necessary to fully realize the potential benefits of posttensioning.

One possible area of development for those engineers who prefer empirical equations over truss models would be to derive empirical equations for statically indeterminate beams. This can probably be done by reevaluating the existing simple-span and continuous beam data and using the shear-span-to-depth ratio as a prime parameter (rather than the ratio of shear to bending moment at the critical section, as currently used by ACI).

6.5   OPENINGS THROUGH BEAMS

In modern building construction, ducts and pipes for air-conditioning, water supply, sewage, and other electrical and mechanical services are accommodated in the space above the false ceiling. Passing these ducts through transverse openings in the floor beams eliminates a significant amount of dead space and results in a more compact and economical design.

Openings through beams may be classified as small or large openings. Small openings are usually circular, square, or nearly square in shape (Fig. 6.33); large openings are rectangular. The effect of these openings on the strength and service load behavior of the beams must be considered in design.

Figure 6.33 shows a simply supported beam with openings under combined bending and shear. For an opening located in a region of positive moment, the struts above and below the opening will be in compression and tension, respectively. The presence of small openings will not affect the flexural capacity of the beam, provided that the depth of the reduced concrete section in compression exceeds the depth of the equivalent concrete stress block at ultimate strength. The shear capacity of the beam can be ensured by designing the compressive strut above the opening to carry the total shear force. Additional longitudinal and diagonal reinforcement must be provided close to the opening to account for stress concentration and to reduce the crack width under service loads.

The provision of large rectangular openings in beams changes their simple mode of behavior into a complex and indeterminate one. Tests (Lorensten, 1965; Nasser et al., 1967; Ragan and Warwaruk, 1967; Barney et al., 1977; Mansur et al., 1984) indicated that the chord members above and below the opening behaved like a vierendeel panel and points of contraflexure occurred at midpoints of the chord members (Fig. 6.34). The free-body diagram at the beam opening can therefore be represented as shown in Fig. 6.35a, with the secondary moments $M_t = M_b = 0$. The external bending moment is resisted by the tensile and compressive stress resultants in the chord members, which can be readily determined from equilibrium. If the distribution of the external shear force between the chord members is known, the beam becomes statically determinate. The critical sections at each corner of the opening that are subjected to combined bending, shear, and axial force can then be designed by any of the current building codes.

The problem, however, lies in apportioning the total shear force between the chord members. Lorensten (1965) regarded the bottom chord as a tension link carrying no shear. Nasser et al. (1967) and Ragan and Warwaruk (1967) have suggested that the amount of transverse shear carried by the chord members can be

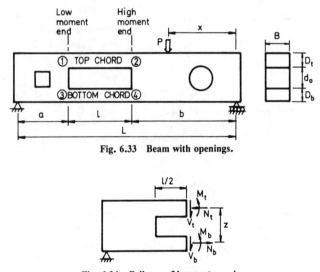

Fig. 6.33 Beam with openings.

Fig. 6.34 Collapse of beam at opening.

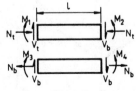

Fig. 6.35 Free-body diagrams.

proportioned according to their cross-sectional areas, while Barney et al. (1977) related it to their flexural stiffnesses.

According to Mansur et al. (1984), the amount of shear force carried by each chord member depends not only on their sectional properties but also on the size and location of the opening. This finding was based on an ultimate strength model for reinforced concrete beams with rectangular openings that are subjected to bending and shear. The model used a collapse load analysis in which the conditions of equilibrium, yield, and a failure mechanism were satisfied simultaneously. The assumed mechanism consisted of four hinges in the chord members, one at each corner of the opening, as shown in Fig. 6.36. The chord members were assumed to be adequately designed for shear, and the interaction relationship between bending moment and axial force was considered as the required yield condition (Fig. 6.37). A computer program has been developed (Tan, 1982) to arrive at a suitable design by successive trial and error.

The analytical model is applicable to beams under any system of vertical loads as long as the shear force along the length of the opening is constant. It can be applied to beams subjected to a uniformly distributed load, which may be replaced by a system of point loads, none of which acts directly on the chord members. In addition, the model is applicable to T-beams, which are typical of floor

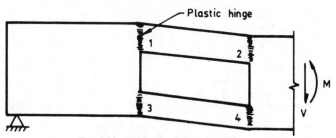

Fig. 6.36 Assumed collapse mechanism.

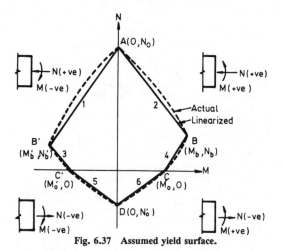

Fig. 6.37 Assumed yield surface.

beams, if the openings are located just below the flange so that the chord members are rectangular.

Based on the exact solution for the collapse load, a method suitable for the direct design of beams with openings has also been proposed by Mansur et al. (1985). The method may be formulated as follows:

Step 1.   Consider the beam as a whole and calculate the values of bending moment $\overline{M}$ and shear force $\overline{V}$ at the center of the opening due to design ultimate load.

Step 2.   Assume a suitable amount and arrangement of reinforcement for the chord members. Construct the interaction diagrams between bending moment and axial force by using the method of equilibrium and strain compatibility.

Step 3.   Determine the axial force N in the chord members. The critical sections are at the ends of the chord members. Forces and moments acting at these ends are shown in the free-body diagram of Fig. 6.35a. It is assumed that no external load acts on the chord members and the shear force remains constant throughout the length of the opening. From the free-body diagram of Fig. 6.35b,

$$V_t = (|M_2| + |M_1|)/l \tag{6.3}$$

$$V_b = (|M_4| + |M_3|)/l \tag{6.4}$$

in which V_t and V_b are the shear forces in the top and bottom chords, respectively; M_1, M_2, M_3, and M_4 are the bending moments at locations 1, 2, 3, and 4, respectively (Fig. 6.33); l is the opening length; and $|\cdot|$ denotes absolute value. The secondary moments M_t and M_b, acting in the top and bottom chord members at the center of the opening, are

$$M_t = (|M_2| - |M_1|)/2 \tag{6.5}$$

$$M_b = (|M_4| - |M_3|)/2 \tag{6.6}$$

At the center of the opening, the external bending moment $\overline{M}$ is resisted by the couple formed by the axial forces N in the chord members and the secondary moments M_t and M_b. Hence,

$$\overline{M} = N_z + M_t + M_b \tag{6.7}$$

in which z is the distance between the plastic centroids of the top and bottom chords. From Eqs. 6.5 to 6.7, the following relation can be obtained:

$$\frac{z}{h} N = \frac{\overline{M} + \frac{1}{2}(|M_1| - |M_2| + |M_3| - |M_4|)}{h} \tag{6.8}$$

in which h is the overall beam depth. Introducing

$$M^* = \overline{M} + \frac{1}{2}(|M_1| - |M_2| + |M_3| - |M_4|)$$

and

$$\frac{z}{h} = \tan \theta$$

the following relationship is obtained:

$$\theta = \tan^{-1}\frac{z}{h} = \tan^{-1}\frac{M^*}{Nh} \tag{6.9}$$

Since collapse of the beam occurs by the formation of four hinges in the chord members, with one at each corner of the opening, the values of the bending moments M_1, M_2, M_3, and M_4 at locations 1, 2, 3, and 4, respectively, must lie on the respective interaction surfaces. The corresponding value of N that must satisfy Eq. 6.8 can be obtained by graphic construction, as illustrated in Fig. 6.38. The applicable portions of the interaction curve (approximated by straight lines) for the top and bottom chords are first drawn so that they appear above the M axis. The values of M_1, M_2, M_3, and M_4 that correspond to any value of N can be obtained from these interaction diagrams; hence the graph of N versus M^*/h. The point of intersection of this graph with the straight line represented by Eq. 6.9 gives the desired value of N.

If the top and bottom chords are each reinforced symmetrically, then the corresponding interaction diagrams are symmetrical about the N axis, and therefore, contraflexure points occur at midpoint of the chord members. Equation 6.7 then reduces to

$$\overline{M} = Nz \tag{6.10}$$

In practice, approximately equal amounts of top and bottom reinforcement for each chord member are provided. In such cases, the values of $\frac{1}{2}(|M_1| - |M_2|)$ and $\frac{1}{2}(|M_3| - |M_4|)$ are found to be very small when compared to $\overline{M}$. Hence N can be obtained directly from Eq. 6.10 without any significant error.

Step 4. Obtain the values of M_1, M_2, M_3, and M_4 that correspond to the value of N as determined from Fig. 6.38. If any of these values are not obtainable, the longitudinal reinforcement in the respective chord member must be increased and step 3 repeated.

Step 5. Calculate the values of V_t and V_b from Eq. 6.3. If $V_t + V_b < \overline{V}$, then the section is not satisfactory and more longitudinal reinforcement has to be provided. If $V_t + V_b > \overline{V}$, a smaller amount of reinforcement could be used. The process is repeated until $V_t + V_b \approx \overline{V}$. Once V_t and V_b are determined, the beam becomes statically determinate and can be designed by any suitable building code.

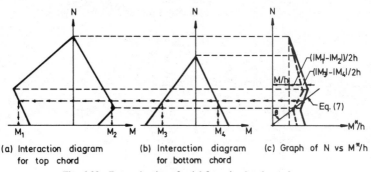

Fig. 6.38 Determination of axial force in chord members.

Step 6. Design the corner reinforcement. Due to a sudden reduction in beam cross section, stress concentration occurs at the corners of the opening. Adequate reinforcement must therefore be provided with proper detailing to avoid wide cracking and premature failure of the beam. In case of stirrups, the required area A_v of vertical legs is given by

$$A_v = \frac{k\overline{V}}{f_{yv}} \tag{6.11}$$

where f_{yv} is the yield strength of stirrup reinforcement and k is the shear concentration factor. When diagonal bars are used as corner reinforcement, the required area A_d can be calculated from

$$A_d = \frac{k\overline{V}}{f_{yd} \sin \alpha} \tag{6.12}$$

where f_{yd} is the yield strength of diagonal reinforcement and α is the angle of inclination of the diagonal bars to the beam axis.

Nasser et al. (1967) have suggested the use of diagonal bars at each corner of the opening and recommended that a sufficient quantity be provided to carry twice the amount of external shear. On the other hand, Lorensten (1965) and Barney et al. (1977) suggested the use of stirrups in the solid section adjacent to each side of the opening to carry the entire shear force, but without any magnification. Recently, Mansur et al. (1985) recommended that a combination of both diagonal bars and vertical stirrups be used with a shear concentration factor of 2 as corner reinforcement, at least 75% of which should be in the form of diagonal bars (Fig. 6.39).

Step 7. Design the solid section beyond the opening by any suitable building code.

In case of predominant torsion, which may occur in spandrel or edge beams, Mansur and Hasnat (1979) and Mansur and Paramasivam (1984) have shown that the familiar *skew-bending* theory for torsion in reinforced concrete solid beams is

Fig. 6.39 Typical corner reinforcement.

also applicable, with little modification, to beams with small transverse openings. When the opening is large, the failure mode changes from skew bending to the one with four hinges in the chord members, one at each corner of the opening, similar to the case of bending and shear. Assuming such a failure mechanism, Mansur et al. (1983a) have developed a *collapse load* analysis for beams with large rectangular openings in pure torsion with adequate experimental substantiation (Mansur et al., 1983b). Daniel and McMullen (1977) have treated vertical instead of transverse openings in beams subjected to predominant torsion. They proposed a method to predict the torsional strength of such a beam. In this method, the stresses due to torsion, bending, and shear in the longitudinal and transverse reinforcements at the ends of the chord members were linearly superimposed. This method is, however, not applicable to beams with transverse (horizontal) openings.

Recently, Mansur (1983) has proposed a simple method for the design of a beam with large rectangular openings under combined torsion and bending. It is based on the concept of limit design in which torsional moments carried by the members above and below the opening are assumed as zero and the points of contraflexure are assumed at midspan of the chord members. This method can be easily extended to include beams under combined torsion, bending, and shear. However, further research is needed to verify this method.

One of the important aspects which require immediate research attention is the calculation of deflections for beams with openings. Studies on prestressed concrete beams are also recommended.

6.6 STAIRS

The stair is an indispensable component of all multistory buildings, and it is usually treated as an inconspicuous detail of minor structural importance. On occasion, the architect and engineer have attempted to make a feature of the stair, and the resulting structural form presents problems for the structural designer.

The most common section for a cast-in-place reinforced concrete stair has a plane underside and may be designed as a slab. A second type has parallel upper and lower profiles resulting in a section which, for lack of a better name, may be designated sawtooth or slabless.

The simplest form of stair is a straight flight between floors, or between floor and landing, in which the stair itself acts as a longitudinal beam or one-way slab, as shown in Fig. 6.40. Alternatively the stair may be supported on one or more longitudinal stringer beams. The principle of cantilevering the stair from a single

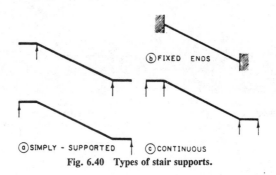

Fig. 6.40 Types of stair supports.

stringer beam or from a wall may also be extended to helical stairs supported from the cylinder forming either the outer or the inner circumference of the helix.

Freestanding stairs represent another development in cast-in-place stair construction. Such stairs are supported only at floor levels and may be curved in plan or rectilinear in plan with an unsupported landing (Fig. 6.41). Again the stair itself may act as the longitudinal beam, or the stair cross sections may have supporting stringer beams. Freestanding stairs are normally designed and constructed with fixed supports; this support condition reduces the maximum value of bending moment and normally results in a more economical design.

The dimensions and slopes of stairs are governed by architectural, economical, and safety considerations. Schuster (1964) recommends that for each step $2R + T = 630$, in which R is the height of the riser and T is the length of the tread. National and city building regulations also specify dimensions.

The design of stairs may be based on elastic analysis and conventional reinforced concrete detailing. The slabless stair should be analyzed as a rigid jointed frame; simple solutions are available for standard cases (Cusens, 1966). Reinforcing of the slabless section creates obvious difficulties due to stress concentrations at the reentrant corners between treads and risers. A pattern of reinforcement (Fig. 6.42) has been suggested by Saenz and Martin (1961), but in experimental tests this has been shown to have some weakness at the reentrant corners. The arrangements suggested in Fig. 6.42b and c develop the full strength of the section.

Freestanding stairs may be analyzed by use of a space frame program. Approximate methods have been formulated for the rectilinear type by Siev (1962) using a plate method, and by Cusens and Kuang (1965) using a simplified space frame technique. Helical stairs are usually analyzed as helical beams with fixed ends, and design charts (Cusens and Santathadaporn, 1966) are available for slab sections subtending angles in plan up to 360°.

In tall buildings, stairs are a highly repetitive element, and hence simple reinforcing details tend to give economy. Frequently, precast stairs are used in conjunction with cast-in-place cores to save forming time and costs.

6.7 BRACKETS AND SHORT FOUNDATION BEAMS

Various approaches have been used for the design of brackets, including beam analogy (Rausch, 1922), truss model (Niedenhoff, 1961), empirical formulas (Kriz and Raths, 1965), and shear-friction hypothesis (Mast, 1968).

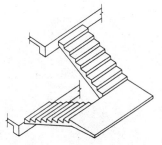

Fig. 6.41 Freestanding stairs.

For these types of structures it is not likely that Bernoulli's theorem of plane sections will apply. For a relation of span width a to height $h \le 1.5$, a simple truss analogy will best satisfy compatibility conditions (Hagberg, 1966). A truss model according to CEB's terminology, used during revision of CEB's model code, is referred to as *strut and tie model*, indicating that the concrete will act as compression strut and the reinforcement as tension tie (see Chapter 5, Section 5.1).

The following derivations are based on a truss analogy that is applicable to vertical and horizontal loads, and which may be used for horizontal and inclined reinforcement (Hagberg, 1983). It will be demonstrated that the results are safe and in acceptable agreement with test results. It should also be emphasized that an objective of this formulation has been to arrive at explicit mathematical formulas which are fitted for the use of computers.

1 Loads on brackets

Figure 6.43 shows a typical bracket configuration. The dimensions are generally small and the loads high. Unintended eccentricities might influence the capacity significantly. It is therefore important to have the location of the loads accurately fixed. Frequently beams have been installed on the bracket without a bearing plate. Through deflection of the beam, the load in such cases may be transferred toward the tip of the bracket, which is particularly unfavorable if significant horizontal loads are acting. In extreme cases the resultant load may act outside the main reinforcement (see Fig. 6.43b).

The following may serve as general guidelines:

1. The location of the loads has to be accurately fixed. The use of a bearing medium is recommended (such as artificial rubber or steel).

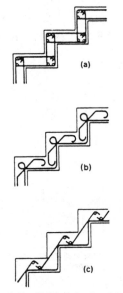

(a)

(b)

(c)

Fig. 6.42 Stair reinforcing details.

2. The geometrical tolerances should be specified, and it should be checked that compliance is achieved.

3. The specified tolerances should be considered in design.

4. Unless special provisions are made, a horizontal force should be accounted for because of friction.

If horizontal forces are to be transferred intentionally from beam to bracket, which might be important to resist seismic and similar loads, this has to be considered carefully in design and detailing.

2 Structural models

Failure modes. For a simple bracket, as shown in Fig. 6.44, tests have indicated the following behavior (Franz and Niedenhoff, 1963). For a certain load, a vertical crack is initiated at the interface between column and bracket. The crack width increases with increasing load. For further load increases, additional cracks develop, the extent depending primarily on the area of the stirrups. These secondary cracks tend to be slightly inclined. For loads near the ultimate load, a small vertical and a dominating horizontal displacement are observed.

It is assumed that failure is introduced through one of the following modes:

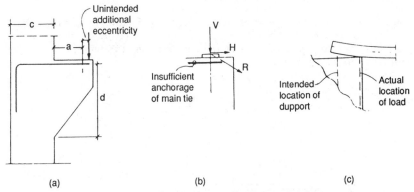

(a)   (b)   (c)

Fig. 6.43 Dimensions and load transfer to bracket.

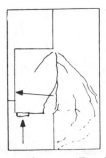

Fig. 6.44 Common crack pattern for a test. (*From Franz and Niedenhoff, 1963.*)

1. The steel is reaching its yield stress (tension failure).
2. The concrete lamellaes between the cracks or the concrete underneath the bearing plate are reaching their compression strength (compression failure).
3. The load transfer between tension tie and compression strut is improper (node or anchorage failure).

Basic assumptions. The following assumptions are made:

1. The equilibrium conditions must be fulfilled.
2. The steel yields or the concrete crushes at failure. (Anchorage failure must be avoided through proper detailing.)
3. The strength of the materials is as determined in uniaxial tests. For design purposes a specified design strength is to be used.
4. The strength of the concrete in tension is neglected.
5. Yielding of the reinforcement is considered a failure criterion.

In the following subsection, capacity formulas are developed for brackets with horizontal reinforcement only and for brackets with combined horizontal and inclined reinforcement as "standard cases."

3 Development of capacity formulas

Capacity with horizontal reinforcement only. Figure 6.45 shows two layers of horizontal reinforcement. The lower layer may represent the center of gravity of horizontal stirrups. Stirrups located near the compression edge will not make any contribution to the tension capacity.

1. Equilibrium conditions:

$$F_c = \frac{V}{\cos \beta} \tag{6.13}$$

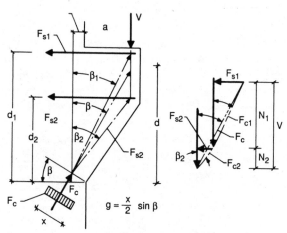

Fig. 6.45   Geometry, forces, and equilibrium conditions based on horizontal reinforcement.

$$F_s = V \cdot \tan \beta \tag{6.14}$$

$$F_s = F_{s_1} + F_{s_2} \tag{6.15}$$

$$V = N_1 + N_2 = \frac{F_{s_1}}{\tan \beta_1} + \frac{F_{s_2}}{\tan \beta_2} \tag{6.16}$$

2. Geometry:

$$\tan \beta_1 = \frac{a + \dfrac{x}{2} \cos \beta}{d_1 - \dfrac{x}{2} \sin \beta} \tag{6.17}$$

$$\tan \beta_2 = \frac{a + \dfrac{x}{2} \cos \beta}{d_2 - \dfrac{x}{2} \sin \beta} \tag{6.18}$$

3. Strength of materials:

$$F_c = f_c bx \tag{6.19a}$$

$$F_{s_1} = A_{s_1} = f_{s_1} \tag{6.19b}$$

$$F_{s_2} = A_{s_2} f_{s_2} \tag{6.19c}$$

Substituting Eqs. 6.17, 6.18, and 6.14 into Eq. 6.16 yields

$$\frac{F_s}{\tan \beta} = \frac{\overbrace{F_{s_1}}}{\left(a + \dfrac{x}{2} \cos \beta\right)} + \frac{\overbrace{F_{s_2}}}{\left(a + \dfrac{x}{2} \cos \beta\right)} \over {d_1 - \dfrac{x}{2} \sin \beta} \quad\quad {d_2 - \dfrac{x}{2} \sin \beta} \tag{6.20a}$$

From Eq. 6.20a one obtains

$$x = \frac{2[\tan \beta(d_1 F_{s_1}/F_s + d_2 F_{s_2}/F_s) - a]}{\cos \beta + \tan \beta \sin \beta} \tag{6.20b}$$

Substituting Eqs. 6.20b, 6.13, and 6.14 into Eq. 6.19a yields

$$\left(1 - \frac{2f_c bd}{F_s}\right)\tan^2 \beta + \frac{2f_2 ba}{F_s} \tan \beta + 1 = 0 \tag{6.21}$$

where $d = d_1 F_{s_1}/F_s + d_2 F_{s_2}/F_s$. Based on Eq. 6.21, all other quantities may be determined. Equation 6.19a combined with Eqs. 6.13 and 6.14 yields

$$x = \frac{F_s}{f_c b \sin \beta}$$

which, used in Eqs. 6.17 and 6.18, determines $\tan \beta_1$ and $\tan \beta_2$. Finally, the capacity *in tension* for vertical load can be calculated using Eq. 6.16.

Upper limit of capacity (compression failure).   In the preceding derivation it has been assumed that the reinforcement will reach its yield strength. However, the geometry of the bracket and the concrete strength may set an upper limit to the capacity. This maximum value is related to the compression failure criterion. The geometric limitations are shown in Fig. 6.46 and yield the following equations:

$$\tan \beta_{max} = \frac{a + w/2}{d} \tag{6.22}$$

and

$$\max x = w \cos \beta_{max} \tag{6.23}$$

Substituting Eq. 6.23 in Eq. 6.19a yields

$$\max F_c = f_c bw \cos \beta_{max} \tag{6.24}$$

Equation 6.13 combined with Eq. 6.24 determines the maximum capacity of the bracket (compression failure):

$$\max V = f_c bw \cos^2 \beta_{max} \tag{6.25}$$

In this formula, all reinforcement is referred to one layer. The simplifications made are conservative as the compressive strut is assumed without any lateral distribution. A lateral distribution would, however, require additional reinforcement to cover the splitting forces.

Capacity with horizontal and inclined reinforcement.   The derivation of formulas for inclined stirrups is analogous to the derivation for horizontal reinforcement (Fig. 6.47). The equilibrium conditions are given by

$$F_c = \frac{V - F_{sv}}{\cos \beta} \tag{6.26}$$

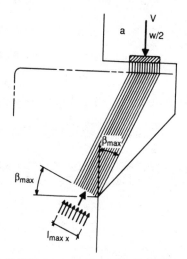

Fig. 6.46   Relation between geometry and maximum capacity.

$$F_{sh} = (V - F_{sv}) \tan \beta \qquad (6.27)$$

$$F_{sh} = F_{s_1} + F_{s_2} \cos v \qquad (6.28)$$

$$F_{sv} = F_{s_2} \sin v \qquad (6.29)$$

The force F_{sh} in Eq. 6.28 is equal to the horizontal force if horizontal reinforcement is present. Hence, the result is that the capacity V of the bracket may be determined as the sum of two capacities as follows: One contribution V' calculated as for horizontal reinforcement, with an effective horizontal force

$$F_{sh} = F_{s_1} + F_{s_2} \cos v \qquad (6.30a)$$

and one contribution equal to the vertical component of the inclined stirrups, that is,

$$V = V' + F_{s_2} \sin v \qquad (6.30b)$$

It can be concluded that inclined stirrups will result in less load in the compression strut than would be the case for horizontal reinforcement, because a part of the load is carried directly by the vertical component of the stirrup force.

Capacity for simultaneously acting horizontal and vertical loads.　It will be assumed that the bracket has horizontal reinforcement only, which will generally be the case if the horizontal force is significant. Further assumptions are evident from Fig. 6.48.

1. Equilibrium conditions:

$$\sum K_v = 0, \qquad R \cos \alpha = F_c \cos \beta \qquad (6.31)$$

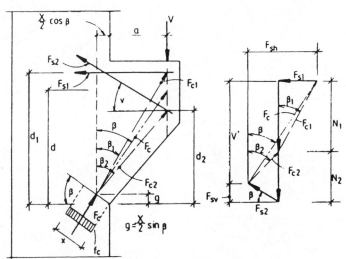

Fig. 6.47　Geometry, forces, and equilibrium conditions based on horizontal and inclined reinforcement.

$$\sum K_h = 0, \qquad R \sin \alpha + F_c \sin \beta = F_{s_1} \qquad (6.32)$$

Where K_v = horizontal force
         K_h = vertical force

2. Geometry:

$$\tan \beta + \frac{a' - \dfrac{x}{2} \cos \beta}{d - \dfrac{x}{2} \sin \beta} \qquad (6.33a)$$

where $a' = a + e$.

Using Eq. 6.33a yields

$$x = \frac{2(d \tan \beta - a')}{\cos \beta + \sin \beta \tan \beta} \qquad (6.33b)$$

Using Eqs. 6.31 and 6.19a yields

$$R = \frac{2f_c b \, d \tan \beta - a'}{\cos \beta 1 + \tan^2 \beta} \qquad (6.34)$$

Substituting Eqs. 6.33b and 6.34 in Eq. 6.32 yields

$$\tan^2 \beta \left(1 - \frac{2f_c bd}{F_{s_1}}\right) + \frac{2f_c b}{F_{s_1}} (a' - d \tan \alpha) \tan \beta + \left(1 + \frac{2f_c ba'}{F_{s_1}} \tan \alpha\right) = 0$$

$$(6.35)$$

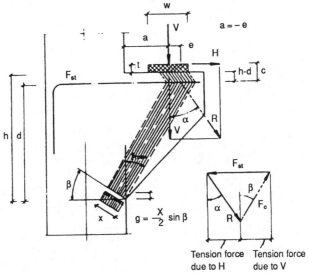

Fig. 6.48 Geometry, forces, and equilibrium conditions for simultaneously acting horizontal and vertical loads.

From Eq. 6.35 all quantities are determined. If $H = 0$, then $\alpha = 0$ and $a' = a$. In this case, Eq. 6.35 is identical to Eq. 6.21.

Furthermore, Eq. 6.35 determines β, Eq. 6.34 determines R, and

$$V = R \cos \alpha \qquad H = R \sin \alpha$$

Maximum capacity (compression failure).   From Fig. 6.48,

$$\tan \beta_{max} = \frac{a + w/2 + (h - d) \tan \alpha}{d} \tag{6.36}$$

and

$$\max x = 2\left(\frac{w}{2} - t \cdot \tan \alpha\right) \cos \beta_{max} \tag{6.37}$$

Equation 6.19a combined with Eq. 6.37 yields

$$\max F_c = 2f_c b\left(\frac{w}{2} - t \cdot \tan \alpha\right) \cos \beta_{max} \tag{6.38}$$

which, using Eq. 6.31, yields the maximum capacity

$$\max R = 2f_c b\left(\frac{w}{2} - t \cdot \tan \alpha\right) \frac{\cos^2 \beta_{max}}{\cos \alpha} \tag{6.39}$$

or

$$\max V = 2f_c b\left(\frac{w}{2} - t \cdot \tan \alpha\right) \cos^2 \beta_{max} \tag{6.40}$$

Equation 6.40 is identical to Eq. 6.25 for $\tan \alpha = 0$, that is, $H = 0$.

4 Various column conditions

The derivations shown in subsection 3 deal with the forces in the bracket only. It is, however, necessary to establish a complete system of equilibrium, which takes the boundary conditions of the column into account and follows the load path into the column. Figure 6.49 shows three different boundary conditions (geometric and static conditions). If in the case of Fig. 6.49c (tension on inner face above bracket) the bracket load is vertical only, it will probably be advantageous to use inclined reinforcement in addition to the horizontal tie. Figure 6.50 shows a possible model for this case. The inclined tie will be effective for a limitation of the cracks in the serviceability limit state. With a horizontal force of some significance it is, however, proper to use only a horizontal tie in the equilibrium model.

5 Dimensioning of bracket

Basis.   The following derivation applies to dimensioning of the bracket solely. It is, however, necessary, as indicated in Subsection 4, to follow the load path into the column and check the section underneath the bracket in particular.

Analyses of tests have shown that stirrups are not necessary to obtain the ultimate load. However, all tests were performed for short-term loads. To maintain the stability of the cracked compression lamellae under sustained loads, a certain area of stirrups should be provided. These stirrups will also be effective in the case of curved compression lamellae, which have been observed in some tests. The stirrups will then cover the tension forces for a change in the direction of compression. Further, observations of test specimens seem to indicate a more distributed crack pattern when stirrups are used; in other words, the requirements of serviceability limit state can be better satisfied. As is obvious from the derivations in Subsection 2, the stirrups will contribute to the total tension capacity if they are located in the upper part of the bracket.

Inclined reinforcement should be considered in two cases:

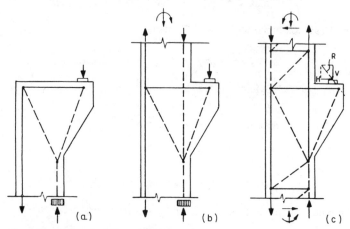

Fig. 6.49   **Various boundary conditions and corresponding strut and tie models.**

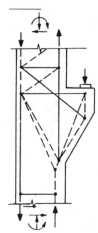

Fig. 6.50   **Possible strut and tie model for given static boundary conditions.**

1. If the height of the bracket is to be limited since a part of the load is carried directly by the vertical component of the inclined reinforcement.

2. If there is tension on the inner face of the column and the vertical load is predominantly on the bracket.

In design, the width b of the bracket will normally be known from the column design. The width w of the load-bearing plate should be designed for a reasonable value of contact stress. The necessary height of the bracket is determined on the basis of the compression failure criterion. Note that lower bracket height is achieved with increased w.

Three checks are necessary:

1. Check of compression failure, such as in the height of the bracket
2. Check of tension failure, such as in the capacity of the main tie
3. Check of anchorage, such as in a check of load transfer between struts and ties in the nodes

Formulas for dimensioning. The formulas are developed to cover checks 1 and 2. The anchorage and node capacity will be checked separately.

Bracket with vertical loads only. From Eq. 6.25, one obtains

$$\cos^2 \beta_{max} = \frac{\max V}{f_{cd} b w}$$

Combined with Eq. 6.22,

$$\tan \beta_{max} = \frac{a + w/2}{d}$$

this yields

$$\frac{1}{1 + \dfrac{(a + w/2)^2}{d^2}} = \frac{\max V}{f_{cd} b w}$$

From this expression, one arrives at

$$d \geq \left(a + \frac{w}{2}\right) \sqrt{\frac{V}{f_{cd} b w - V}} \tag{6.41}$$

For inclined stirrups, V' is used in Eq. 6.41, where

$$V' = V - F_{s_2} \sin v = V - f_{s_2} A_{s_2} \sin v$$

The reinforcement for a balanced design may be achieved using Eqs. 6.25, 6.22, and 6.14,

$$\max F_s = \tan \beta_{max} \cdot \max V - \max A_s f_{sd}$$

In other words,

$$\max A_s = \frac{f_{cd} bw \, \cos^2 \beta_{max}}{f_{sd}} \left(a + \frac{w}{2} \right) d$$

which may be written as

$$\max A_s = \frac{f_{cd}}{f_{sd}} \frac{a + w/2}{d} bw \, \cos^2 \beta_{max} \qquad (6.42)$$

or

$$\max A_s = \frac{f_{cd}}{f_{sd}} bw \, \sin \beta_{max} \cos \beta_{max} \qquad (6.43)$$

A balanced design determines the maximum amount of reinforcement that may be used at its yield stress. If d is chosen greater than the value used in Eq. 6.41, then required $A_s < \max A_s$.

Bracket with vertical and horizontal loads. With horizontal reinforcement assumed, one obtains from Eq. 6.40

$$\frac{V}{2f_{cd}b(w/2 - t \cdot \tan \alpha)} = \cos^2 \beta_{max}$$

From Eq. 6.36,

$$\cos^2 \beta_{max} = \frac{1}{1 + \dfrac{[a + w/2 + (h - d) \tan \alpha]^2}{d^2}}$$

which may be rewritten as

$$d \geq \left[a - \frac{w}{2} + (h - d) \tan \alpha \right] \sqrt{\frac{V}{2f_{cd}b(w/2 - t \cdot \tan \alpha) - V}} \qquad (6.44)$$

If $\tan \alpha = 0$, that is, $H = 0$, Eq. 6.44 is identical to Eq. 6.41. Balanced design may be determined as shown for a bracket with vertical load only. Applying Eqs. 6.40, 6.36, 6.32, and 6.31, one obtains

$$\max A_s = \frac{f_{cd}}{f_{sd}} 2b \left(\frac{w}{2} - t \cdot \tan \alpha \right) \qquad (6.45)$$

$$\left[\tan \alpha + \frac{a + w/2 + (h - d)\tan \alpha}{d} \right] \cos^2 \beta_{max}$$

Equation 6.45 is identical to Eq. 6.43 for $\tan \alpha = 0$. Based on these formulas, the design may be performed for arbitrary loading.

Check of anchorages and nodes. In the node beneath the bearing plate, three members are connected: the compression strut from the bearing plate, the inclined strut, and the tension tie. It is essential that the reinforcement be so detailed that the horizontal component of the inclined strut can be transferred into the tie. Recommendations for such an anchorage have been given by various authors, such as Franz and Niedenhoff (1963) and Leonhardt (1974). The most common types of anchorages are welded anchor plates and horizontally bent bars (Fig. 6.51). Tests have shown that horizontally bent U-bars are safe when executed properly. The force is transferred into the bar mainly by direct contact and partly by compression against the ribs on the deformed bars. The area of direct compression will be increased if the reinforcement is arranged in two layers (Fig. 6.51*b*).

With horizontal loads, the node will be transferred outward (Fig. 6.51*c*), which has to be considered in detailing. Transfer of the horizontal component from the top of the bearing plate to the tie may be achieved by utilizing friction between bearing plate and bracket. Figure 6.51*c* indicates that the bearing plate is inserted into the bracket. A completely rigid connection is obtained if the bearing plate is welded to the tie (for example, see Mattock et al., 1976).

Stresses to be used in dimensioning

Reinforcement. The reinforcement should be dimensioned in the ultimate limit state with a design stress

$$f_s = \frac{f_y}{\gamma_{m1}} \quad \text{or} \quad \frac{f_{02}}{\gamma_{m1}} \tag{6.46}$$

where γ_{m1} is the material factor according to the design code.

Concrete. If there is tension crossing a compression field, as is the case in the node area, the design stress should be reduced. However, if the widths of the struts are determined according to the derivations in Subsection 3, calculated capacities are well in agreement with test results and the design is safe. When detailing the structure, some horizontal stirrups should, however, be provided for. Such stirrups will keep the compression lamellae together. It is therefore recommended to use a design stress in the ultimate limit state equal to

$$f_{cd} = \frac{f_c}{\lambda_{m2}} \tag{6.47}$$

where f_c is the concrete strength for uniaxial compression according to the design code.

Dimensioning procedure. The following procedure may be used:

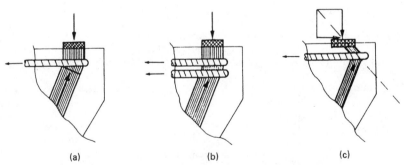

(a)   (b)   (c)

Fig. 6.51 Node connections between tie and inclined strut.

1. The width b is usually known from dimensioning of the column. If not, assume b from previous experience.
2. Determine min w (width of bearing plate),

$$\text{min } w = \frac{V}{\lambda f_{cd} b} \tag{6.48}$$

where $\lambda < 1$; for example, between 0.5 and 0.8. Smaller λ leads to lower bracket heights.

3. With vertical loading only, inclined stirrups may be used to reduce the compression force when the allowable height of the bracket is limited. For higher a values, the use of inclined stirrups is also convenient to improve the serviceability limit state, as the cracks tend to be more inclined in this case.

4. The minimum effective height d is given from Eq. 6.41, or from Eq. 6.44 for brackets with both vertical and horizontal loading.

5. A balanced design is obtained for reinforcement calculated according to Eq. 6.43 or Eq. 6.45. The inclination β_{max} is taken according to Eq. 6.22 or Eq. 6.36. The reinforcement shall have its resultant tension force at a distance d from the compressed edge. If the capacity of the stirrups is to be considered, a certain part, say one-fourth, should be assumed to consist of stirrups. Further, a reasonable distribution of the stirrups should be used, for example, $d_2 \cong 0.7 d_1$.

6. If d is chosen greater than necessary as calculated according to Subsection 3, $\beta < \beta_{max}$ and the reinforcement needed is less than that for balanced design. The required reinforcement area can be calculated with the formulas given in Subsection 3. As an example, for vertical loads only and horizontal reinforcement, Eq. 6.21 can be reformulated using Eq. 6.14,

$$\tan^2 \beta - 2\frac{f_c bd}{V} \tan \beta + \left(1 + \frac{2f_c ba}{V}\right) = 0 \tag{6.21'}$$

and

$$F_s V \cdot \tan \beta$$

$$A_s = \frac{V \cdot \tan \beta}{f_{sd}}$$

For dimensioning, V is given; for check of capacity, F_s is given.

7. Proper detailing of the reinforcement is required according to Subsection 5 (Check of anchorages and nodes) to achieve the calculated capacities without node failure. In particular, failure in the anchorage should be avoided.

Design example.   Figures in parentheses are approximate values in U.S. customary units.

Given:

$$a = 406 \text{ mm (16 in.)}$$
$$b = 508 \text{ mm (20 in.)}$$

$$f = 45 \text{ N/mm}^2 \text{ (6525 psi)}$$

$$f_c = 45/1.5 = 30 \text{ N/mm}^2 \text{ (4350 psi)}$$

$$f_{cd} = 400 \text{ N/mm}^2 \text{ (58,000 psi)}$$

$$V_{sd} = 700 \text{ kN (157.4 kips)}$$

Problem: Calculate necessary effective height d and reinforcement A_s for a balanced design.

Solution:

1. Minimum width of bearing plate

$$\min w = \frac{700.00}{0.8 \times 80 \times 508} = 57.4 \text{ (2¼ in.)}$$

Choose $w = 58$ mm.

2. From Eq. 6.41,

$$d > \left(406 + \frac{58}{2}\right) \sqrt{\frac{700.000}{30 \cdot 508 \cdot 58 - 700.000}} = 435 \cdot 1.95 = 848 \text{ mm (33½ in.)}$$

Choose $h = 900$ mm (35 in.).

3. Balanced design is obtained using Eqs. 6.43 and 6.22. From Eq. 6.22,

$$\tan \beta_{max} = \frac{206 + 58/2}{848} = 0.51$$

that is, $\beta_{max} = 27.1°$. From Eq. 6.43,

$$\max A_s = \frac{30}{400} 508 \cdot 58 \cdot \sin 27.1 \cdot \cos 27.1° = 896 \text{ mm}^2 \text{ (1.39 in.}^2)$$

The actual steel area:

Use   2 × 2   16 mm (⅝ in.) in upper part   804 mm²

                  1 × 2   10 mm (⅜ in.) for stirrup   160 mm²

$$A_s = 964 \text{ mm}^2$$

Then

$$d = \frac{804 d_1 + 160 d_2}{964} = \frac{804 \cdot 870 \cdot + 160 \cdot 750}{964}$$

Use $d = 850$ mm, as found in step 2.

If an underreinforced section is requested, the procedure may be as follows: From step 2, $d > 848$ mm. Choose $h = 1000$ mm. Assuming for main tie $3A_s/4$ and for stirrups $A_s/4$, one obtains

$$A_s d = \frac{3}{4} A_s d_1 + \frac{1}{4} A_s d_2$$

that is,

$$d = \frac{3}{4} d_1 + \frac{1}{4} d_2 = \frac{3}{4} \cdot 970 + \frac{1}{4} \cdot 0.75 \cdot 970 = 910 \text{ mm}$$

Equation 6.21 is reformulated as

$$\tan^2 \beta - 2\frac{f_c bd}{V} \tan \beta + \left(1 + \frac{2f_c ba}{V}\right) = 0$$

yielding

$$\tan^2 \beta - 2 \cdot 19.812 \tan \beta + 18.68 = 0$$
$$\tan \beta = 0.477$$

which with Eq. 6.14 yields

$$F_s = V \cdot \tan \beta = 700 \cdot 0.477 = 334 \text{ kN}$$

Then $A_s \geq 344/0.4 = 834 \text{ mm}^2$ as compared with 896 mm^2 found in step 3. The correlation between w and d and between d and A_s is illustrated in Fig. 6.52.

6   Test results

Results from three test series have been compared with the results from calculated capacities obtained with the formulas developed in Subsection 3. The tests cover a/d values between 0.114 and 0.72 and reinforcement ratios between 0.21 and 3.10%. Some specimens had inclined stirrups and some had both vertical and horizontal loading. A total of 118 tests were analyzed. The calculated load capacities were based on the concrete cylinder strength and the yield stress of the reinforcement. Figure 6.53 shows the calculated ultimate load versus tested values. Figure 6.54 shows calculated yield load versus measured yield load for tests by

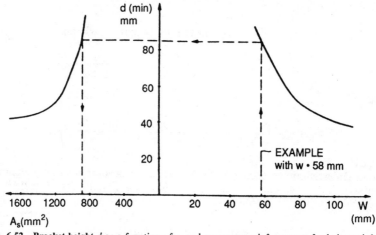

Fig. 6.52   Bracket height d as a function of w and necessary reinforcement for balanced design.

Kriz and Raths (1965). For further details of the test analyses, see Hagberg (1983).

7 Short foundation beams

Types and loadings.   Foundation beams transfer the loads directly to soil or to piles (Fig. 6.55).

Structural system.   The structural system of foundation beams (strut and tie model) should be developed according to the same principles as those applied on brackets. Figure 6.56 shows a foundation resting directly on the soil, with a suggested strut or tie model.

A check of compression failure may be performed, as shown for the brackets. The resultant force R is to be used in the check. The main reinforcement (main tie) is suggested as closed stirrups with two lengths, according to the structural model. A surface reinforcement and a splicing reinforcement to the column are recommended.

If the foundation beam is supported on piles, the direction of the struts and ties is rather well defined. Figure 6.57 gives examples of foundation beams on

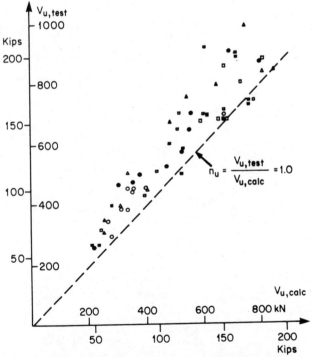

Fig. 6.53   Calculated and measured ultimate loads. Legend: ■ Hermansen, calc. tension failure, horizontal stirrups. ▲ Hermansen, calc. tension failure, inclined stirrups. ● Hermansen, calc. compression failure. □ Sware/Jonsson, calc. tension failure, horizontal stirrups. △ Sware/Jonsson, calc. tension failure, inclined stirrups. ○ Both horizontal and vertical load.

two and four piles. Figure 6.57*a* illustrates strut and tie models, Fig. 6.57*b* shows proposed reinforcement layouts.

The main ties are proposed as closed shapes analogous to the main ties in the brackets. It is recommended to use more layers rather than one, such that smaller and medium diameters can be used. With small and medium sized bar diameters, proper bending radii can be achieved. In the case of four piles, diagonal main ties are recommended in accordance with the strut and tie model.

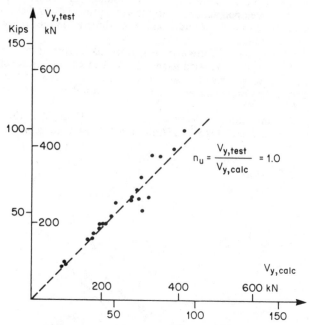

Fig. 6.54   Calculated and measured yield loads.

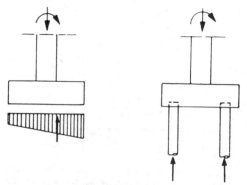

Fig. 6.55   Foundation beams, system and loading.

6.8 CONDENSED REFERENCES / BIBLIOGRAPHY

ACI 1986, *Building Code Requirements for Reinforced Concrete (Supplement)*
ACI 318 1989, *Building Code Requirements for Reinforced Concrete and Commentary*

Barney 1977, *Behavior and Design of Prestressed Concrete Beams with Large Web Open-*
Bobrowski 1969, *A Method of Calculating the Ultimate Strength of Reinforced and Pre-*
Bobrowski 1982, *Origins of Safety in Concrete Structures*
BSI 1985, *Code of Practice for Design and Construction (BS 8110)*

CEB-FIP 1978, *Model Code for Concrete Structures*
CIRIA 1977, *The Design of Deep Beams in Reinforced Concrete*
Colaco 1970, *End Moments for Floor Beams Framing into Spandrels*
Colaco 1975, *Haunched-Girder Concept for High Rise Office Buildings*

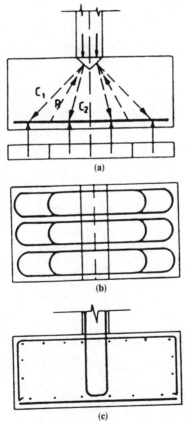

(a)

(b)

(c)

Fig. 6.56   Directly supported foundation beam. (*a*) Structural model. (*b*) Horizontal reinforcement. (*c*) Complete reinforcement layout.

Cook 1988, *Studies of Disturbed Regions Near Discontinuities in Reinforced*
CSA 1984, *Design of Concrete Structures for Buildings (CAN3-A23.3-M84)*
Cusens 1965, *Analysis of Free-Standing Stairs under Symmetrical Loading*
Cusens 1966, *Analysis of Slabless Stairs*
Cusens 1966, *Design Charts for Helical Stairs with Fixed Supports*

Daniel 1977, *Torsion in Concrete Beams Containing an Opening*

Fenwick 1968, *Mechanisms of Shear Resistance of Concrete Beams*
Ferguson 1973, *Reinforced Concrete Fundamentals*
Fintel 1978, *Case Study of Effects of Post-Tensioning the Beams in a 45-Story*
Fintel 1965, *Effects of Column Exposure in Tall Structures—Temperature*
Fintel 1969, *Effects of Column Creep and Shrinkage in Tall Structures*
Franz 1963, *Reinforcement for Brackets and Short Beams*

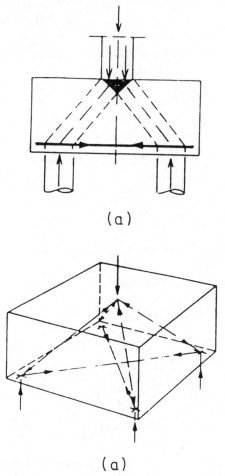

(a)

(a)

Fig. 6.57   Short foundation beams on piles. (*a*) Strut and tie models.

Franz 1980, *Design Proposal for Side Face Crack Control Reinforcement*

Grob 1976, *Ultimate Strength and Design of Reinforced Concrete Beams*
Gustaferro 1972, *Fire Resistance of Post-Tensioned Structures*

Hagberg 1966, *On the Design of Brackets*
Hagberg 1977, *Design of Concrete Brackets*
Hagberg 1983, *Design of Concrete Brackets: On the Application of the Truss*
Hermansen 1974, *Modified Shear-Friction Theory for Bracket Design*

Jonsson 1976, *Tests on Brackets in Concrete*

Kani 1964, *The Riddle of Shear and Its Solution*
Kong 1975, *Design of Reinforced Concrete Deep Beams in Current Practice*
Kong 1980, *Reinforced and Prestressed Concrete*
Kong 1990, *Reinforced Concrete Deep Beams*
Kotsovos 1979, *Fracture Processes of Concrete under Generalized Stress*

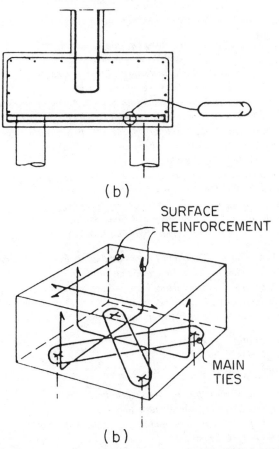

(b)

SURFACE
REINFORCEMENT

MAIN
TIES

(b)

Fig 6.57   (*Continued*) Short foundation beams on piles. (*b*) Proposed reinforcement layouts.

Kotsovos 1981, *An Analytical Investigation of the Behaviour of Concrete under Concen-*
Kotsovos 1981a, *Fracture Mechanics and Concrete Behaviour*
Kotsovos 1981b, *Effect of Boundary Conditions upon the Behaviour of Concrete*
Kotsovos 1982, *A Fundamental Explanation of the Behaviour of RC Beams*
Kotsovos 1983, *Mechanisms of "Shear" Failure*
Kotsovos 1984a, *Behaviour of RC Beams with Shear Span to Depth Ratios*
Kotsovos 1984b, *Deformation and Failure of Concrete in a Structure*
Kotsovos to be published, *The Use of Fundamental Properties of Concrete for the Design*
Kotsovos to be published (c), *Shear Failure of RC Beams*
Kotsovos to be published (d), *Behaviour of RC Beams with Shear Span to Depth Ratios*
Kriz 1965, *Connection in Precast Concrete Structures—Strength of Corbels*

Leonhardt 1961/62, *The Stuttgart Shear Tests*
Leonhardt 1966, *Wandartige Träger. Deutscher Ausschuss für Stahlbeton*
Leonhardt 1974, *Lectures on the Design of Concrete Structures*
Leonhardt 1977, *Crack Control in Concrete Structures*
Lorensten 1965, *Holes in Reinforced Concrete Girders*
Lyn 1963, *Load Balancing Methods for Design and Analysis of Prestressed Concrete*

Mansur 1979, *Concrete Beams with Small Openings under Torsion*
Mansur 1983, *Combined Bending and Torsion in Reinforced Concrete Beams*
Mansur 1983a, *Torsion Tests of R C Beams with Large Openings*
Mansur 1983b, *Ultimate Torque of R C Beam with Large Openings*
Mansur 1984, *Reinforced Concrete Beams with Small Opening in Bending and Torsion*
Mansur 1984, *Collapse Loads of R C Beams with Large Openings*
Mansur 1985, *Design Method for Reinforced Concrete Beams with Large Openings*
Marti 1985a, *Basic Tools of Reinforced Concrete Beam Design*
Marti 1985b, *Truss Models in Detailing*
Marti 1990, *Personal Communication*
Mast 1968, *Auxiliary Reinforcement in Concrete Connections*
Mattock 1976, *The Behavior of Reinforced Concrete Corbels*
Mehmel 1967, *Tests on the Load Capacity of Concrete Brackets*
Mokhtar 1985, *Stud Shear Reinforcement for Flat Concrete Plates*

Nasser 1967, *Behaviour and Design of Large Openings in Reinforced Concrete Beams*
Niedenhoff 1961, *Studies on the Structural Behavior of Brackets*
Nielson 1978, *Concrete Plasticity: Beam Shear—Shear in Joints*
Nylander 1967, *Deep Beams I. Effects Produced on Stress Distribution under Concentrated*
Nylander 1967, *Deep Beams II. Moment and Stress Distribution in Continuous Deep*

PCA 1980, *Design of Deep Girders*
PCI 1980, *Design Handbook*
PTI 1984, *Design of Post-Tensioned Slabs*

Ragan 1967, *Tee Members with Large Web Openings*
Rausch 1922, *Direct Shear in Concrete Structures*
Rausch 1963, *Design for Shear in Reinforced Concrete Structures*
Regan 1969, *Shear in RC Beams*
Reinhardt 1982, *Cracks in Concrete Subject to Shear*

Rice 1985, *Structural Design Guide to the ACI Building Code*
Rogowsky 1986, *Tests of Reinforced Concrete Deep Beams*
Rogowsky 1986, *The Design of Reinforced Concrete Beams*

Saenz and Martin 1961, *Slabless Tread-Riser Stairs*
Schlaich 1984, *Design of Reinforced Concrete*
Schlaich 1987, *Toward a Consistent Design of Structural Concrete*
Schuster 1964, *Helical Stairs*
Siev 1962, *Analysis of Free Straight Multiflight Staircases*
Somerville 1974, *The Behavior and Design of Reinforced Concrete Corbels*

Tan 1982, *Ultimate Strength of Reinforced Concrete Beams with Rectangular*
Taylor 1968, *Shear Stresses in RC Beams without Shear Reinforcement*

Underwriters Laboratories 1971, *Building Materials List*

7

Vertical Members

To discuss vertical members in tall buildings requires a comprehensive coverage of columns, shear walls, and retaining walls. Many routine but important aspects of column design are well known and are included in widely available textbooks on the design of reinforced concrete. The presentation of these aspects in this chapter is brief and general. Other types of column construction such as concrete-filled steel tubes or topics such as detailing of columns are less frequently addressed in design books and, hence, are covered in rather extensive detail in this chapter. The section on retaining walls is essentially the same as that presented in the Council's previous publications (Monograph Volume CB, *Tall Concrete and Masonry Buildings*) as the Committee believed that no major new development in this area has taken place to warrant an update of this section.

A detailed discussion of shear walls is presented in Chapter 8, which is concerned with structural systems subjected to seismic loads.

7.1 SHORT COLUMNS

1 Strength considerations

For practical design considerations, columns are always required to resist a combination of axial load *and* bending moment. Column moments will necessarily exist as the result of direct loading (direct placement of load with known or accidental eccentricity) or due to deformations incurred by the frame, of which the column forms a part. This section does not only address strength considerations, but it gives some treatment to the stiffness of column sections.

The following discussion of axial load–moment interaction is intended to give design engineers the necessary background and tools to enable them to develop a fairly simple personal-computer-based program for the construction of column interaction design diagrams. Initially the method for computing three key points on a typical axial load–moment interaction diagram is presented. The procedure for computing other points on the diagram is extrapolated from this information.

An approximate, and conservative, representation of column strengths for compressive axial loads can be constructed using three select points from a complete interaction diagram. Those points correspond to (1) the pure axial load capacity (zero moment), (2) the pure moment capacity (zero axial load), and (3) the axial load–moment combination associated with what is commonly referred to as the *balanced strain condition*. Such a diagram is shown in Fig. 7.1 for a typical square column section with longitudinal reinforcement distributed uniformly about the perimeter of the section.

An earlier study conducted by Hognestad (1951) indicated that the strain gradient across a section remains approximately linear for any axial load and moment combination at failure. In addition, the maximum concrete strain ε_{cu} observed at failure at the extreme compression fiber was relatively constant (he proposed 0.0038). A more conservative value of 0.003, as suggested by ACI code 318-89 (ACI, 1989), will be used here.

The point labeled P_{no} in Fig. 7.1 corresponds to the axial load capacity of the column and is computed as

$$P_{no} = 0.85f'_c(A_g - A_{st}) + A_{st}f_y \qquad (7.1)$$

where A_g = gross area of column section
A_{st} = total area of longitudinal reinforcement
f'_c = compressive strength of concrete
f_y = yield strength of reinforcement

The other two points used to define the approximate interaction diagram are obtained by applying the strain distributions shown in Fig. 7.2*a* and *b*. Note that the maximum compression strain is constant (0.003), while maximum strains on the opposite side of the section are tensile and vary from ε_y (yield strain) to much greater than ε_y.

The point denoted by (M_b, P_b), sometimes referred to as the balanced point, is computed by imposing a strain distribution on the column section that is intended to produce simultaneous crushing of concrete on one face and yield of the extreme tensile reinforcement on the opposite side of the section. Steel strains for Fig. 7.2*a* are computed as:

$$\varepsilon_{s_1} = \frac{c - d_1}{c}\varepsilon_{cu} \qquad (7.2)$$

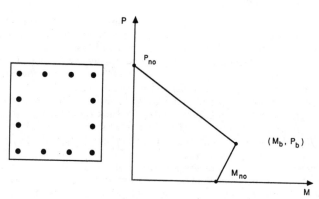

Fig. 7.1 Approximate *P-M* interaction diagram.

$$\varepsilon_{s_2} = \frac{c - d_2}{c} \varepsilon_{cu} \tag{7.3}$$

$$\varepsilon_{s_3} = \frac{d_3 - c}{d - c} \varepsilon_y \tag{7.4}$$

where the neutral axis depth c is defined by the unique strain distribution

$$c = \frac{\varepsilon_{cu}}{\varepsilon_{cu} + \varepsilon_y} d \tag{7.5}$$

Compressive stresses in the concrete are represented by an equivalent rectangular stress block, as suggested by ACI 318, and steel stresses are computed using the calculated steel strains shown and assuming an elastoplastic response for the steel. Force components for the column section are computed as follows:

$$C = 0.85f'_c ba$$

where $a = \beta_1 c$. Also,

$$C_1 = A_{s_1}(\varepsilon_{s_1}E_s - 0.85f'_c) \le A_{s_1}(f_y - 0.85f'_c)$$

$$C_2 = A_{s_2}(\varepsilon_{s_2}E_s - 0.85f'_c)$$

$$T_3 = A_{s_3}\varepsilon_{s_3}E_s$$

$$T_4 = A_{s_4}f_y$$

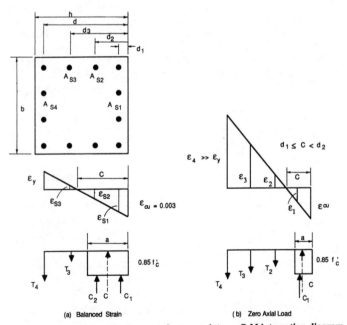

(a) Balanced Strain   (b) Zero Axial Load

Fig. 7.2 **Stress and strain diagrams for two points on *P-M* interaction diagram.**

Note that two of the relations include a term that effectively reduces the steel stress. This term, which is included to account for the force that was not excluded in the calculation of C, corresponds to the steel area times a stress equal to $0.85f_c'$. The axial load and moment that correspond to the balanced point are computed by summing force components, and by summing the moment of each force component about the plastic centroid of the section,

$$P_b = C + C_1 + C_2 - T_3 - T_4 \tag{7.6}$$

$$M_b = C\left(\frac{h}{2} - \frac{a}{2}\right) + (C_1 + T_4)\left(\frac{h}{2} - d_1\right) + (C_2 + T_3)\left(\frac{h}{2} - d_2\right) \tag{7.7}$$

The third point, denoted by M_{no} in Fig. 7.1, can be computed using a trial-and-error approach. For a strain distribution similar to that shown in Fig 7.2b, the depth C of the neutral axis can be varied slightly until a value is found that yields a sum of the force components approximately equal to zero (in other words, $P = 0$).

Note that once a particular strain distribution is selected for a given column section, the neutral axis depth, stresses, force components, and resultant axial load and moment can be computed. A better representation of the interaction diagram for column strength is obtained by making incremental changes in the strain distribution, beginning with the uniform strain associated with P_{no} and ending with a strain profile that yields a net axial load M_{no} of zero. Smaller incremental changes in the strain profile will yield a more precise interaction diagram, such as that shown in Fig. 7.3. Notice that selected strain profiles for a variety of axial load–moment combinations are included in the figure.

The interaction diagram for design is constructed from the strength diagram by multiplying each axial load–moment pair by the appropriate strength reduction factor ϕ. For a tied column, most of the design diagram is constructed with $\phi = 0.7$. For low axial loads, the ϕ factor is gradually increased from 0.7 to 0.9 as the factored axial load P is reduced from 10% of $f_c'A_g$ to zero. Furthermore, because it is assumed that loads cannot be applied to a column without imparting some moment, a cap of 80% of ϕP_{no} is placed on the design diagram. This plateau on the design diagram loosely corresponds to some minimum level of expected eccentricity of the load with respect to the centroid of the column. The design diagram for the example column is shown in Fig. 7.3 by a broken line.

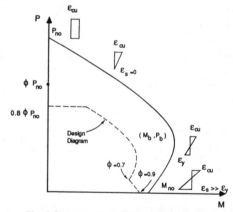

Fig. 7.3 Complete *P-M* interaction diagram.

2 Serviceability concerns

Controlling deflections under service-level loads is a concern in almost every reinforced concrete structure, especially tall buildings. Depending on the magnitude of vertical and lateral loading on a tall building, as well as the history of
previous loads, the effective stiffness of individual columns can vary substantially. Edge or corner columns, for example, can experience variations in axial
load equal to changes in reactions at the exterior end of adjacent beams. These
changes accumulate over the height of the structure and can be very significant
for lower-story columns. The effect of varying axial load on column stiffness is
illustrated in Fig. 7.4 using test data from a column specimen that was subjected
to lateral load reversals and simultaneous changes in axial load (Linbeck, 1987).
The axial load was increased linearly as increments of positive lateral load were
applied, and was decreased linearly as increments of negative lateral load were
applied. The hysteretic response illustrated in Fig. 7.4 indicates dramatically different stiffness characteristics for lateral loads applied in the two directions. Large
reductions in the stiffness of exterior columns have a limited effect on story stiffness
for most tall buildings. However, structures with a small plan area and a high percentage of exterior columns have a greater potential to be significantly influenced by
this effect. Various methods are available for computing column stiffnesses for
varying axial load levels and can be implemented on modern personal computers
(Aktan et al., 1973; Kaba and Mahin, 1984; Lai et al., 1984; Saiidi et al., 1989).

7.2 SLENDER COLUMNS

Moments in columns which result from applied gravity loads acting through column deformations, and which are a significant percentage of the moments computed using first-order linear elastic analysis procedures, are sometimes referred
to as *secondary moments,* or moments resulting from *slenderness effects.* Col-

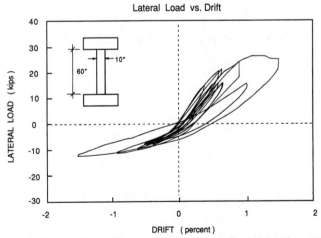

Fig. 7.4 **Hysteresis for column subjected to simultaneously varying axial and lateral loads.** (*From Linbeck, 1987.*)

umns which have a potential for developing significant secondary moments are often referred to as *slender columns.*

The most common method used today by design engineers to account for the slender column effect is embodied in modern North American design codes, and is commonly called the moment magnifier method. The basis for this approximate method is discussed in this chapter.

Consider a braced, pin-ended slender column with an axial load that is applied with the same eccentricity at both ends of the member (as shown in Fig. 7.5). The primary moment diagram and the corresponding elastically deformed shape are also shown. As one moves along the member, away from the column ends, the eccentricity of the load increases by the amount the column has deformed. The product of the applied axial load and increased eccentricity is the first-order approximation of the secondary moments, and is illustrated in Fig. 7.5 by the broken line superimposed on the primary moment diagram. The member curvatures associated with these additional moments will result in increased column displacements. The added displacements, which correspond exactly to additional eccentricities for the applied load, result in further contributions to secondary moments, which lead to additional column displacements, and the like. If the column is stable under the applied axial load, then the additional column deformation for each successive iteration will become smaller and converge to zero. The final maximum deflection y_{max} attained by the column illustrated in Fig. 7.5 is approximated by

$$y_{max} = \frac{y_o}{1 - P/P_c} \qquad (7.8)$$

where y_0 = elastic, first-order deflection
$\quad\quad P$ = applied axial load
$\quad\quad P_c$ = Euler buckling load for column

Using this approximation and Fig. 7.5, the maximum moment M_{max}, including secondary moments, is

$$M_{max} = M_1 + P y_{max} = M_1 + P\frac{y_o}{1 - P/P_c} \qquad (7.9)$$

where $M_1 = P \cdot e$. After substituting the elastic deflection relationship for y_0,

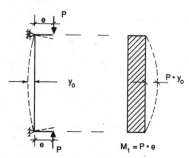

Fig. 7.5 Illustration of slenderness effect for braced, pin-ended column.

$$M_{max} = \frac{M_1(1 + 0.23P/P_c)}{1 - P/P_c}$$

For the single-curvature case shown in Fig. 7.5, the error in omitting the $0.23P/P_c$ term is only 11.5% when $P/P_c = 0.5$. As a result, code equations associated with this approach are generally based on

$$M_{max} = \frac{M_1}{1 - P/P_c} \tag{7.10}$$

If

$$\delta = \frac{1}{1 - P/P_c} \tag{7.11}$$

then the equation for the maximum moment takes the form

$$M_{max} = \delta M_1$$

Because δ has a value always greater than unity, the name *moment magnifier* was adopted by the ACI 318 Committee during the early 1970s. The name is still in use today. To account for conditions different from the unique case illustrated in Fig. 7.5, such as unequal end moments and sidesway, modifications are made in, or additional factors are applied to, the basic magnifier relationship (ACI, 1989).

Other approximate methods that are more precise and more rational exist for estimating and including secondary moments during the structural analysis process. One of these methods was described by Wood et al. in 1976 and is commonly referred to as the P-delta method. It is an iterative approach which first estimates the additional story shears that are caused by the vertical loads acting through the interstory displacements that occur due to the original external loads on the structure. These additional story shears are computed as

$$V_i = \frac{\sum P_i}{h_i} (\Delta_{i+1} - \Delta_i) \tag{7.12}$$

where V_i = additional story shear in story i
P_i = sum of column axial loads in story i
h_i = height of story i
Δ_{i+1} = displacement of level $i + 1$

The additional story shears are applied to the structure as additional sway forces at each level,

$$H_i = V_{i-1} - V_i \tag{7.13}$$

and the entire structure is analyzed again. When the displacements computed at every level at the end of a cycle are nearly the same as those from the previous cycle, then the method has converged. The final computed moments contain the moments due to second-order effects.

For many years the ACI 318 (1989) has contained a statement that allows engineers to perform any type of analysis that adequately considers slenderness effects in columns, but has provided little guidance for performing such an analysis (aside from the moment magnifier approach). A task committee from ACI Committee 318 is currently studying a proposal by Furlong (1989) that incorporates an alternate approximate method like the P-delta method described. In his proposal he also recommends that a section stiffness of $0.4E_cI_g$ be used for all members in the analysis. This recommendation is based on a not yet published investigation conducted by Furlong at the University of Texas at Austin.

7.3 CONCRETE-FILLED STEEL TUBES

Tubular sections, either empty or filled with concrete, are being increasingly used as structural members. When a tube is acting as a compression member, filling the tube with concrete is advantageous because it increases the load-carrying capacity without increasing the size of the column. Traditionally, concrete-filled steel tubular columns have been made of circular steel tubes. Square and rectangular tubular sections are now available and are also being used.

Two state-of-the-art reviews on concrete-filled steel tubular structures have been published (Tomii et al., 1973; Roik et al., 1975). A review on the development of concrete-filled steel tubular structures in China was summarized by Zhong (1985). The latest state-of-the-art report on concrete-filled steel tubular columns is included in one of the five volumes that make up the Monograph on the Planning and Design of Tall Buildings, specifically *Structural Design of Tall Steel Buildings* (Volume SB) published in 1979. That report reviewed the investigations reported until 1976, the vast majority of which discussed the mechanical behavior, especially with regard to ultimate strength, of concrete-filled circular steel tubular columns subjected to concentric axial loading.

Extensive experimental studies on the seismic performance of concrete-filled steel tubular columns with square and circular sections have been undertaken in the 1980s. A review of those investigations carried out after 1976 is presented in this section. The emphasis of this section will be placed on the deformation capacity of the columns, which is an important criterion for the satisfactory seismic performance of the columns.

1 Columns under axial compression

Many experiments on concrete-filled steel tubular columns subjected to concentric axial load had been conducted prior to 1976. The results of those experiments are summarized in Fig. 7.6, which shows the relationship between the ultimate load and the nominal slenderness ratio. Ultimate loads are normalized by the nominal axial load capacity, which is the sum of the compressive strengths of concrete and steel. The minimum radius of gyration for calculating the nominal slenderness ratio is taken as 0.25 times the diameter for circular columns, or 0.29 times the outside dimension in the case of square columns. Ultimate load curves for encased steel columns and reinforced concrete columns obtained from tests conducted by Stevens (1965) are also shown in Fig. 7.6 for reference.

The ultimate loads of short columns with circular section are considerably larger than their nominal axial load capacity, as shown in Fig. 7.6. The reasons for this increase in ultimate load are attributed to the strain-hardening effect of the steel tube and the triaxial containment effect of concrete. The increase in ultimate load due to both effects depends, among other factors, on the magnitude of the longitudinal strain at failure, and therefore these effects are diminished with increasing length. Confinement does not increase the ultimate load capacity when the slenderness ratio of the concrete core exceeds 44.3 (Knowles and Park, 1969). Consequently the triaxial effect is usually not taken into account for columns of practical proportions, but the influence of confinement does guarantee highly ductile behavior, which is useful for an aseismic design of the columns, as described later.

The increase in the ultimate load of short columns is considered to vary according to many structural factors, such as the shape and size of the steel tube and the mechanical properties of the materials. To examine the effects of those factors on the mechanical behavior of short columns, Tomii et al. (1977) have conducted tests on about 270 stub columns with slenderness ratios less than 36. In their tests, all the steel tubes with circular, octagonal, and square sections were annealed to determine the effect of strain hardening on the ultimate load. The test results showed that the axial load–longitudinal strain relationships, which were remarkably affected by the cross-sectional shape, the diameter-to-wall-thickness ratio, and the concrete strength, can be classified into three types: strain-hardening type, elastic–perfectly plastic type, and degrading type, as illustrated in Fig. 7.7. The strain-hardening type and the elastic–perfectly plastic type were observed in the circular and octagonal columns, and the degrading type was seen in all the square columns and some of the octagonal columns. The concept of yielding load N_y, defined in Fig. 7.7, was proposed as the column strength instead of the ultimate load N_u, which was remarkably affected by the slenderness ratio and the wall thickness of the tube and was widely scattered as those factors varied. The yielding loads, which were scarcely affected by the slenderness ratio, were 1.0 to 1.25 times the nominal axial load capacity for circular columns, 1.0 to 1.15 times for octagonal columns, and 0.9 to 1.1 times for square columns. Based on the plastic theory, they proposed semiempirical formula to calculate the yield-

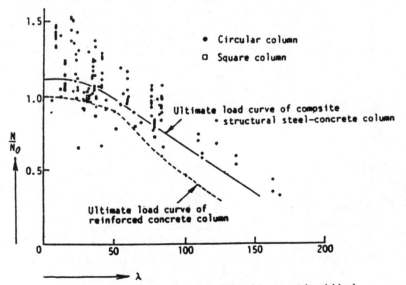

Fig. 7.6   Ultimate loads of columns subjected to concentric axial load.

ing load of circular short columns. For square columns, they concluded that there was no increase in ultimate load, which was equal to the yielding load. This conclusion is consistent with one obtained from the tests conducted by Knowles and Park (1969).

2 Columns under combined compression and bending

A load-deformation behavior of short columns under combined axial compression and bending moment (short beam columns) is usually described as a moment-thrust-curvature relationship. Tomii and Sakino (1979a) have conducted tests on the concrete-filled square steel tubular columns subjected to monotonically increasing bending moments under constant axial load, and obtained moment-thrust-curvature relationships that were ductile compared to those of ordinary reinforced concrete columns, despite the occurrence of local buckling of the steel tube. Tomii and Sakino (1979b) made a simple analysis based on the equivalent stress-strain relationships for steel and concrete to be used in numerically simulating the experimental moment-thrust-curvature relationships. They also proposed a simplified procedure, which could be used without computer facilities, for determining the moment-thrust-curvature relationships. Figure 7.8 shows an example of experimental relationships along with analytical ones, which were calculated based on the equivalent stress-strain relationships given in Fig. 7.9. The proposed stress-strain curve for concrete with a gentle falling branch, the slope of which depends on the width-to-wall-thickness ratio of the steel tube, indicates the ductile behavior of concrete confined by the square steel tube.

The ultimate strength of short columns subjected to axial compression and bending moment is usually described as an interaction curve between axial compression and bending moment, called the *N-M* interaction curve. Furlong (1967) proposed to determine the *N-M* interaction curve of concrete-filled steel tubular columns based on an ultimate compressive strain of 0.003, the concrete compressive strength f'_c instead of $0.85f'_c$, and the ACI stress block for concrete in compression (referred to as modified ACI method). However, this calculation procedure is complicated because of the stress distribution in the steel tube web. Considering that the equivalent stress-strain curve for concrete shown in Fig. 7.9 is ductile, Tomii and Sakino (1979a) proposed to determine the *N-M* interaction curve of the concrete-filled square steel tubular columns based on the simple stress blocks shown in Fig. 7.10 without limited ultimate compressive strain (re-

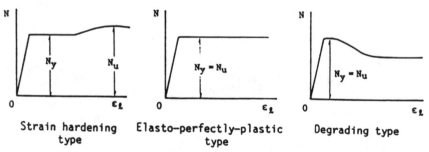

Fig. 7.7   Schematic axial load versus axial shortening for columns.

ferred to as simple method). Figure 7.11 compares the *N-M* interaction curves obtained by the modified ACI method and the simple method, along with experimental results represented by circles. This simple method can be applied to circular columns conservatively, because the augmentation of the concrete strength due to the confinement provided by the circular steel tube is ignored in the stress block shown in Fig. 7.10.

The material characteristics of strength and the confinement effect are important ingredients of cross-sectional capacity. However, slenderness, which depends on the material characteristics of stiffness, becomes more important for determining the capacity of long beam columns. The *N-M* interaction curve of long or intermediate-length beam columns should be determined by taking the slenderness effects into consideration. Knowles and Park (1969) reported that the buckling loads of concrete-filled steel tubular long columns could be predicted accurately by summing the tangent modulus loads for the steel tube and the concrete core acting as independent columns.

Traditionally, the Architectural Institute of Japan (AIJ) Standard for Structural Calculation of Steel Reinforced Concrete Structures has adopted the simple superposition method, in which the strength of a composite column is determined

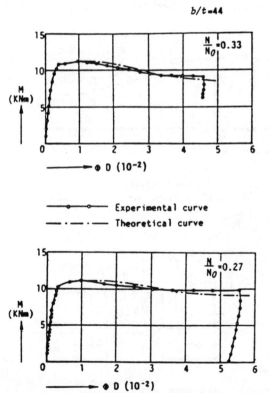

Fig. 7.8 Moment-thrust-curvature relationships of square columns subjected to bending moment under constant axial load.

as a simple sum of separately computed strengths of the steel and reinforced concrete columns. Wakabayashi (1977) extended this simple superposition method to the method for determining the N-M interaction curves of long composite beam columns. In the extended method, the slenderness effects are taken into account

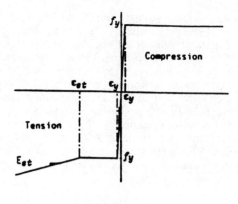

Steel tube

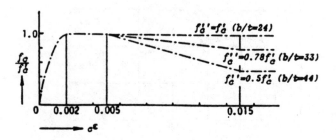

Encased concrete

Fig. 7.9   Equivalent stress-strain curves.

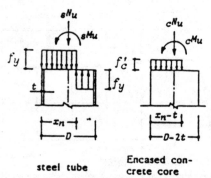

steel tube

Encased concrete core

Fig. 7.10   Assumed stress blocks to estimate ultimate strength of square short beam columns.

not only when the *N-M* interaction curves of two component columns are determined, but also when the *N-M* interaction curves are summed up, as shown in Fig. 7.12. This extended method has been adopted in the AIJ Standard for Structural Calculation of Mixed Tubular Steel-Concrete Composite Structures since 1980.

3 Columns under combined compression, bending, and shear

It is generally uneconomical to design structures to withstand lateral forces corresponding to the elastic response to design-level earthquakes. The alternative and widely accepted approach is to design for a lower lateral force level, and to

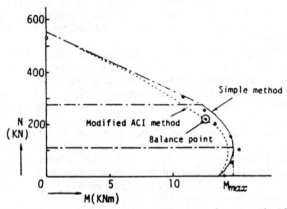

Fig. 7.11 Axial load–ultimate moment interaction curves for square short beam columns.

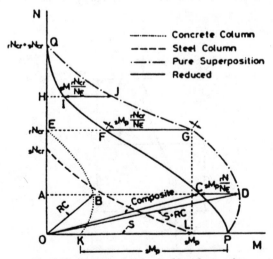

Fig. 7.12 Superposed strength of long beam columns.

detail the structure for ductility to ensure that it can sustain the inelastic deformations and absorb energy without significant degradation of strength. Thus lateral design forces specified by many codes have generally been much less than
the elastic response inertia forces induced by earthquakes. Although current seismic design philosophy for reinforced concrete frame buildings is directed toward
ensuring the formation of plastic hinges in the beams rather than in the columns,
it is necessary to develop plastic hinges at the base of the bottom columns to obtain a full plastic mechanism. Even if the design of frame buildings is based on the
design philosophy of strong columns–weak girders, significant column hinging
can develop at the other regions as well as at the base of the bottom columns
because of the effects of higher modes and inelastic moment redistribution on the
actual response of the buildings, and because of the effects of nonstructural elements which introduce short columns into the frame buildings. Then it is necessary to investigate the hysteretic behavior and the energy absorption capacity of
the concrete-filled steel tubular columns subjected to alternately repeated shear
under axial load to establish an aseismic design method for the concrete-filled
steel tubular structures.

The tests of 80 concrete-filled square steel tubular columns, which were subjected to combined forces and deformed in a double-curvature pattern as shown
in Fig. 7.13, have been conducted for short and intermediate-length columns subjected to monotonically increasing shear (Tomii and Sakino, 1979c), for intermediate-length columns subjected to alternately repeated shear (Sakino and Tomii,
1981), and for short columns subjected to alternately repeated shear (Sakino and
Ishibashi, 1985). The term *short* columns used here implies that the effect of the
shearing force on a failure mode and the ultimate strength cannot be ignored.
Two distinguished failure modes shown in Fig. 7.14 were observed in monotonic
loading tests: (1) shear failure observed in the short columns whose shear-span-
to-depth ratios a/D (see Fig. 7.13) were equal to or smaller than 1.0, and (2) flexural failure observed in the columns whose a/D ratios were equal to or larger than
1.5. Then the critical a/D ratio was between 1.0 and 1.5.

Figure 7.15 shows typical examples of hysteretic loops and failure modes of
the short and intermediate-length columns subjected to alternately repeated shear

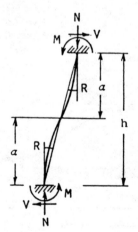

Fig. 7.13   Loading condition.

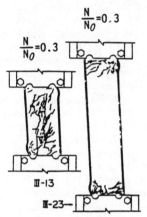

Fig. 7.14　Typical crack patterns in encased concrete of square columns.

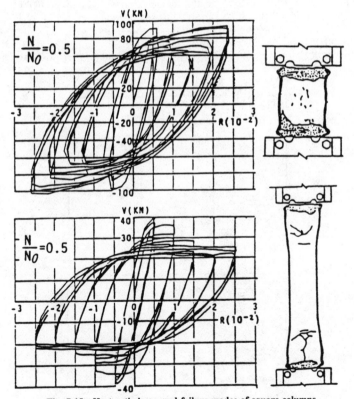

Fig. 7.15　Hysteretic loops and failure modes of square columns.

under high axial compression ($N/N_0 = 0.5$). Although a certain amount of degradation in strength is observed, hysteretic loops are stable and considerable energy absorption is available in both cases. The reason for the degradation in strength is the local buckling of the flanges and webs of the steel tube with a width-to-wall-thickness ratio of 44, which results in crushing of the encased concrete. The square section gradually becomes circular in the top and bottom critical regions due to local buckling, and this transformed circular steel tube leads to stable behavior of the columns after a certain degradation in strength. It is noteworthy that the cyclic deterioration of the short column failing in shear is less than that of the column failing in flexure. This result was consistent in columns with smaller width-to-wall-thickness ratios (Sakino and Ishibashi, 1985). The other serious problem resulting from local buckling and concrete crushing was a considerable amount of cumulative axial shortening, which was about 30% of the column depth for the columns shown in Fig. 7.15. It is necessary to limit the magnitude of the axial load to avoid major axial shortening.

The test results on the ultimate strength of the columns failing in flexure are summarized in Fig. 7.16 in terms of column end moments, which includes secondary moments due to axial load and lateral displacement. The experimental ultimate moments M_u are compared with theoretical values obtained by the simple method based on the stress blocks shown in Fig. 7.10. As shown in Fig. 7.16, the experimental values are larger than the theoretical ones. The reasons for this are the strain hardening of the steel tube and the additional confinement from the stiff loading jig (see Fig. 7.14), which should shift the critical sections away from the column ends as inferred from the failure mode shown in Fig. 7.14.

On the other hand, the short columns failing in shear attained only 90 to 100% of the theoretical ultimate moments. An analytical method to predict a lower

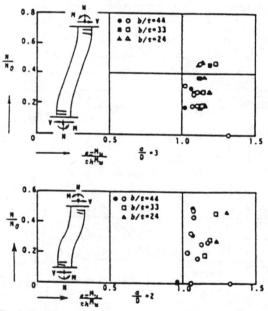

Fig. 7.16   Ultimate strengths of square columns failing in flexure.

bound of the ultimate shear strength of the short columns was proposed by Sakino and Ishibashi (1985). According to their method, the ultimate shear strength of concrete-filled square steel tubular columns was obtained by summing the shear strengths of the plain concrete column (Tomii et al., 1981) and the hollow square steel tubular column. Figure 7.17 compares experimental and theoretical shear strengths.

4 Limitation on width-to-wall-thickness ratios of square steel tubes

To design concrete-filled steel tubular columns economically it is desirable to use steel tubes with thinner wall thicknesses. However, when a steel tube with a thin wall thickness is used, there is some danger of local buckling. It is necessary to limit the value of the width-to-wall-thickness ratio b/t of the steel tube according to one of the following viewpoints:

1. To ensure that the steel tube wall will attain longitudinal yield stress before buckling (local buckling strength)
2. To ensure that the rotational capacity of the plastic hinge developed in the columns is large enough for the frame to develop a full, plastic mechanism (deformation capacity)
3. To ensure that the energy absorption capacity of the plastic hinge developed in the columns is large enough for the structure to survive earthquakes (energy absorption capacity)

From the viewpoint of local buckling strength, the ACI code and the AIJ standard prescribe the limitation on the width-to-wall-thickness ratio of rectangular steel tubes using the following equations:

$$\frac{b}{t} \leq \sqrt{\frac{3_s E}{f_y}} \qquad \text{for each face of width } b \qquad (7.14)$$

○ □ △ Monotonic loading

● ■ ▲ Cyclic loading

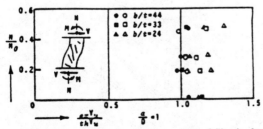

Fig. 7.17   Ultimate strengths of square columns failing in shear.

$$\frac{b'}{t} \leq \frac{734}{\sqrt{F}} \qquad \text{for flange plates} \tag{7.15}$$

where F is defined as the standard value used in determining allowable stresses and taken as minimum yield stress of 235 MPa (34,000 psi) for mild steel with a thickness of less than 40 mm (1.6 in.). The definitions of the other symbols are given in Fig. 7.18. Equations 7.14 and 7.15 give the same b/t value of 51 for the mild steel tube with rounded corners whose radius is equal to the plate thickness t. It should be pointed out as a problem that Eqs. 7.14 and 7.15 do not take into account the effect of the encased concrete, which can change the buckling mode of the hollow steel tube shown in Fig. 7.19a into the higher buckling mode shown in Fig. 7.19b.

Suzuki et al. (1984) have conducted tests on stub columns subjected to concentric axial load to examine the effect of the encased concrete on the local buckling strength of the square steel tube wall. In their tests, the axial load was applied to the columns by loading the steel tube alone, as shown in Fig. 7.20, for the encased concrete not to sustain any part of the axial load but to change the buckling mode. They reported that the axial load in the encased concrete transferred by the bond stress was negligible. The test results showed that the local buckling strength of the concrete-filled steel tube with a b/t ratio of 80 was similar to that of the hollow steel tube with a b/t ratio of 33, which was the limit value given by Eq. 7.15 when the measured yield strength was used.

In Fig. 7.21 the rotational capacities of the plastic hinges developed in the concrete-filled steel tubular columns subjected to monotonically increasing bend-

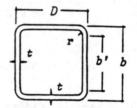

Fig. 7.18 Shape of square tube.

a) Hollow steel tube

b) Concrete filled
steel tube

Fig. 7.19 Local buckling modes.

ing moments (Tomii and Sakino, 1979c) are directly compared to those of the hollow steel tubular columns (Kato et al., 1978). This figure implies that the limitation on the b/t ratio of the steel tube can be mitigated by filling the tube with concrete, although the experimental results of concrete-filled steel tubular columns with thinner walls are not included in Fig. 7.21.

The main factor that limits the rotational capacity of the plastic hinge developed in concrete-filled steel tubular columns is the local buckling accompanied by concrete crushing. The degradation in mechanical behavior due to local buckling can be observed clearly in the load-deformation curve of the columns subjected to concentric axial load. Tomii et al. (1977) conducted the tests on concrete-filled and hollow steel tubular columns with different b/t ratios subjected to concentric axial load to examine the effect of the b/t ratio on the mechanical behavior at large deformation. Figure 7.22 compares the load-deformation curve of the concrete-filled steel tubular column having a b/t ratio of 75 with that of the hollow steel tubular column having a b/t ratio of 35. Both columns have similar nominal axial load capacities. The concrete-filled steel tubular column can attain the longitudinal yield stress prior to local buckling and behaves in a more ductile manner after local buckling than the hollow steel tubular column.

Matsui (1985b) conducted an analytical study on the behavior of the plastic hinge subsequent to local buckling on the basis of plastic limit analysis. He assumed local buckling mechanisms of the concrete-filled and hollow steel tubes as shown in Fig. 7.23. In his analysis, he took into account two factors through which the behavior following local buckling was improved by filling the tube with concrete: (1) difference in the local buckling mechanism as shown in Fig. 7.23, and (2) transfer of axial load from the steel tube to the encased concrete. It was pointed out that the latter factor was more important than the former. The numerical examples showed that the energy absorption capacity of the plastic hinge developed in the concrete-filled steel tubular column with a b/t ratio of 75 at the ductility factor level of 5 was equal to that of the hollow steel tubular column with a b/t ratio of 50, which was nearly equal to the limit value given by Eq. 7.14 for mild steel tubes.

All the investigations reviewed in this section suggest that the limit value of the b/t ratio can be increased by at least 1.5 times by filling the tube with concrete as far as local buckling strength, deformation capacity, and energy absorption capacity are concerned.

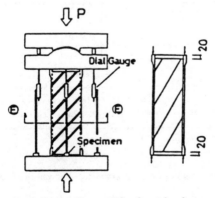

Fig. 7.20 Loading condition for stub columns.

5   Columns in frames

Matsui (1985b) has conducted lateral load tests of frames composed of concrete-filled or hollow steel tubular columns and wide-flange beams. The mechanical behavior of the frame with concrete-filled steel tubular columns is compared in Fig.

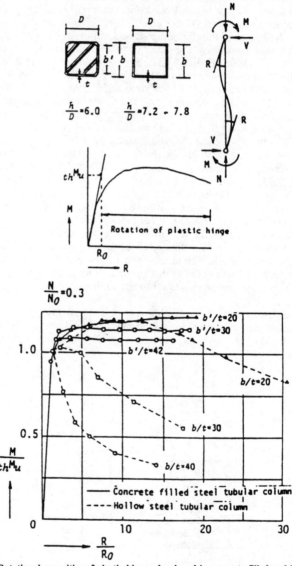

Fig. 7.21   Rotational capacities of plastic hinges developed in concrete-filled and hollow steel tubular columns.

7.24 to that of the frame with hollow steel tubular columns. The figure also includes theoretical curves as explained in the preceding section. Steel tubular columns and wide-flange beams of the same size and mechanical property were used for two frames. A plastic mechanism of both frames was the so-called column mechanism, in which the plastic hinges were developed at the top and bottom of both columns. Hence the mechanical behavior at the large lateral drift was dominated by the behavior of the columns. The stiffness characteristic, lateral load capacity, and ductility of the frame with the hollow steel tubular columns are improved remarkably by filling the tube with concrete. The local buckling of the steel tube web, which brings a drastic degradation in the lateral load capacity of the frame with the hollow steel tubular columns, does not affect the behavior of the frame with the concrete-filled steel tubular columns.

Matsui (1985b) also conducted alternately repeated lateral load tests of the frames composed of wide-flange beams and concrete-filled steel tubular columns with a b/t ratio of 68, which was 1.5 times the limit value given by Eq. 7.15 when the measured yield strength was used. Figure 7.25 shows the hysteretic loops of

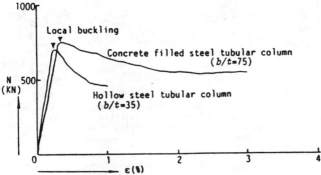

Fig. 7.22   Axial load versus axial shortening for concrete-filled and hollow steel tubular stub columns.

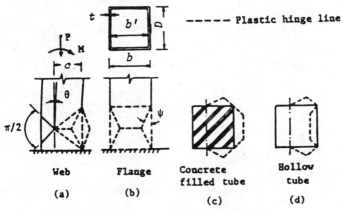

Fig. 7.23   Collapse mechanisms of plastic hinges.

the frames whose plastic mechanism is also that of the columns. The considerable amount of energy absorption shown in Fig. 7.25 supports the conclusion with regard to the limitation of the *b/t* ratio described in the preceding subsection.

To ensure a ductile behavior of the frame subjected to lateral load, beam-to-column connections should be designed to have enough strength to transfer the stresses from the beam to the column. Investigations on the behavior and the design method of the beam-to-column connections have been carried out in Japan (Matsui, 1985a; Suzuki et al., 1985, 1986).

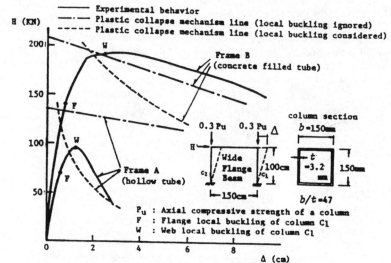

Fig. 7.24   Mechanical behavior of frames.

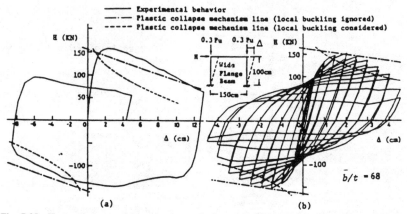

Fig. 7.25   Hysteretic loops of frames composed of concrete-filled steel tubular columns with thin wall thickness.

6 Bond

The concrete-filled steel tubular column is a composite column composed of the concrete core and the steel tube. A composite action is brought by the bond stress between the concrete core and the steel tube or mechanical devices such as shear connectors, diaphragms, or stiffeners provided on the inside of the steel tube. The actual composite action, which depends on the bond characteristics and the properties of the mechanical devices, is between the following two extreme cases:

1. Noncomposite action, that is, there exists no bond stress or mechanical device. The axial force, which is usually transferred directly to the steel tube from the steel beam at the beam-to-column connection, is never transferred to the concrete core. Hence the concrete core sustains only its own weight.

2. Full composite action, that is, there is no slippage between the concrete core and the steel tube in any section due to the rigid bond behavior and the stiff diaphragm with holes for casting the concrete at each beam-to-column connection. In this case, plane sections remain plane through the concrete core and the steel tube after flexural or axial deformations.

In the case of full composite action, the concrete core sustains part of the axial load. The magnitude of the axial force resultant in the concrete core $_cN$ depends on the magnitude of the bending moment as well as on the magnitude of the axial force in the column section, provided that the bending moment causes the plastic strain in the concrete core or steel tube, or the tensile strain in the concrete whose tensile strength is neglected, or both. Hence the magnitude of $_cN$ varies along the longitudinal axis of the column with the moment gradient despite the constant axial force. This variation in the magnitude of $_cN$ can be determined by the moment-thrust-curvature analysis, although the procedure is rather complicated. The magnitude of $_cN$ in the section with zero bending moment can be estimated easily, because the axial force in that section is shared by the steel tube and the concrete core according to their axial stiffnesses. The magnitude of $_cN$ in the plastic hinge developed in the column can also be estimated easily by assuming the simple stress blocks for the steel tube and the concrete core (Tomii, 1984). The magnitude of $_cN$ in the plastic hinge so obtained is the optimum value of the axial compression for the plastic hinge to display a maximum flexural strength corresponding to the given axial force. The axial bond stress resultant of unit length, which transfers the axial force between the steel tube and the concrete core, can be determined from the variation of $_cN$ along the longitudinal axis. It is very difficult, however, to determine the distribution of the bond stress along the perimeter of the concrete core.

In the case of the actual column, the full composite action cannot be expected to be realized due to the limited bond strength, which is very low, as described later. Tomii (1984) has proposed design procedures to transfer the axial force between steel tube and concrete core by the bond stress, based on the following two criteria:

1. A portion where cross sections remain plane and the axial bond stress resultant between steel tube and concrete core is zero should exist in the column of each story in the case of long-term loading such that the encased concrete core may carry as much long-term axial compression force as possible. In this por-

tion, the axial compression force is shared by the steel tube and the concrete core according to their axial stiffnesses.

2. The concrete core should carry the optimum axial compression force at the critical sections at the top and bottom of the column in the case of seismic loading such that the concrete-filled steel tubular column may display a maximum flexural strength corresponding to the axial force at the critical sections.

He proposed the following formula to determine the axial length l_b which is required to transfer $\Delta_c N$ from the steel tube to the concrete core:

$$l_b = \frac{\Delta_c N}{_s\psi_s f_a} \tag{7.16}$$

where $_s\psi$ is the inside perimeter of the steel tube and $_s f_a$ is the allowable bond stress. The values of $\Delta_c N$ for each beam-to-column connection are determined based on criteria 1 and 2 for long-term loading and earthquake loading, respectively.

It was necessary to conduct experimental studies to specify an allowable axial bond stress resultant $_s\psi_s f_a$ in Eq. 7.16. Virdi and Dowling (1975) have carried out about 100 push-out tests on concrete-filled steel tubular sections to investigate the bond strength between circular steel tube sections and concrete cores. The test results showed that the 0.2% offset bond strength exceeded a value of 2.1 MPa (305 psi) in most cases. It is well known, however, that the bond strength obtained by experiments highly depends on the test method. Morishita et al. (1979a, 1979b) have carried out tests on concrete-filled steel tubular columns with circular, octagonal, and square sections to investigate the bond strength at long-term loading by using the test method shown in Fig. 7.26, which was considered to reproduce the actual load transfer mechanism in the column under gravity load. The axial bond stress resultant was estimated by measuring the variations of the axial strain in the steel tube. The tests results showed that the bond strength between steel tubes and concrete cores was not influenced to any appreciable degree by the concrete strength, and was quite low compared with the bond strength between embedded reinforcements and the surrounding concrete. Based on these test results, the AIJ standard specified allowable bond stresses for long-term loading as shown in Table 7.1.

Morishita and Tomii (1982) have carried out tests on concrete-filled square steel tubular columns subjected to alternately repeated shear under constant axial force to investigate the bond strength at earthquake loading by using the test method illustrated in Fig. 7.27. The axial bond stress resultant was estimated in a manner similar to that described before. The test results supported the AIJ specified allowable stresses for earthquake loading shown in Table 7.1.

To improve the bond behavior and obtain firm composite action, Tomii et al. (1980a, 1980b) proposed two methods: (1) to use a steel tube with checkered (deformed) internal surface, and (2) to cast expansive concrete in the steel tubes. They conducted tests on columns with circular, octagonal, and square sections, and reported that the former method was more effective than the latter.

7 Steel-encased reinforced concrete columns

Circular steel tubes are used to form the underground portions of bridge piles in New Zealand. In this case the bridge pile designated as steel-encased reinforced concrete pile is composed of the steel tube and reinforced concrete, although existing New Zealand Railway design practice ignores the contribution of the steel tube casing toward the strength and ductility of the bridge pile because of a corrosion problem of steel tubes with a typical thickness of 10 mm (0.4 in.)

Priestly and Park (1984, 1985) have conducted tests on steel-encased reinforced concrete columns subjected to alternately repeated shear under constant axial compression to investigate the seismic performance of the bridge piles. Satisfactory cyclic performance at large displacements is exhibited, as shown in Fig. 7.28. They reported that estimates of flexural strength based on the ACI stress block for concrete and an ultimate compressive strain of 0.003 were conservative. They also made theoretical upper- and lower-bound predictions. In the upper-bound predictions it was assumed that the steel tube followed its uniaxial stress-strain relationship in the axial direction and, in addition, contributed fully to concrete confinement. In the lower-bound predictions it was assumed that the steel tube followed its uniaxial stress-strain relationship in the axial direction and

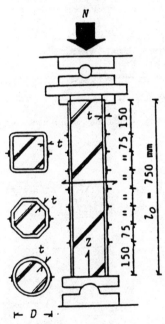

Fig. 7.26   Loading condition for columns under long-term loading.

Table 7.1   Allowable bond stresses between steel tubes and concrete cores, defined by AIJ standard

| | Shape of tube | |
Application	Circular	Square
Long-term loading	0.15 MPa	0.10 MPa
Earthquake loading	0.22 MPa	0.15 MPa

did not have any confining effect on the concrete. In both cases, full composite action of the reinforced concrete section with the steel tube was assumed. The behavior of the columns was observed to follow the upper-bound prediction up to displacement ductility levels of 4. At large ductility levels the experimental response tended to lie between the upper- and lower-bound predictions.

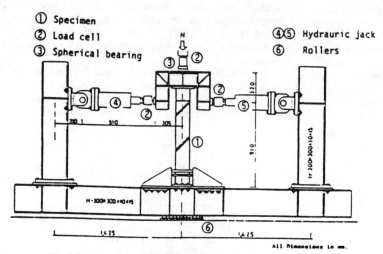

Fig. 7.27   Loading condition for columns under earthquake loading.

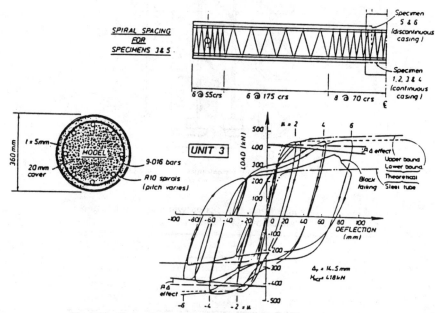

Fig. 7.28   Hysteretic loop of steel-encased reinforced concrete column.

Tomii et al. (1985a, 1985b) proposed a new type of composite column which is similar to the steel-encased reinforced column in appearance. In this column, the steel tubes were used only as transverse reinforcement of reinforced concrete short columns or edge columns of a framed shear wall, as shown in Fig. 7.29. The roles of the steel tube were to prevent shear failure, bond splitting failure, and buckling of the longitudinal bars, and to confine the concrete. This composite column was called tubed column simply or superreinforced concrete column because the steel tube confined all the concrete, including the cover concrete, which was apt to spall off in the case of ordinary reinforced concrete columns.

The axial load capacity of circular tubed plain concrete stub columns subjected to concentric axial load was larger than that of concrete-filled circular steel tubular columns (Sakino et al., 1985). This means that it is effective to use the steel tube as transverse reinforcement rather than as longitudinal reinforcement as far as the ultimate strength is concerned.

Tomii et al. (1985a, 1985b) have conducted tests on superreinforced concrete short columns with circular and square sections subjected to alternately repeated shear under constant axial compression. Examples of the hysteretic loops of the superreinforced concrete columns and ordinary reinforced concrete columns are shown in Fig. 7.30. The welded hoops in the ordinary reinforced concrete col-

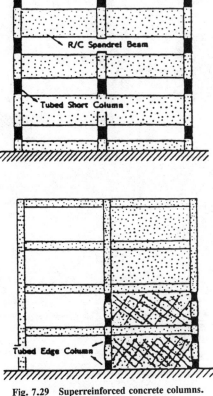

Fig. 7.29 Superreinforced concrete columns.

umns were replaced by steel tubes in the superreinforced concrete columns. The brittle behavior of the hooped columns was improved remarkably in the super-reinforced concrete columns. The ultimate strengths of the superreinforced concrete columns with circular and square sections are far beyond the predictions based on the ACI stress block for concrete and an ultimate compressive strain of 0.003 because of the superconfinement effect provided by the steel tubes. The experimental study on superreinforced concrete columns is in progress at Kyushu University in Japan.

7.4 DETAILING PRACTICE FOR REINFORCED CONCRETE COLUMNS

Good detailing of longitudinal and transverse steel reinforcement in concrete columns is necessary to ensure satisfactory performance of the column from the point of view of serviceability, strength, and ductility. The detailing of the reinforcement should be based on a thorough understanding of the properties of steel reinforcement and concrete, and of the internal forces to be resisted by the column. Steel reinforcement is necessary to provide resistance to tensile and compressive forces in concrete columns arising from bending, shear, and axial forces. Steel reinforcement is also necessary to prevent compressed bars from buckling and to provide confinement to concrete in highly compressed regions.

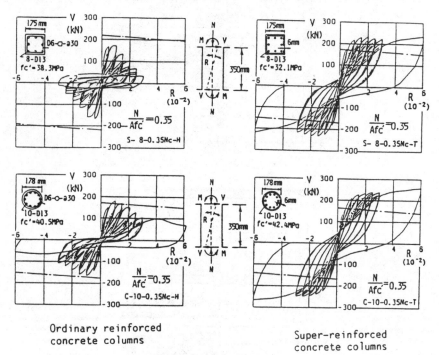

Ordinary reinforced
concrete columns

Super-reinforced
concrete columns

Fig. 7.30   Hysteretic loops of ordinary reinforced and superreinforced concrete columns.

1   Stress-strain behavior of reinforcing steel and concrete

Stress-strain behavior of reinforcing steel.   The stress-strain behavior of typical steel reinforcing bars, measured during monotonic loading tests, is shown in Fig. 7.31. The curves are characterized by an elastic region, a yield plateau, and a strain-hardening region. The design of reinforcement for structures not resisting earthquake forces is based on data from monotonic stress-strain curves.

Reinforcing bars in structures resisting earthquake forces will be subjected to cyclic (reversed) loading. If cyclic (tension-compression) loading is applied in the yield range, the measured stress-strain curve shows the Bauschinger effect, in which the stress-strain curve becomes nonlinear at stresses much lower than the initial yield stress.

Figure 7.32 shows measured stress-strain behavior for cyclic stressing with

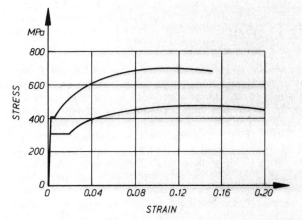

Fig. 7.31   Typical stress-strain curves for steel reinforcement measured in monotonic load tests (1 MPa = 145 psi).

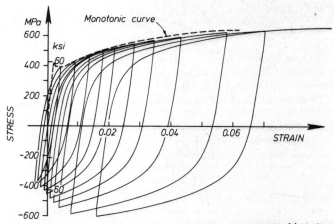

Fig. 7.32   Typical cyclic stress-strain curves for steel reinforcement measured in tests with unsymmetrical strain cycles.

strain mainly in the tensile range. This cyclic strain history would be typical of a longitudinal reinforcing bar in a building column during cyclic flexure with low axial load where, since the neutral axis is close to the extreme compression fiber of the column section, the steel strains in compression would be much smaller than the steel strains in tension. The stress-strain curve for monotonic loading is also shown in Fig. 7.32. For the type of cyclic strain history shown in the figure, it is evident that the monotonic stress-strain curve with origin at the original position gives a satisfactory envelope for the cyclic stress-strain curves.

Figure 7.33 shows the results for cyclic stressing with gradually increasing symmetrical straining in the tension and compression range. This strain history would be typical of a longitudinal reinforcing bar in a building column during cyclic flexure with high axial load in which the neutral axis is close to middepth of the column section. The particular specimen in Fig. 7.33 yielded in compression first. It is evident that symmetrical straining of the type shown in Fig. 7.33 results in a buildup of steel stress to much greater stress levels than that given by the monotonic stress-strain curve with the origin in the original position. The buildup of steel stress for this type of loading with increasing strain amplitudes is particularly high for steel that strain-hardens early.

Stress-strain behavior of concrete confined by transverse reinforcement. Unconfined concrete, such as a plain concrete cylinder, when loaded uniaxially in compression, has a Poisson ratio of about 0.15 to 0.2 at low levels of longitudinal stress. However, as the unconfined compressive strength f'_c is approached, the transverse strains become very large because of progressive internal longitudinal microcracking (Fig. 7.34), and failure occurs eventually by longitudinal splitting of the concrete. When compressed concrete contains closed transverse reinforcement, at low levels of longitudinal stress the transverse reinforcement is hardly stressed, and hence the concrete is unconfined. The concrete becomes confined when the transverse strains become significant and cause the concrete to bear out against the transverse reinforcement, which then applies a confining reaction to

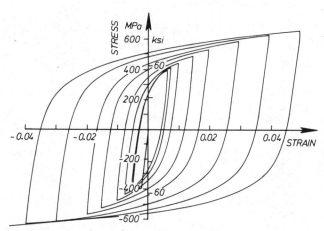

Fig. 7.33   Typical cyclic stress-strain curves for steel reinforcement measured in tests with symmetrical strain cycles.

the concrete. The passive confining pressure applied by the transverse reinforcement can improve the longitudinal stress-strain characteristics of the concrete considerably. The compressive strength of the concrete is increased, and the ductility at high strains is enhanced.

Spirals or circular hoops, because of their shape, are in hoop tension and provide a continuous confining pressure around the circumference, as illustrated in Fig. 7.35a and b. As a rule, however, square hoops can only apply confining reactions near the corners of the hoops, because the pressure of the concrete against the side of the hoops tends to bend the sides outward, as illustrated in Fig. 7.35c. Transverse bars of small diameter will generally act merely as ties between the corners of square hoops, because the flexural stiffness of the hoop bar is small and the hoop sides bow outward rather than effectively confining the concrete in the regions between the corners. In that case confinement occurs by arching of the concrete between the corners of the hoops, and the concrete is only effectively confined in the corners and central region of the section, as shown in Fig. 7.35c.

The confinement of concrete is improved if the transverse reinforcement is placed at relatively close spacing. Small spacing of spirals or hoops leads to better confinement, as is illustrated in Fig. 7.36. This is because the arching of the concrete is more efficient since the arches are shallower, and hence more of the concrete section area is effectively confined.

The confinement provided by square or rectangular hoops can be improved significantly by the use of overlapping hoops, or hoops with cross ties, which results in several legs crossing the section. The better confinement resulting from the presence of a number of transverse bar legs is illustrated in Fig. 7.37a and b. Again the arching is more efficient since the arches are shallower, and hence more of the concrete area is confined effectively.

The presence of a number of longitudinal bars, well distributed around the perimeter of the section and tied across the section, will also aid the confinement of the concrete. The concrete bears against the longitudinal bars, and the transverse reinforcement provides the confining reactions to the longitudinal bars. Thus confinement arises by the arching of the concrete between the longitudinal bars as well as between the transverse bars, as is illustrated in Fig. 7.37a, b, and c. The longitudinal bars generally have sufficient flexural stiffness not to bend signifi-

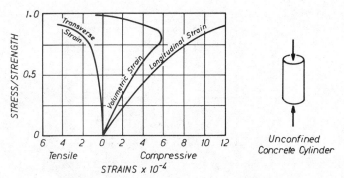

Fig. 7.34   Strains measured on plain concrete cylinder loaded concentrically in compression. (*From Park and Paulay, 1975.*)

cantly between the spirals or hoops when subjected to lateral pressures (Fig. 7.37d). Hence closely spaced and laterally tied longitudinal bars provide effective confinement to the concrete.

Further variables influencing confinement are the ratio of the volume of the transverse reinforcement to the volume of the concrete core and the yield strength of the transverse reinforcement, since a large volumetric ratio and a high yield strength of transverse reinforcement will both lead to higher confining pressures. The effectiveness of confinement is also a function of the ratio of the area of effectively confined concrete core to the area of the core within the perimeter spiral or hoop. Hence for the same volume ratio of transverse reinforcement, the

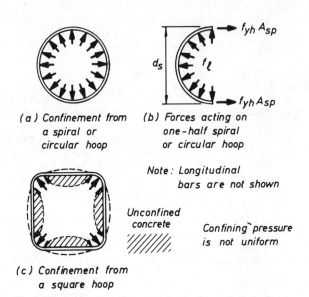

(a) Confinement from a spiral or circular hoop

(b) Forces acting on one-half spiral or circular hoop

Note: Longitudinal bars are not shown

Unconfined concrete

Confining pressure is not uniform

(c) Confinement from a square hoop

Fig. 7.35 Confinement of concrete by circular and square hoops.

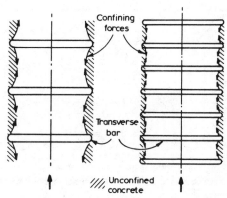

Confining forces

Transverse bar

Unconfined concrete

Fig. 7.36 Effect of spacing of transverse reinforcement on confinement of concrete.

performance of a spirally reinforced column is better than that of a column with rectangular hoops.

Outside the transverse reinforcement, the concrete is not confined. This cover or shell concrete generally commences to spall after the unconfined strength is reached, particularly if the content of transverse reinforcement is high, because the presence of a large number of transverse and longitudinal bars creates a plane or surface of weakness between core and cover concrete and precipitates spalling. If the reinforcement content is low, the cover concrete will tend to spall less readily and will tend to act with the confined core.

The stress-strain curve for confined concrete can be predicted by an analytical relationship which takes into account the quantity and arrangement of transverse and longitudinal reinforcement in the section. In an example of such an analytical relation derived by Mander et al. (1984) the main variables are the strength of the confined concrete, which is a function of the effective lateral confining pressure and the unconfined strength, the strain at the confined strength, and the tangent modulus of elasticity of the concrete.

Figures 7.38 to 7.40 give stress-strain relations for circular, square, and rectangular concrete columns with various quantities and arrangements of reinforcement. Figure 7.38 shows the increase in strength and ductility of the confined core of circular columns resulting from an increase in the volume ratio of spiral reinforcement ρ_s. Figure 7.39 compares the stress-strain curves for the confined core of 8-bar and 12-bar square columns with similar amounts of longitudinal and transverse reinforcement. Again improved behavior results from an increase in the quantity of transverse reinforcement. Also better confinement is obtained when the longitudinal bars are closely spaced. Figure 7.40 compares the stress-

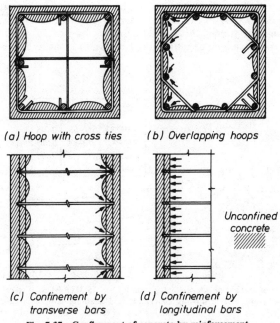

(a) Hoop with cross ties   (b) Overlapping hoops

(c) Confinement by   (d) Confinement by
   transverse bars   longitudinal bars

Unconfined concrete

Fig. 7.37   Confinement of concrete by reinforcement.

strain curves for the confined core of two rectangular walls with approximately the same transverse steel content but different spacings of longitudinal bars. It is evident that the closer spacing of the longitudinal bars and cross ties led to more effectively confined concrete. In Figs. 7.38 and 7.40 the stress-strain curves predicted using the analytical model of Mander et al. (1984) are shown as dashed lines and are seen to be in reasonably close agreement with the experimental curves. At far advanced longitudinal compressive strains the lateral pressure applied by the confined concrete to the transverse reinforcement can eventually be sufficient to cause the transverse reinforcement to fracture. The longitudinal strains at first fracture of the transverse reinforcement are shown as steps in the measured curves.

2 Design actions in columns

Columns in structures not designed for seismic actions.   Column bending moments are found using elastic frame analysis for the factored loads and forces in such combinations as recommended by the appropriate loading codes. The effects of column slenderness need also be considered in the determination of the design actions.

Columns in structures designed for seismic actions.   In order to survive severe earthquakes, structures designed to the level of seismic loading recommended by codes generally need to be capable of undergoing horizontal displacements in a ductile manner in the inelastic range when subjected to severe earthquake loading (Park and Paulay, 1975). The rational approach for achieving this aim in earthquake-resistant design is to choose the most suitable mechanism of inelastic deformation for the structure and to ensure, by appropriate design procedures, that yielding will occur only in the chosen manner during a severe earthquake. For reinforced concrete frames this is best achieved by flexural yielding at selected plastic hinge positions, since with proper design the plastic hinges can be made adequately ductile.

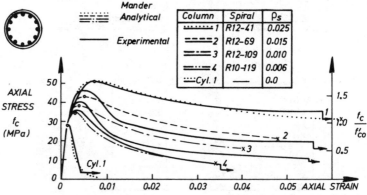

Fig. 7.38   Effect of amount of intermediate-grade $[f_{yh} \geq 275$ MPa (40 ksi)] spiral reinforcement of stress-strain relationships for concentrically loaded 500-mm (19.9-in.)-diameter by 1500-mm (59.1-in.)-high columns with high strain rate ($\varepsilon = 0.013/s$) and comparison of experimental and analytical relationships. (*From Mander et al., 1984.*)

The ductility required at a plastic hinge in a yielding structure may be expressed by the curvature ductility factor ϕ_u/ϕ_y, where ϕ_u is the maximum curvature (rotation per unit length) at the critical section and ϕ_y is the curvature at the section at first yield.

For moment-resisting frames, mechanisms which involve flexural yielding at plastic hinges are shown in Fig. 7.41. If columns begin to yield before the beams, a column sidesway mechanism can form. In the worst case the plastic hinges may

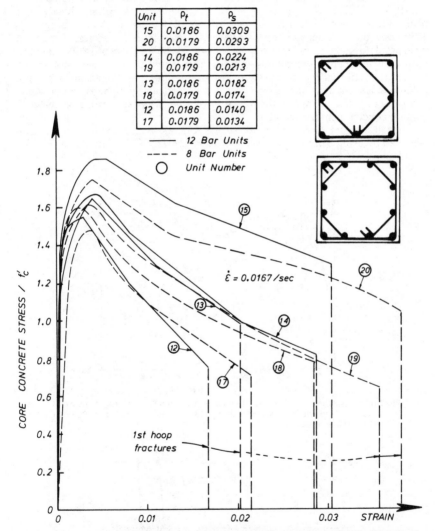

Unit	ρ_t	ρ_s
15	0.0186	0.0309
20	0.0179	0.0293
14	0.0186	0.0224
19	0.0179	0.0213
13	0.0186	0.0182
18	0.0179	0.0174
12	0.0186	0.0140
17	0.0179	0.0134

Fig. 7.39   Effect of amount and arrangement of intermediate-grade [f_{yh} = 275 MPa (40 ksi)] reinforcement on experimental stress-strain relationships for core concrete of concentrically loaded 450-mm (17.7-in.)-square by 1200-mm (47.2-in.)-high reinforced concrete columns with high strain rate (ε = 0.0617/s). (*From Scott et al., 1982.*)

form in the columns in only on story, as in Fig. 7.41*b,* since the columns of the other stories are stronger. Such a mechanism can make very large curvature ductility demands on the plastic hinges of the critical story (Park and Paulay, 1975), particularly for tall buildings. The curvature ductility required at the plastic hinges of a column sidesway mechanism may also be so large that it cannot be met, and in that case collapse of the structure will occur. On the other hand, if beams yield before the columns, a beam sidesway mechanism will develop, as illustrated in Fig. 7.41*c,* which makes more moderate demands on the curvature ductility required at the plastic hinges in the beams and at the column bases (Park and Paulay, 1975). The curvature ductility demands at the plastic hinges of a beam sidesway mechanism can be met by careful detailing of the reinforcement. Therefore for tall frames, a beam sidesway mechanism is the preferred mode of inelastic deformation, and a strong column–weak beam concept is advocated to ensure beam hinging. For frames with less than about three stories, and for the top story of tall frames, the curvature ductility required at the plastic hinges if a column sidesway mechanism develops is not particularly high. Hence for one- and two-story frames, and in the top story of taller frames, a strong beam–weak column concept can be permitted.

For tall moment-resisting frames, strong column–weak beam behavior can be achieved by using a capacity design approach (SANZ, 1982) to determine the de-

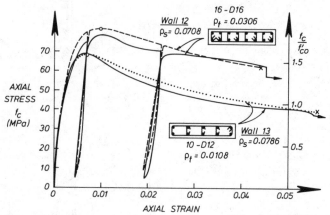

Fig. 7.40 **Effect of longitudinal bar distribution on experimental stress-strain relationships for core concrete of concentrically loaded walls of 150-mm (5.9-in.) width and 700-mm (27.6-in.) length.** (*From Mander et al., 1984.*)

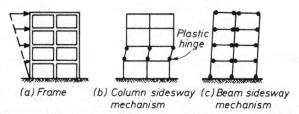

(a) Frame   (b) Column sidesway   (c) Beam sidesway
                       mechanism   mechanism

Fig. 7.41 **Moment-resisting frames with horizontal seismic loading and possible mechanisms.**

sign actions in the columns. In this approach the column bending moments found from elastic frame analysis for the code factored load combinations are amplified to take the following criteria into account.

1. *The flexural overstrength at the beam plastic hinges,* due to the actual steel yield strength f_y being higher than specified and due to strain hardening of the steel at high strains, which results in higher moments being applied to the columns.

2. *The higher-mode effects of dynamic loading,* which can cause much higher column moments than calculated from the code static seismic loading, which is based mainly on a first-mode response. Nonlinear dynamic analyses have shown that in frames, due to higher modes of vibration, the points of contraflexure may occur well away from the midheight of columns at various stages during an earthquake (Park and Paulay, 1975). For example, Fig. 7.42 shows a possible bending moment distribution in a column at an instant during an earthquake. It is evident that the total beam input moment $M_{b1} + M_{b2}$ may have to be resisted almost entirely by one column section, rather than be shared almost equally between the column sections above and below the joints, as would be implied by the bending moment diagrams obtained using the code static seismic loading.

3. *The greater column moments in a two-way frame,* caused by the possible simultaneous yielding of beams in two directions due to seismic loading acting in a general (skew) direction and having components of load along both principal axes of the structure. For example, for the symmetrical building shown in Fig. 7.43, if a displacement of four times that at first yielding of the beams is reached in direction 2, it only requires $\Delta_1 = \Delta_2/4$ to cause yielding of the beams in direction 1 as well, and this occurs when θ is only 14°. Thus, yielding in the beams in both directions may occur simultaneously for much of the seismic loading, and for a structure with beams of equal strength in each direction, the resultant beam moment input applied biaxially to the columns is $\sqrt{2}$ times the uniaxial beam moment input. Also biaxial bending will generally reduce the flexural strength of the column. Typically the flexural strength of a square column for bending about a diagonal may be 15% less than the flexural strength for uniaxial bending. Therefore, concurrent earthquake loading may cause the columns to yield before the beams, unless columns are strengthened to take this effect into account.

It is evident that column flexural strengths much greater than the bending moments derived from the code static seismic loading are needed if plastic hinges in

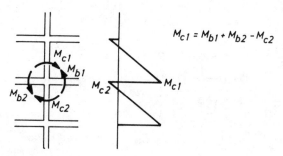

Part of frame   Column bending moments

Fig. 7.42   Possible column moments during dynamic response.

columns are to be avoided. The difficulty of preventing plastic hinges from forming in columns is such that some column yielding must be considered to be inevitable. The degree of protection of columns against plastic hinging is a debatable issue and needs to be approached on a probabilistic basis.

A method for evaluating the column actions in ductile multistory frames due to Paulay has been placed in the commentary of the New Zealand concrete design code (SANZ, 1982). This procedure is aimed at giving reasonable protection against column yielding. The design uniaxial bending moment for the column, acting separately in each of the two principal directions of the building, is given by multiplying the column moment derived from code loading by a factor to account for beam flexural overstrength, higher-mode effects, and concurrent earthquake loading. The design axial loads in the columns also take into account beam flexural overstrengths. The multiplier to obtain the design columns moments from the code moments can vary from 1.8 to much higher values depending on the frame.

By comparison the approach of Chapter 21 of the ACI code (ACI, 1989) is to require the sum of the moments at the center of the joint corresponding to the design flexural strengths of the columns at the joint, to be at least equal to ⁶⁄₅ times the sum of the moments at the center of the joint corresponding to the design flexural strengths of the beams at the joint.

3   Longitudinal reinforcement in columns

Limits for longitudinal reinforcement.   The area of longitudinal reinforcement required in reinforced concrete columns can be determined using design charts, tables, computer programs, or hand calculations based on the analysis procedures described in earlier sections. That is, the required area of longitudinal steel can be calculated for a given column size, material strength, distribution of reinforcement, and design load and moment (Park and Paulay, 1975). Codes generally specify limits on the areas of longitudinal steel used and the number of bars in the section, in order to ensure ease of construction and satisfactory behavior of the column.

The minimum and maximum allowable areas of longitudinal reinforcement are normally specified as percentages of the gross area of the column. For example, it is recommended in the ACI code (ACI, 1989) that the area of longitudinal reinforcement shall be not less than 1% nor greater than 8% of the gross area of the column. The minimum percentage is to ensure that some reinforcement is there

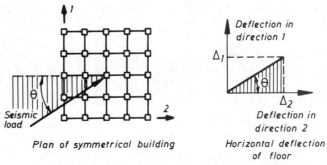

Plan of symmetrical building   Horizontal deflection of floor

Fig. 7.43   General direction of earthquake loading on building.

to provide resistance to bending, which may exist regardless of whether or not the calculations indicate bending is present, and to reduce the effect of shrinkage and creep under sustained compressive loading. The maximum percentage is mainly to minimize the difficulties of placing concrete when the reinforcement is congested. The percentage of longitudinal reinforcement in columns should not usually exceed 4% when the bars are to be lap spliced.

It is generally considered that for longitudinal bars in a circular arrangement, enclosed by spirals or circular hoops, the number of bars should not be less than six, in order to provide proper support to the transverse steel during construction and to ensure that the flexural strength of the column is not significantly dependent on the direction of bending. For longitudinal bars enclosed by transverse ties or hoops of other shapes, at least one longitudinal bar should exist in each corner of the transverse reinforcement. For example, the minimum number of longitudinal bars is four for rectangular columns and three for triangular columns. In seismic design there are also limitations on the maximum distance between adjacent longitudinal bars, which may govern the minimum number of bars in a section. For example, in the seismic provisions of the New Zealand concrete design code (SANZ, 1982) it is required that in the potential plastic hinge regions of columns the longitudinal bars shall not be spaced further apart between centers than 200 mm (7.9 in.). This requirement is to ensure adequate confinement of the compressed concrete by transverse reinforcement passing around the longitudinal bars.

Lap splices. In structures designed for significant seismic actions the columns may be subjected to cyclic (reversed) bending moments large enough to cause plastic hinges to form at the top and bottom ends of the columns. Lap splices are considered to be undesirable in plastic hinge regions subjected to cyclic flexure, and seismic codes generally require lap splices to be placed near the midheight of columns. Tests have been conducted by Paulay (1982) to investigate the performance of columns with lap splices. When the lap splices were placed in plastic hinge regions, it was found that a large amount of transverse reinforcement was necessary to ensure that the longitudinal bar forces could be transferred satisfactorily within the lap length. The transverse reinforcement was needed to apply clamping forces across the potential longitudinal splitting cracks and therefore enable a shear friction mechanism to transfer forces from one spliced bar to another. In that case, however, yielding of the longitudinal reinforcement was found to be restricted to a small length at the end of the laps, leading to an undesirable concentration of curvature there and resulting in extremely large steel strains, premature buckling of bars, and in some cases fracture of the longitudinal bars; that is, the yielding did not spread along the column. It is evident that lap splices should be positioned away from the plastic hinge regions of columns of frames designed to resist seismic actions, unless precautions are taken to reduce the possibility of plastic hinges forming in columns by a suitable strong column–weak beam design approach.

Also, whenever the longitudinal steel force changes direction, for example, where longitudinal bars are bent to provide an offset at lap splices, transverse tensile forces will be generated in the concrete, which need to be resisted by transverse reinforcement.

4   Transverse reinforcement

The role of transverse reinforcement.   Transverse reinforcement, placed in reinforced concrete columns, is in the form of spirals or circular hoops, or rectangular arrangements of hoops with or without cross ties. The role of transverse reinforcement is to aid the development of longitudinal bars, to confine the compressed concrete, to prevent premature buckling of the longitudinal reinforcement, and to prevent shear failure of the member. Transverse reinforcement needs to be anchored adequately if it is to function effectively. The quantities of transverse reinforcement required can be calculated using procedures specified by codes. Codes also state rules for the minimum and maximum spacing, and for achieving adequate anchorage of transverse reinforcement.

The quantity of transverse reinforcement of circular shape is generally expressed in terms of the volumetric ratio ρ_s, which is the ratio of the volume of spiral or circular hoop reinforcement to the volume of the concrete core, namely,

$$\rho_s = \frac{A_{sp}\pi d_s}{s\pi(d_s/2)^2} = \frac{4A_{sp}}{d_s s} \tag{7.17}$$

where A_{sp} = area of spiral bar
$\quad\quad d_s$ = diameter of spiral
$\quad\quad s$ = center-to-center spacing of spiral bar

For transverse reinforcement of rectangular shape, with or without cross ties, the quantity of transverse reinforcement is generally expressed in terms of A_{sh}, which is the total area of transverse reinforcement, including cross ties, in the direction under consideration within longitudinal spacing s_h of the hoop sets. The requirements for structures not designed for seismic actions and for structures designed for seismic actions are treated separately in the following subsections.

Transverse reinforcement in columns of structures not designed for seismic actions

Transverse reinforcement for shear. For columns of structures not designed for seismic actions, shear is not generally critical. Nevertheless, the transverse reinforcement provided should be checked to ensure that it is adequate to resist the design shear forces.

Rectangular ties. If arrangement of rectangular ties are used in columns, the bar size and spacings are generally governed entirely by considerations of providing adequate lateral support to the longitudinal bars. It is recommended by the ACI code (ACI, 1989) that the diameter of the transverse bar be at least 9.5 mm (⅜ in.) for longitudinal bars 32 mm (1¼ in.) or smaller, and at least 12.7 mm (½ in.) for larger-diameter and bundled longitudinal bars. The vertical spacing of the ties is not to exceed 16 longitudinal bar diameters, 48 tie bar diameters, or the least lateral dimension of the column. The ties are to be arranged in such a way that every corner and alternate longitudinal bar has lateral support provided by the corner of a tie with an included angle of not more than 135° and so that no bar is further than 152 mm (6 in.) clear on each side along the tie from such a laterally supported bar. For rectangular columns tied in this manner, it is not considered that the ties apply sufficient confinement to increase the load-carrying capacity of the concrete core within the ties.

Spiral reinforcement. If spiral reinforcement is used for transverse reinforcement the ACI code (ACI, 1989) specifies that the ratio of spiral reinforcement is to be not less than

$$\rho_s = 0.45\left(\frac{A_g}{A_c} - 1\right)\frac{f_c'}{f_{yh}} \tag{7.18}$$

where A_g = gross area of column section
    A_c = area of core of column section measured to outside of spiral
    f'_c = specified compressive strength of concrete
    f_{yh} = specified yield strength of spiral reinforcement, not to exceed 414
        MPa (60,000 psi)

The diameter of the spiral bar is to be not less than 9.5 mm (⅜ in.) and the clear spacing between spirals is not to exceed 76 mm (3 in.) nor be less than 25 mm (1 in.).

Tests (see, for example, Park and Paulay, 1975) have shown that columns with properly anchored spirals containing the amount of spiral reinforcement required by Eq. 7.18 behave in a ductile manner when loaded concentrically to failure. This is because the confinement of the concrete core, provided by the spiral reinforcement as failure of the column is approached, enhances the strength and ductility of the core concrete, which compensates for the loss of load-carrying capacity of the shell concrete which spalls off at large deformations.

Transverse reinforcement in columns of structures designed for seismic actions. In seismic design, arrangements of spirals or hoops used in potential plastic hinge regions are placed at close centers, and rectangular hoops are overlapped or incorporate cross ties, so that the column core is well confined. Figure 7.44 illustrates examples of damage caused to inadequately confined reinforced concrete columns, which occurred during the 1971 San Fernando earthquake. Figure 7.45 shows examples of the plastic hinge regions of well-confined reinforced concrete columns after being subjected to simulated severe seismic loading in laboratory tests, and illustrates that although the cover concrete has been lost, the core is well confined, allowing the strength of the column to be maintained. Hence the proper detailing of transverse reinforcement in the plastic hinge regions of the

Fig. 7.44 Damage caused to some reinforced concrete columns in bridge and building structures during 1971 San Fernando earthquake.

columns is necessary to achieve adequate ductility for the structure to survive severe earthquake actions without collapse.

Length of potential plastic hinge regions of columns. In the ACI code (ACI, 1989) the length of the potential plastic hinge regions in the ends of columns adjacent to the joint face is specified as not less than (1) the depth of the section in the direction of bending, (2) one-sixth of the clear height of the column, and (3) 457 mm (18 in.).

In the New Zealand concrete design code (SANZ, 1982) the length of the potential plastic hinge regions in the ends of columns adjacent to the joint face is dependent on the magnitude of the ratio $P_e/\phi f'_c A_g$, where P_e is the column load compression due to the design gravity and seismic loading, ϕ is the strength reduction factor ($\phi = 0.9$ for confined members), f'_c is the concrete compressive cylinder strength, and A_g is the gross area of the column cross section. When $P_e \leq 0.3\phi f'_c A_g$, the potential plastic hinge region is taken as the longer column section dimension in the case of a rectangular section, or the diameter in the case of a circular section, or the region where the moment exceeds 0.8 of the maximum moment at that end of the member, whichever is larger. These requirements are illustrated in Fig. 7.46. The bending moment diagram for a column is known quite accurately in the case of cantilever columns and in the case of low frames where higher-mode effects during earthquake shaking are not significant. In tall frames, where higher-mode effects are significant, the column moments will differ from those given by code static equivalent loading, which is based mainly on first-mode effects (Park and Paulay, 1975). In lieu of more accurate analysis, the bending moment diagram in the columns of tall frames used to determine the length of the potential plastic hinge region can be considered to extend linearly from maximum moment at the end under consideration to zero moment at the other end of the column in that story. When $P_e > 0.3\phi f'_c A_g$, the potential plastic hinge region is increased by 50%. Tests in New Zealand (for example, Priestley et al. 1981) have shown that at high axial load levels, the plastic hinge region tends to spread along the column because the flexural strength at the critical section is enhanced by the larger confining steel content. Thus flexural failure could occur

Fig. 7.45   Well-confined reinforced concrete columns with spiral and rectangular hoop reinforcement after being subjected to simulated severe seismic loading. (*From Priestley et al., 1981; Park et al., 1982.*)

in the less heavily confined adjacent regions of columns unless the heavy confining steel is spread over a longer length of the column (Fig. 7.47).

Spacing of transverse reinforcement in potential plastic hinge regions of columns.   According to the ACI code (ACI, 1989), for both circular and rectangular shaped transverse reinforcement, the spacing in the longitudinal direction of the column in potential plastic hinge regions is not to exceed (1) one-quarter of the

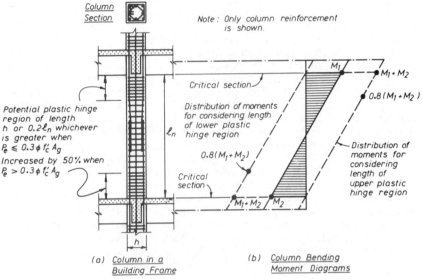

Fig. 7.46   Length of potential hinge regions of columns in tall moment-resisting frames subjected to seismic loading. (*From SANZ, 1982.*)

Fig. 7.47   Failure occurring outside well-confined end region of reinforced concrete column as a result of simulated severe seismic loading. (*From Priestley et al., 1981.*)

minimum column section dimension, and (2) 102 mm (4 in.). Also, cross ties or legs of overlapping hoops are not to be spaced more than 356 mm (14 in.) across the section.

According to the New Zealand concrete design code (SANZ, 1982), for both circular and rectangular shaped transverse reinforcement, the spacing in the longitudinal direction of the column is not to exceed (1) one-fifth of the minimum column section dimension, (2) six longitudinal bar diameters, and (3) 200 mm (7.9 in.). Also, cross bars or legs of overlapping hoops are not to be spaced at more than 200 mm (7.9 in.) across the section. In addition, for rectangular hoops the yield force in the hoop bar or cross tie is to be at least one-sixteenth of the yield force of the longitudinal bar or bars it is to restrain laterally. With regard to the limits on longitudinal spacing of transverse reinforcement, the requirement of one-fifth of the least column lateral dimension is to ensure that the bars are close enough to effectively confine the compressed concrete, and the requirement of six longitudinal bar diameters is to ensure that premature buckling of compressed longitudinal reinforcing bars does not occur during cyclic (tension-compression) loading when the tangent modulus of the steel is reduced by the Bauschinger effect (see Figs. 7.32 and 7.33). The maximum transverse spacing of 200 mm (7.9 in.) of hoop legs or cross ties is also to permit effective confinement of concrete. The tie force of at least one-sixteenth of the longitudinal bar force is to provide adequate restraint against premature buckling of the longitudinal bar.

Figures 7.48 to 7.50, taken from the commentary of the New Zealand concrete design code (SANZ, 1982), the ACI code (ACI, 1989), and the recommendations of the Structural Engineers Association of California (SEAOC, 1975), illustrate typical arrangements of transverse reinforcement in the potential plastic hinge regions of rectangular columns recommended in New Zealand and in the United States. Typical details for columns, recommended by the second draft of the seismic design appendix to the model code of the European Concrete Committee— International Federation of Prestressing (CEB-FIP, 1982), are similar to those in Fig. 7.48.

It is evident that in most rectangular sections a single perimeter hoop will be insufficient to confine the concrete properly and to laterally restrain the longitudinal steel against buckling. Therefore an arrangement of rectangular hoops, either overlapping or with cross ties, or both, will be necessary. Also, transverse reinforcement can only be expected to function effectively if fitted reasonably tightly around the bars making up the reinforcement cage, a rather difficult requirement in practice. Note that in Fig. 7.48 a cross tie can engage either the longitudinal bar or the peripheral hoop beside the longitudinal bar, that is, the concrete is confined by arching between hoops, cross ties, and longitudinal bars. In a set of overlapping hoops it is preferable to have one peripheral hoop enclosing all the longitudinal bars together with one or more hoops covering smaller areas of the section. That is because such a detail is more easy to construct, since the longitudinal bars are held more firmly in place if they are all enclosed by one hoop. An inclined hoop (for example, that in the 16-bar column illustrated in Fig. 7.48) can be counted on as making a contribution to A_{sh} by determining the equivalent bar area of the component of transverse force in the required direction. In the case of that 16-bar column, it is evident that A_{sh} may be taken as $5.41A_b$, where A_b is the area of each hoop bar.

Anchorage of transverse reinforcement in potential plastic hinge regions of columns. Anchorage failure of the transverse reinforcement must be prevented if that reinforcement is to function effectively. The New Zealand concrete design code (SANZ, 1982) specifies that hoops and cross tie reinforcement in reinforced concrete columns are to be anchored by end hooks formed by a 135° turn around a longitudinal bar plus an extension of at least eight hoop or cross tie bar diameters at the free end of the bar into the core concrete, as shown in Figs. 7.48 and 7.51a. Alternatively, the bar ends can be welded to achieve anchorage. These anchorage details mean that when the reinforcement cages are being fabricated, the hoops and cross ties first need to be placed over the ends of the longitudinal bars and then shifted along the longitudinal bars to their correct positions in the rein-

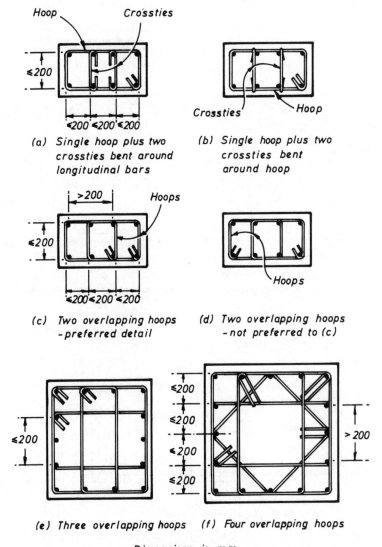

(a) Single hoop plus two crossties bent around longitudinal bars

(b) Single hoop plus two crossties bent around hoop

(c) Two overlapping hoops – preferred detail

(d) Two overlapping hoops – not preferred to (c)

(e) Three overlapping hoops

(f) Four overlapping hoops

Dimensions in mm

Fig. 7.48 Examples of transverse reinforcement on columns according to commentary of New Zealand concrete design code. Dimensions in mm. (SANZ, 1982).

forcing cage, that is, the hoops and cross ties cannot be inserted directly through the side of the cage into their final locations.

United States codes permit alternative details, which simplify the fabrication of reinforcing cages, as shown in Figs. 7.49 and 7.50. The cross ties with 90° and 135° end hooks alternating along the member, also illustrated in Fig. 7.51b, can be inserted directly into position from each side of the cage after the hoops are in place. The use of J bars, which have a 135° end hook and are inserted from each

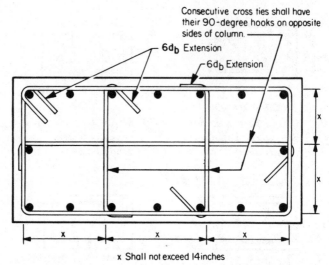

Fig. 7.49 Example of transverse reinforcement in columns according to commentary of ACI code (ACI 318, 1989).

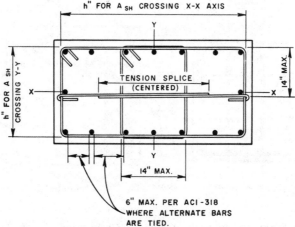

Fig. 7.50 Example of transverse reinforcement in columns according to recommendations of Structural Engineers' Association of California (SEAOC, 1975).

side of the cage and lapped in the core concrete, also illustrated in Fig. 7.51c, is possible if the column size permits development of the tension splice. The U bar detail of Fig. 51d is satisfactory if the lap has sufficient length to develop the tension splice in the core concrete. However, the U bar detail is definitely not recommended for transverse bars passing around the longitudinal bars in the corners of columns, since the tension splice will not be effective in the cover concrete if the cover concrete spalls at large column deformations during severe seismic loading.

Figure 7.52 compares the anchorage requirements of transverse reinforcement by bending around a longitudinal bar according to some seismic codes. It is of interest that the extension beyond the 135° bend into the core concrete varies from $6d_b$ specified in the appendix of the commentary of the code of the Architectural Institute of Japan (AIJ, 1982), to $8d_b$ specified in the New Zealand concrete design code (SANZ, 1982), to $10d_b$ specified in the ACI code (ACI, 1989), the recommendations of the Structural Engineers' Association of California (SEAOC, 1975), and the second draft of the seismic design appendix of the model code of the European Concrete Committee (CEB-FIP, 1982), where d_b is the diameter of the transverse bar.

The cross tie with the 90° bend illustrated in the commentary of the ACI code

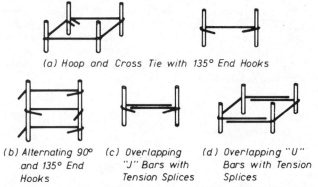

(a) Hoop and Cross Tie with 135° End Hooks

(b) Alternating 90°
and 135° End
Hooks

(c) Overlapping
"J" Bars with
Tension Splices

(d) Overlapping "U"
Bars with Tension
Splices

Fig. 7.51   Alternative details for anchoring transverse reinforcement for reinforced concrete columns.

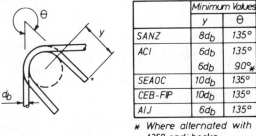

	Minimum Values	
	y	θ
SANZ	8d$_b$	135°
ACI	6d$_b$	135°
	6d$_b$	90°*
SEAOC	10d$_b$	135°
CEB-FIP	10d$_b$	135°
AIJ	6d$_b$	135°

* Where alternated with
135° end hooks

Fig. 7.52   Anchorage of transverse reinforcement around longitudinal bar according to some seismic codes.

(ACI, 1989) has an extension of $6d_b$. As discussed earlier, a cross tie with a 90° bend at one end and a 135° bend at the other end has the construction advantage that it can be inserted into the reinforcing cage from the side when placing the steel. However, it is considered in the New Zealand code (SANZ, 1982) that the 90° bend is undesirable since the extension of the bar beyond the 90° bend is not embedded in the concrete core. Thus when the cover concrete spalls, the 90° bend anchorage may become ineffective.

A column recently tested in New Zealand (Tanaka et al., 1985) has shown that the 90° bend anchorage for cross ties, as illustrated in Fig. 7.51b, does eventually become ineffective at large column deformations. Two other columns tested demonstrated that the tension splice detail for cross ties shown in Fig. 7.51c is satisfactory, provided sufficient lap length is available for adequate anchorage.

It is evident that more tests are needed on reinforced concrete columns subjected to seismic loading to compare the performance of various anchorage details for transverse reinforcement. The importance of good detailing of reinforcement in reinforced concrete structures designed for earthquake resistance cannot be overemphasized. Significant protection against damage will be provided by properly detailed reinforcement.

Quantity of transverse reinforcement required for concrete confinement in potential plastic hinge regions of columns

1. *New Zealand code provisions.* According to the New Zealand concrete design code (SANZ, 1982), the quantity of transverse reinforcement specified is intended to ensure adequate ductility at the potential plastic hinge regions of columns in the event plastic hinging occurs, for the level of seismic design force used. In potential plastic hinge regions when spirals or circular hoops are used, the volumetric ratio ρ_s should not be less than

$$\rho_s = 0.45\left(\frac{A_g}{A_c} - 1\right)\frac{f_c'}{f_{yh}}\left(0.5 + 1.25\frac{P_e}{\phi f_c' A_g}\right) \tag{7.19}$$

or

$$\rho_s = 0.12\frac{f_c'}{f_{yh}}\left(0.5 + 1.25\frac{P_e}{\phi f_c' A_g}\right) \tag{7.20}$$

whichever is greater,

where A_g = gross area of column cross section

A_c = area of concrete core of section measured to outside of spiral or hoop steel

f_{yh} = yield strength of transverse reinforcement

f_c' = concrete compressive cylinder strength

P_e = axial load on column

ϕ = strength reduction factor

The strength reduction factor ϕ = 0.9 if plastic hinging can occur or 1.0 if the column is protected from plastic hinging by a suitable strong column–weak beam design procedure. In potential plastic hinge regions where rectangular hoops with or without cross ties are used, the total area of transverse bars A_{sh} in each of the transverse directions within spacing s_h should not be less than

$$A_{sh} = 0.3s_h h'' \left(\frac{A_g}{A_c} - 1\right)\frac{f_c'}{f_{yh}}\left(0.5 + 1.25\frac{P_e}{\phi f_c' A_g}\right) \tag{7.21}$$

or

$$A_{sh} = 0.12s_h h'' \frac{f_c'}{f_{yh}}\left(0.5 + 1.25\frac{P_e}{\phi f_c' A_g}\right) \tag{7.22}$$

whichever is greater,

where h'' = dimension of concrete core of section measured perpendicular to direction of hoop bars to outside of perimeter hoop

s_h = center-to-center spacing of hoop sets.

The other notation is as for Eqs. 7.19 and 7.20.

The maximum design axial load in columns is limited to $0.7f_c'A_g$ or $0.7P_0$, whichever is greater, where f_c' is the concrete compressive cylinder strength, A_g the gross area of the column section, and P_0 the axial load strength of the column, since the ductility of very heavily loaded columns may be small even with extensive confining steel.

In moment-resisting frames where a strong column–weak beam design procedure is used to protect the columns from plastic hinging, the required quantity of transverse reinforcement in the potential plastic hinge regions may be one-half that required by Eqs. 7.19 and 7.22, but the previous spacing and anchorage requirements should be maintained. It is to be noted that it is impracticable to make the column strong enough to eliminate column hinging entirely, but at least the likelihood of column hinging can be reduced significantly (Park and Paulay, 1975). Hence some available column ductility is always necessary. This reduction in the quantity of transverse reinforcement is not permitted at the base of columns of frames nor in columns forming part of frames designed using a weak column–strong beam concept.

2. *United States provisions.* In the ACI code (ACI, 1989) and in the recommendations of the SEAOC (1975) it is specified that in the potential plastic hinge regions when spiral reinforcement is used, ρ_s should not be less than

$$\rho_s = 0.45\left(\frac{A_g}{A_c} - 1\right)\frac{f_c'}{f_{yh}} \tag{7.23}$$

or

$$\rho_s = 0.12\frac{f_c'}{f_{yh}} \tag{7.24}$$

whichever is greater. In the potential plastic hinge regions where rectangular hoops with or without cross ties are used, A_{sh} should not be less than

$$A_{sh} = 0.3s_h h'' \frac{f_c'}{f_{yh}}\left(\frac{A_g}{A_c} - 1\right) \tag{7.25}$$

or

$$A_{sh} = 0.12s_h h'' \frac{f_c'}{f_{yh}} \tag{7.26}$$

whichever is greater. The notation used in Eqs. 7.23 to 7.26 is the same as that for

Eqs. 7.19 to 7.22, except that in the ACI code h'' is the dimension of the concrete core measured to the centers of the perimeter hoop.

3. *Background of New Zealand and United States provisions for quantity of transverse reinforcement required for concrete confinement in potential plastic hinge regions of columns.* It is evident that the New Zealand equations (Eqs. 7.19 to 7.22) are similar to the United States equations (Eqs. 7.23 to 7.26), except for the term $(0.5 + 1.25P_e/\phi f'_c A_g)$. The reason for this difference is that the United States equations are based on a philosophy of preserving the axial load-carrying capacity of the column after spalling of the cover concrete has occurred rather than aiming to achieve a particular curvature ductility factor for the section (Park and Paulay, 1975). The philosophy of maintaining the axial load strength of the section after spalling of the cover concrete does not properly relate to the detailing requirements of adequate plastic rotation capacity of eccentrically loaded members. A more logical approach for the determination of the amount of transverse reinforcement necessary to achieve adequate curvature ductility would be based on ensuring a satisfactory moment-curvature relationship.

Theoretical moment-curvature analyses have been conducted in New Zealand by Park et al. (1972, 1975, 1977) to determine the effect of confinement on the available curvature ductility of reinforced concrete columns. The idealized stress-strain curves for confined concrete used in these analyses took into account the influence of the variation in the quantity of transverse reinforcement on the shape of the curves. The complete stress-strain curve for confined concrete was used in the moment-curvature analyses, that is, the full extent of the "falling branch" of the stress-strain curve after the maximum stress was reached was utilized and hence no arbitrary value for the "ultimate" concrete compressive strain was assumed. Instead, the available curvature ductility factor of the section was judged by assessing the curvature after maximum moment was reached when the section was still carrying a reasonable proportion of the maximum moment. The theoretical moment-curvature relations for a range of transverse steel contents and axial load levels were computed. The analyses showed that the quantities of transverse steel specified by the ACI and SEAOC equations are conservative for low axial load levels but are unconservative for high axial load levels. Hence Eqs. 7.19 and 7.22 are based on the ACI and SEAOC equations, but with a modification factor $(0.5 + 1.25P_e/\phi f'_c A_g)$ to account for the effect of axial load level.

The amount of transverse reinforcement required by Eqs. 7.19 and 7.22 increases with the axial load level because a higher axial load means a larger neutral axis depth, which in turn means that the flexural strength of the column is more dependent on the contribution of the concrete compressive stress block. Thus the higher the axial load, the more important it becomes to maintain the strength and ductility of the concrete, thus leading to a greater quantity of transverse steel.

The behavior of reinforced concrete columns subjected to simulated seismic loading has been studied extensively in New Zealand in recent years (Priestley and Park, 1984). Test results have been obtained from a wide range of columns. Figure 7.53 shows two typical test results from columns detailed according to the New Zealand concrete design code (SANZ, 1982). The column units had a stub at midheight to simulate a beam. During the tests the compressive column load was held constant at a predetermined level and a reversible static horizontal load was applied to the stub, which was either load- or displacement-controlled. The maximum bending moment occurred adjacent to the beam stub. Very good stability of the load-displacement hysteresis loops was observed up to displacement ductility

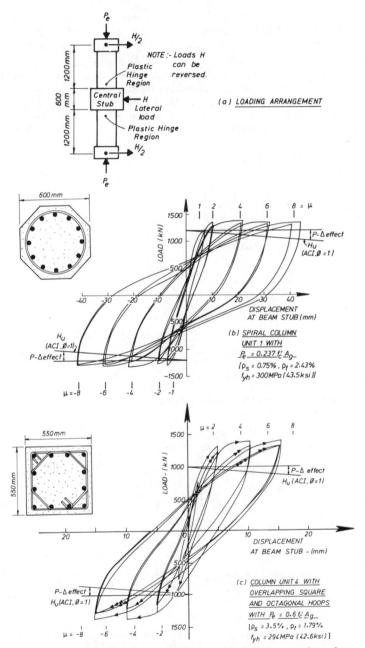

Fig. 7.53 Loading arrangements and measured horizontal load-displacement loops for two reinforced concrete columns subjected to simulated severe seismic loading. (*From Priestley et
al., 1981; Park et al., 1982.*)

factors of at least 6 with little strength degradation. The results from the wide range of columns tested have indicated that the New Zealand equations for the quantity of confining reinforcement results in columns with satisfactory ductility.

   4. *Comparisons of the quantity of confining steel required in potential plastic hinge regions of columns by New Zealand and United States codes.*   The differences between the provisions for transverse reinforcement of the New Zealand concrete design code (SANZ, 1982), the ACI code (ACI, 1989) and the recommendations of the SEAOC (1975) are illustrated in Fig. 7.54 for a typical 1.5-m (59.1-in.)-diameter circular column confined by a spiral, and in Fig. 7.55 for a typ-

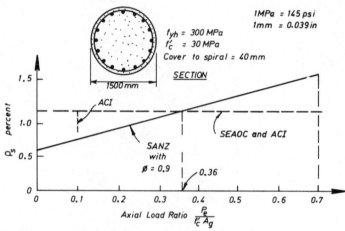

Fig. 7.54   Comparison of United States and New Zealand code spiral steel requirements for circular column.

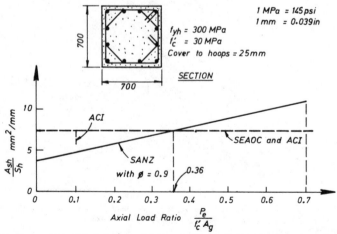

Fig. 7.55   Comparison of United States and New Zealand code hoop steel requirements for square column.

ical 700-mm (27.6-in.)-square column confined by an arrangement of square and octagonal hoops.

It is evident from Figs. 7.54 and 7.55 that the ACI and SEAOC provisions stipulate a constant quantity of transverse steel, regardless of the level of axial compressive load on the column. It should be noted, however, that for column compressive loads less than $0.1f'_cA_g$ the member could be defined as a beam according to the ACI code and then contain the reduced quantity of transverse steel specified for a beam. The New Zealand code quantity of transverse steel shows a linear increase with axial load from 50% of the ACI/SEAOC quantities at zero axial load to 100% of the ACI/SEAOC amount at an axial load of $0.36f'_cA_g$, to 1.47 times the ACI/SEAOC amount at an axial load of $0.7f'_cA_g$, assuming $\phi = 0.9$ in the New Zealand code equations.

For the circular column of Fig. 7.54, the quantity of spiral steel required by the New Zealand code at an axial load level of $0.36f'_cA_g$, and by the ACI and SEAOC codes at all load levels, could be met using a spiral with $f_{yh} = 300$ MPa (43.5 ksi) from a 20-mm (0.79-in.)-diameter bar at 74-mm (2.9-in.) center-to-center spacing. If a higher-strength spiral steel was used, the spiral bar diameter could be reduced or the spacing increased, or both. For example, if $f_{yh} = 414$-MPa (60-ksi) spiral steel is used, a 19.1-mm (3/4-in.)-diameter spiral bar at 93-mm (3.7-in.) center-to-center spacing would be sufficient. It is obvious that large-diameter columns require large-diameter spiral steel bars at close centers for confinement.

For the square column of Fig. 7.55, the quantity of hoop steel required by the New Zealand code at an axial load level of $0.36f'_cA_g$, and by the ACI and SEAOC codes at all load levels, could be met using hoops with $f_{yh} = 300$ MPa (43.5 ksi) from 16-mm (0.63-in.)-diameter bar with the hoop sets placed at 88-mm (3.5-in.) centers. Again the quantity of transverse steel used could be reduced by using higher-strength steel. For example, if $f_{yh} = 414$-MPa (60-ksi) hoop steel is used, a 15.9-mm (⅝ in.)-diameter hoop bar with hoop sets at 120-mm (4.7-in.)-center-to-center spacing would be sufficient.

Figures 7.56 and 7.57 show theoretical moment-curvature relations derived for the columns of Figs. 7.54 and 7.55 for three different axial load levels, namely, 0, $0.36f'_cA_g$, and $0.72f'_cA_g$. The stress-strain relation for the longitudinal steel used

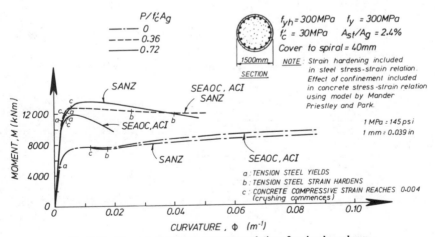

Fig. 7.56 Theoretical moment-curvature relations for circular column.

in the analysis included the effect of strain hardening. The stress-strain relation for confined concrete used was that due to Mander et al. (1984). It is of interest that at the high axial load level of $0.72f'_cA_g$ the curve obtained for the ACI/ SEAOC amount of confining steel shows a significant reduction in moment at curvatures beyond the maximum moment (that is, relatively poor ductility), while the curve obtained for the New Zealand amount of confining steel shows more ductility. At zero axial load the curves obtained for the ACI/SEAOC and New Zealand amounts of confining steel are almost identical and show good ductility, indicating that the smaller New Zealand amount of confining steel is adequate.

5. *Comparisons of the quantity of confining steel required in potential plastic hinge regions of circular and square column sections.* It is of interest to compare the volumes of transverse steel required for the three column sections shown in Fig. 7.58. Each section has 12 longitudinal bars. The circular column has spiral reinforcement; the square columns have two alternative arrangements of hoops. Case 1 has three overlapping hoops per set, made up of one square perimeter hoop surrounding all 12 bars and two interior rectangular hoops, each surrounding four bars. Case 2 has two overlapping hoops per set, made up of one square perimeter hoop surrounding all 12 bars and one octagonal interior hoop surrounding eight bars.

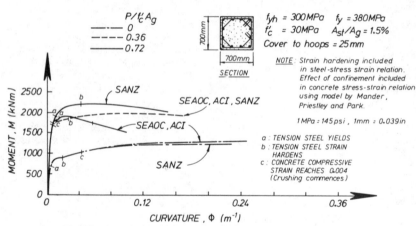

Fig. 7.57   Theoretical moment-curvature relations for square column.

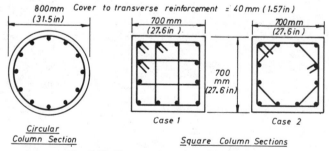

Fig. 7.58   Cross sections of example columns.

The relative sizes of the circular and square cross sections are such that the nominal (ideal) flexural strengths of the three columns are approximately the same if the columns all have longitudinal reinforcement with f_y = 380 MPa (55 ksi) and $\rho_t = A_{st}/A_g$ = 0.02, concrete with f'_c = 30 MPa (4350 psi), and an axial load level of $0.3f'_c A_g$, where A_{st} in the total area of longitudinal reinforcement, A_g the gross area of the column section, and f'_c the concrete compressive cylinder strength. This equality of flexural strength may be demonstrated as follows. In both columns the distance between the bar centroids in extreme faces of the column is close to 0.8 of the overall column depth (within 2% of this proportion), and $\rho_t f_y/0.85f'_c = 0.02 \cdot 380/(0.85 \cdot 30) = 0.30$. If the strength reduction factor ϕ equals 1.0, the nominal (ideal) flexural strength is 1690 kN · m (1246 kip · ft) for the circular column and 1730 kN · m (1275 kip · ft) for the square column, as may be obtained from design charts, tables, or calculation from first principles (Park and Paulay, 1975).

For the same axial load level $P_e/\phi f'_c A_g$ on all three columns, the following can be shown, using Eqs. 7.19 to 7.22 to calculate the quantities of transverse reinforcement:

1. The volume of overlapping hoops in the square column is 2.0 to 2.2 times the volume of the spiral in the circular column.

2. The square column with sets of overlapping square and octagonal hoops (case 2) required 11% less transverse reinforcement volume than the square column with sets of overlapping square and rectangular hoops (case 1).

3. For the same transverse bar diameter, the clear spacing between transverse bars is greatest in the circular column with the spiral. For example, if $P_e/\phi f'_c A_g$ = 0.4 and if 16-mm (0.63-in.)-diameter bar with f_{yh} = 380 MPa (55 ksi) is used for transverse reinforcement, the center-to-center spacing of the spirals or hoop sets is as follows. From Eqs. 7.19 to 7.22, for *circular columns,*

$$s = 118 \text{ mm (4.6 in.)}$$

Clear spacing between spirals is 118 − 16 = 102 mm (4.0 in.).
For *square column, case 1* (three overlapping hoops)

$$s_h = 137 \text{ mm (5.4 in.)}$$

Clear spacing between hoop sets is 137 − 48 = 89 mm (3.5 in.).
For *square column, case 2* (two overlapping hoops),

$$s_h = 117 \text{ mm (4.6 in.)}$$

Clear spacing between hoop sets is 117 − 32 = 85 mm (3.3 in.).

Note that this example points to the considerable reduction in the volume of transverse reinforcement possible if circular columns with spirals are used.

Transverse reinforcement for confinement away from potential plastic hinge regions. In the regions of columns outside the potential plastic hinge regions, the spacing of the transverse reinforcement can be increased since yield of longitudinal steel is not likely to occur there and the concrete does not need as much confinement. However, the reduction in the quantity of transverse reinforcement should occur reasonably gradually. Hence in the length of the member equal to the length of the potential plastic hinge region, and immediately adjacent to the potential plastic hinge region, the quantity of transverse steel could be reduced to one-half that in the potential plastic hinge region. Elsewhere between the potential plastic hinge regions, the requirements of shear will govern the quantity of transverse steel placed.

Transverse reinforcement for shear.   The transverse reinforcement placed for confinement may be assumed to contribute to the shear strength of the member, provided it effectively crosses the section, that is, interior hoops passing around only a few longitudinal bars are not effective as shear reinforcement if they do not extend to the area near the extreme tension and compression fibers of the section.

Congestion of reinforcement.   A serious problem in the construction of columns of ductile reinforced concrete frames is the congestion of steel reinforcement in the critical regions adjacent to the beam-column joints, which makes the fabrication of the reinforcement cages and the placing of concrete difficult. The congestion in those regions arises mainly from the close spacing and the multileg arrangements of the transverse reinforcement.

The fabrication of reinforcement cages is best carried out as far as possible under factory conditions, where good workmanship is more readily achieved than on the building site. Construction problems can be eased by giving careful attention to the manner in which the reinforcement will be placed on the site in the forms. For work to proceed rapidly and efficiently, standardization of detailing of the reinforcement should be sought.

Congestion can be made a less serious problem if larger concrete cross section dimensions are used for column members so that relatively low reinforcement ratios are adequate to achieve the required flexural strength. The use of larger column sections also results in lower average compressive stresses on the gross area of the column, and then the required amount of horizontal confining steel in the column ends is not as large.

The placement of the concrete in congested reinforced concrete cages is difficult. However, proper compaction of the concrete is obviously essential if the structure is to perform adequately under service load conditions and when subjected to large deformations during major earthquakes.

7.5 RETAINING WALLS

1 Types of walls and stability

In connection with tall buildings, retaining walls are generally basement walls, often extending several stories below grade level. Design problems associated with such walls differ from those normally encountered for retaining walls, which are not an integral part of a building, such as gravity walls, cantilever walls, and counterfort or buttress walls.

When dealing with the latter category, special attention must be paid to stability, overturning, and sliding of the walls.

In retaining walls in buildings, which are generally found in basements, the instability problem either disappears, since the walls have support at the floor slabs, or the problem pertains to the building as a whole, as in the case of building basements dug into a slope.

2 Loads on walls

Because of the characteristics of basement walls of this type, they are generally subjected to bending and axial load. Bending is produced by the earth pressure, and the axial load by the part of the vertical load transmitted by the floor slabs.

Usually the walls have a considerable stiffness and can neither rotate nor move laterally. Therefore the design earth pressure must be greater than the active pressure. In fact, it has been common practice in these cases to use a pressure at least 20% greater than the active pressure.

Particular attention should also be given to the additional effects that may be caused by earthquakes. It has been established that the horizontal forces induced are obtained by the mass in "Coulomb's wedge" multiplied by the accelerations of the earthquake. The resulting dynamic pressure of the displaced soil is located at approximately two-thirds of the height of the wall from its base.

3 Design

In its final condition the wall will be subjected to both bending and axial load. The standard requirements for the design of elements with this type of load combination must be met.

In the process of constructing basement walls, unfavorable loading conditions, different from the final conditions, may be obtained temporarily, such as temporary loads from excavation bracing, or when backfill is placed and compacted before the full axial dead load is present.

A good protection against water infiltration may be obtained by tough, sealed membranes applied to the outside of the walls and protected against puncture damage from the backfilling operation by pargeting. The so-called integral water proofing cannot be effective unless honeycombs and cracks in the concrete can be eliminated.

7.6 CONDENSED REFERENCES / BIBLIOGRAPHY

ACI 318 1983, *Building Code Requirements for Reinforced Concrete*
ACI 318 1989, *Building Code Requirements for Reinforced Concrete*
AIJ 1982, *Reinforced Concrete Structures, Design Code and Interpretation*
Aktan 1973, *Effect of Two-Dimensional Earthquake Motion on a Reinforced Concrete*

CEB-FIP 1982, *Seismic Design of Concrete Structures*

Ferguson 1988, *Reinforced Concrete Fundamentals*
Furlong 1967, *Strength of Steel-Encased Concrete Beam Columns*
Furlong 1989, *Personal communication*

Hognestad 1951, *A Study of Combined Bending and Axial Load*

Kaba 1984, *Refined Modeling of Reinforced Concrete Columns for Seismic Analysis*
Kato 1978, *Deformation Characteristics of Box-Shaped Steel Members*
Knowles 1969, *Strength of Concrete Filled Steel Tubular Columns*

Lai 1984, *Model for Inelastic Biaxial Bending of Reinforced Concrete Members*
Linbeck 1987, *Behavior of Reinforced Concrete Columns Subjected to Cyclic Axial*

Mander 1984, *Seismic Design of Bridge Piers*
Matsui 1985a, *Strength and Behaviour of Frames with Concrete Filled Square Steel*
Matsui 1985b, *Local Buckling of Concrete Filled Steel Square Tubular Columns*
Morishita 1979a, *Experimental Studies on Bond Strength in Concrete Filled Circular*

Morishita 1979b, *Experimental Studies on Bond Strength in Concrete Filled Square*
Morishita 1982, *Experimental Studies on Bond Strength between Square Steel Tube*

Park 1972, *Ductility of Reinforced Concrete Column Sections in Seismic Design*
Park 1974, *Effects of Confining Reinforcement on the Flexural Ductility of Rectangular*
Park 1975, *Reinforced Concrete Structures*
Park 1977, *Curvature Ductility of Circular Reinforced Concrete Columns*
Park 1982, *Ductility of Square-Confined Concrete Columns*
Park 1982, *The Seismic Performance of Steel Encased Reinforced Concrete Bridge*
Paulay 1982, *Lap Splices in Earthquake-Resisting Columns*
Potyondy 1985, *Concrete Filled Tubular Steel Structures in Marine Environment*
Priestley 1981, *Ductility of Spirally-Confined Concrete Columns*
Priestley 1984, *Strength and Ductility of Bridge Substructures*
Priestley 1985, *Concrete Filled Steel Tubular Piles under Seismic Loading*

Roik 1975, *Tragfähigkeit von ausbetonierten Hohlprofilstützen aus Baustahl*

Saiidi 1989, *Five-Spring Element for Biaxially Bent R/C Columns*
Sakino 1981, *Hysteretic Behavior of Concrete Filled Square Steel Tubular*
Sakino 1985, *Sustaining Load Capacity of Plain Concrete Stub Columns Confined*
Sakino 1985, *Experimental Studies on Concrete Filled Square Steel Tubular Short*
SANZ 1982, *Code of Practice for the Design of Concrete Structures (NZS 3101)*
Scott 1982, *Stress-Strain Behavior of Concrete by Overlapping Hoops at Low and High*
SEAOC 1975, *Recommended Lateral Force Requirements and Commentary*
Stevens 1965, *Encased Stanchions*
Suzuki 1984, *Elasto-Plastic Behaviors of Concrete-Filled Square Steel Tubular Columns*
Suzuki 1985, *Elasto-Plastic Behavior of Concrete-Filled Square Steel Tubular Columns*
Suzuki 1986, *Elasto-Plastic Behavior of Concrete-Filled Square Steel Tubular Columns*

Tanaka 1985, *Anchorage of Transverse Reinforcement in Rectangular Reinforced Concrete*
Tomii 1973, *Concrete Filled Steel Tube Structures*
Tomii 1977, *Experimental Studies on Concrete Filled Steel Tubular Stub Columns*
Tomii 1979a, *Experimental Studies on the Ultimate Moment of Concrete Filled*
Tomii 1979b, *Elasto-Plastic Behavior of Concrete Filled Square Steel Tubular Beam-*
Tomii 1979c, *Experimental Studies on Concrete Filled Square Steel Tubular Beam-*
Tomii 1980a, *A Method of Improving Bond Strength between Steel Tube and Concrete*
Tomii 1980b, *A Method of Improving Bond Strength between Steel Tube and Concrete*
Tomii 1981, *Experimental Studies on Plain Concrete Columns Subjected to Monotonic*
Tomii 1984, *Bond Check for Concrete-Filled Steel Tubular Columns*
Tomii 1985a, *Lateral Load Capacity of Reinforced Concrete Short Columns*
Tomii 1985b, *Earthquake-Resisting Hysteretic Behavior of Reinforced Concrete*

Virdi 1975, *Bond Strength in Concrete Filled Circular Steel Tubes*

Wakabayashi 1977, *A New Design Method of Long Composite Beam-Columns*
Wood 1976, *Column Design by P Delta Method*

Zhong 1985, *The Use of Concrete Filled Steel Tubular Structures in China*

8

Seismic Design of Reinforced Concrete Systems

For the majority of ordinary tall buildings, the overriding seismic design criterion will be the prevention of collapse, and hence loss of life, as a possible consequence of the largest earthquake which could be expected during the useful life of that building. It is generally recognized that structural survival is closely related to the ability of the structure to offer a specific level of resistance against lateral loading while extreme ground motions may impose significant ductility demands on various parts. Other criteria, such as availability of adequate stiffness and strength, must also be satisfied. These latter criteria relate to damage control in the event of moderate but more frequent earthquakes.

To ensure a predictably satisfactory inelastic response of a reinforced concrete building during an extreme seismic event, the designer must rely on viable energy-dissipating mechanisms within the structure. These will then provide the necessary hysteretic damping. Subsequently a significant part of the design effort must concentrate on the techniques of detailing potential plastic regions where ductility demands will arise. In the context of design for survival, the importance of the accuracy of elastic structural analyses must be deemphasized because of the inevitable gross approximations involved in the specifications of building codes for using equivalent lateral static design loads (UBC, 1982; IAEE, 1984), and the uncertainties associated with inelastic dynamic structural response to ground motions, the characteristics of which are yet impossible to predict. Specified static lateral loads or elastic modal analysis techniques should be considered mainly as means to ensure that there is a rational distribution of potential resistance throughout the structure. It should be remembered that strength resulting from requirements of lateral code loadings is considerably less (typically 25%) than what would be required if buildings were to respond elastically to the design earthquake. Therefore in the design of ductile structures any elastic analysis technique that preserves consistency in the treatment of structural members should be considered satisfactory.

These considerations led to the development in New Zealand of a simple deterministic seismic design approach, to be reviewed in this chapter. In this, the results of traditional elastic analyses for specified lateral static loads are utilized to establish an acceptable hierarchy in the development of energy-dissipating mechanisms. This hierarchy must be formulated by the designer in an effort to "tell" the structure "what to do" in the case of an extreme seismic event. Once the choice is made, each member is given appropriate strength resistance to ensure that, when required, only the chosen plastic mechanisms can develop within the structure. As will be seen, this powerful design tool is very simple. Its simplicity arises from the intent of the designer to order the structure "what it must do," rather than to ask, by way of analyses, "what it might do." The aim is thus to ensure desirable and predictable elastoplastic behavior during an extreme event with unpredictable characteristics.

A justification of these expectations relies on high quality in the detailing of the potential plastic regions of concrete components. Utilizing experimental research findings of the last 20 years, determined efforts were also made in New Zealand (SANZ 3101, 1982) to unambiguously quantify the "goodness" of detailing. Because of the need for "good" detailing, numerous and quantified recommendations are made in the following sections, particularly for components which are not, or only superficially, covered in most codes.

8.1 THE CONCEPTS OF CAPACITY DESIGN

If a hierarchy in the chain of resistance is to be established, then the designer must rationally choose weak links and strong links. Thus strengths or capacities must be compared. It is for this reason that the term *capacity design* was coined. In the capacity design of earthquake-resisting structures, elements of primary load-resisting systems are chosen and suitably designed and detailed for energy dissipation under severe inelastic deformations. All other structural elements are provided with sufficient strength so that the chosen means of energy dissipation can be maintained.

When the strength of one element is compared with that of another, it is necessary to evaluate the likely strengths mobilized during large displacements imposed by severe earthquakes. The common term used in the strength design approach (ACI 318, 1989) is the nominal, or ideal, strength S_i. This is obtained from theory predicting the failure geometry and specified material strengths. The dependable strength is then obtained from $S_d = \phi S_i$, where ϕ is a specified strength reduction factor (ACI 318, 1989). During a large inelastic seismic pulse, material strengths considerably larger than assumed or specified values may be mobilized. For example, steel strength at strain hardening may develop. Concrete strength may be enhanced by confinement. Moreover, for practical or other reasons, more reinforcement may have been provided at critical sections than what design equations indicated. All factors taken into account allow the overstrength to be estimated as

$$S_o = \rho_o S_i \tag{8.1}$$

where ρ_o is the overstrength factor relevant to a particular section. Its value ranges typically from 1.25 to 1.45, depending mainly on the grade of steel used (Park and Paulay, 1975).

When comparing the strengths of two adjacent elements, for example, beams and columns of a ductile frame, it is convenient to relate these to a code-specified seismic load demand. For example, the flexural overstrength factor for a beam, applicable to computed moments at the centerline of an exterior column, is

$$\phi_o = \frac{M^o}{M_{e,\text{code}}} \tag{8.2}$$

where M^o is the flexural overstrength of the beam as built and derived with the use of Eq. 8.1, and $M_{e,\text{ code}}$ is the moment at the same section, derived from the appropriately factored code-specified lateral static seismic load. In this, the maximum likely developed strength of a beam is compared with the intended moment demand due to the specified earthquake load only. The strength of the beam, as built, may well have been governed by other load considerations, such as gravity. If it is the designer's intention to make a column stronger than the adjacent beam, a moment input from the beam $\phi_o M_{e,\text{code}}$ will need to be considered.

The second important consideration in the establishment of the strength hierarchy is the recognition that the pattern of design actions within the structure, such as moments, shear, and axial forces, during the inelastic dynamic response of the ductile structure may markedly differ from those derived for a specified lateral static load acting on an elastic structure. To allow for this phenomenon in the estimation of the maximum likely load demand on the strong links of the chain of resistance during a large earthquake, a dynamic magnification factor ω is introduced.

The essence of the capacity design philosophy may thus be expressed by

$$S_i = \omega\phi_o S_{ed} \tag{8.3}$$

where S_i is the required ideal strength of a strong link, S_{ed} is the dependable strength assigned to the adjacent weak link with the use of the specified lateral earthquake loading, ϕ_o is the overstrength factor (Eq. 8.2) derived from the maximum likely strength of this weak link, and ω is the dynamic magnification factor, which estimates the deviation of load patterns during the inelastic dynamic response of the structure from corresponding patterns predicted by elastic analyses for specified lateral static loads. The application of this simple concept is illustrated in the following sections with respect to two different structural systems. Capacity design procedures for concrete structures have been in use in New Zealand since 1982 (SANZ 3101, 1982) and have also been incorporated in parts of other codes (CEB, 1983; CSA, 1984).

As the ideal strength, assigned by this technique to the strong links in the chain of resistance (Eq. 8.3), is an upper-bound estimate of load input at a stage when significant damage has already occurred in the structure, no further precautions need be applied. Hence the ideal strength S_i of the strong links need not be reduced by the customary strength reduction factor ϕ (ACI 318, 1989). Therefore $\phi = 1$ may be applied throughout when capacity design procedures are used.

8.2 MOMENT-RESISTING DUCTILE FRAMES

1 Aims and purpose of the design approach

To illustrate the application of capacity design principles and their implementation in terms of special detailing for ductility, the major steps of the design procedure are reviewed in the following sections. For multistory frames, the primary aim is to ensure that a story mechanism that consists of plastic hinges at both ends of all columns in any story, will not occur. This principle is generally accepted in most codes (IAEE, 1984). It led to the weak beam–strong column system in ductile frames. However, the amount of reserve strength of strong columns in comparison with the weak beam is still a subject of debate.

Case studies (Paulay, 1980) indicated that without imposing economic penalties, it is possible to provide columns with sufficient flexural strength so that plastic hinges should not be expected in any column in the upper stories. In this context limited yielding of the steel is not synonymous with a plastic hinge and associated plastic rotations. This approach may require slightly larger amounts of vertical reinforcement in columns, but accrued benefits are substantial. These are:

1. Ductility demand in the end regions of columns does not arise or is negligible. Hence there is no need to provide substantial transverse confining reinforcement. Congestion may thus be reduced.

2. As reversed cyclic inelastic response is not expected at the ends of columns, the contribution of concrete mechanisms to shear strength during an earthquake is not diminished. Therefore less shear reinforcement may be used.

3. Columns, which are more difficult to repair, enjoy a much greater degree of protection against structural damage.

4. Lapped splices, which should never be located in potential plastic hinge regions, can be used immediately above floors (Paulay, 1981a). If a plastic hinge in a column is to be expected, and this is the case with most current design procedures, splices must be located at the midheight of the columns. This represents some construction difficulties.

5. The prevention of yielding of column bars will improve the response of beam-column joints (Paulay et al., 1978).

6. Slightly larger columns will provide improved anchorage for beam bars, a task which is generally difficult to fulfill in beam-column joints of ductile frames.

The steps that follow aim to ensure that, when required, energy dissipation will occur in beam plastic hinges at any or all levels and in column plastic hinges at column bases only. Column hinges may be admitted, however, in the top story of a building.

2 Design steps

Step 1: Bending moments due to lateral load.   The bending moments due to the code-specified lateral factored static loading are derived for all beams and columns of all frames. Standard or approximate techniques of elastic analyses (Council on Tall Buildings, Group CB, 1978) may be used. M_{code} refers to column moments so obtained.

Step 2: Total beam bending moments.   Beam moments so derived are then superimposed upon those induced by appropriately factored gravity loads. Elastic analyses are used.

Step 3: Redistribution of beam moments.   If desired, design moments for beams may be redistributed among all spans of a bent. Thereby maximum moments, requiring large amounts of flexural reinforcement in the top of beams, may be reduced at the expense of smaller and often noncritical moments, requiring bottom beam reinforcement, which needs to be increased correspondingly. The design moments at column faces, for both directions of earthquake attack, can be equalized. Also minimum compression reinforcement in the bottom of beams, specified by codes (ACI 318, 1989), to ensure adequate curvature ductility (Council on Tall Buildings, Group CB, 1978) can be used more effectively in tension. Thereby the possible and unnecessary excess strength of beams, to be matched subsequently by adjacent columns, can be reduced. With the proper detailing of beam plastic hinges, reviewed in the following sections, their curvature ductility potential will be typically 10 times greater than the ductility associated with the redistribution of design moments. It has been recommended (SANZ 3101, 1982) that peak beam moments may be reduced by up to 30% of the maximum obtained in a span for any combination of loading on that span. However, in practice much smaller moments are redistributed to obtain practical solutions.

Step 4: Design of beams for flexure. Design all critical beam sections so as to provide the required dependable strength S_{ed} and determine and detail the flexural reinforcement for all beams of the building. Specific areas and features of the detailing of beams, as shown in Fig. 8.1, are discussed in Subsection 3 of this section.

Step 5: Beam flexural overstrengths and shear demands. Compute the flexural overstrength of each potential plastic hinge, as detailed, in each span of each continuous beam for both directions of the applied lateral load. Subsequently, using bending moment diagrams or otherwise, determine the corresponding beam overstrength moments at each column centerline.

Once the flexural overstrengths at each of the two possible plastic hinges in a span are determined, an upper-bound estimate of the earthquake-induced shear force in that span can be made. Because a shear failure is associated with limited ductility and significant loss of energy dissipation, it should be avoided. To this end the forces developed with flexural overstrength should be considered. This is the simplest example of the application of the capacity design philosophy. With respect to the beam shown in Fig. 8.1, the maximum shear which is not likely to be exceeded at the right-hand support is

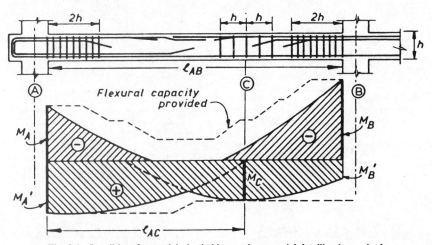

Fig. 8.1 Localities of potential plastic hinges where special detailing is required.

$$V_{uB} = \frac{M_{oB} + M_{oA}'}{\ell_{AB}} + V_{gB} \qquad (8.4a)$$

where M_{oB} and M_{oA}' are the moments at the development of flexural overstrength at the respective ends, ℓ_{AB} is the clear span, that is, the distance between critical end sections, and V_{gB} is the shear force at B due to the gravity load placed on the simply supported span. Similarly at the other end of this beam,

$$V_{uA} = \frac{M_{oA} + M_{oB}'}{\ell_{AB}} + V_{gA} \qquad (8.4b)$$

where M_{oB}' must be evaluated from the flexural overstrength at C, namely, M_{oC}.

In the evaluation of the flexural strength of beam sections, allowance should be made for all tension reinforcement which could be mobilized during inelastic story displacements. When floor slabs are interacting with beams, as in the case of cast-in-place slabs, some slab reinforcement, placed parallel with a beam, will also be stressed. Thus the flexural strength of a section may be increased considerably when the top fibers of the beam are in tension. In the design for gravity loads, the contribution of such slab reinforcement is normally neglected.

The effective width of the flange of a T- or L-beam in tension cannot be determined uniquely. The larger the imposed plastic rotation, the more slab reinforcement is stressed in tension. As a compromise, it is suggested that the effective width of a flange in tension should be assumed as shown in Fig. 8.2. All bars within the shaded area in each case should be included when estimating the area of the steel in tension for both dependable strengths and overstrengths. The effective widths shown in Fig. 8.2 are affected by the presence of a transverse

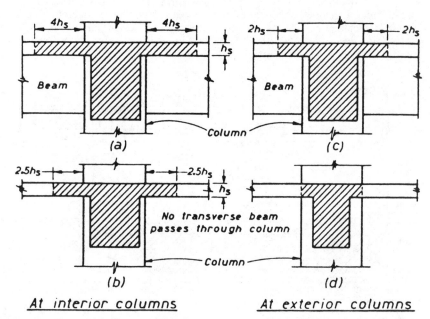

Fig. 8.2 Beam areas within which flexural reinforcement should be considered as being fully effective.

beam and the position of the section in question, in other words, situated at an exterior or at an interior joint. The effective participation of slab bars in flexural resistance was also observed in experiments (Ma et al., 1976; Yoshimura and Kurose, 1985).

Step 6: Beam overstrength factors. Determine the beam overstrength factor ϕ_o from Eq. 8.2 at each column for both directions of the lateral loading on the beam. The beam overstrength factor ϕ_o at a column is the ratio of the sum of the flexural overstrength values developed by adjacent beams, as detailed, to the total of the flexural strength required in the given direction by the code-specified lateral seismic loading alone, both sets of values being taken at the centerline of the relevant column.

Because the overstrength factor enables the total moment input from beams into columns during inelastic lateral interstory displacements to be evaluated, gravity-induced moments in either beams or adjacent columns need not be considered separately. (For typical values of ϕ_o and their effects on final column moments see Fig. 8.4.) There are three areas where special consideration must be given to the value of ϕ_o:

1. At the ground floor or at foundation level, where the full column flexural capacity could be developed, no beams may frame into the column. Consequently, a ϕ_o factor applicable to that locality would appear to be irrelevant. Moreover, a plastic column hinge at this level is to be expected. To make the ideal strength of the column at that level compatible with the strength of the remainder of the frame, designed in accordance with common strength design principles (ACI 318, 1989), the value of ϕ_o at this level should not be less than 1.4.

2. At roof level, generally gravity load will govern the design of beams. At a roof beam-column joint it is not necessary to avoid the formation of a column plas-

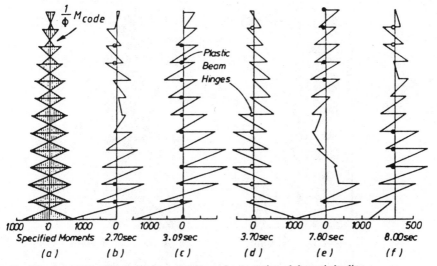

Fig. 8.3 Comparison of column moment patterns due to static and dynamic loading.

tic hinge. Therefore a value of ϕ_o = 1.1 should be used to compensate for the capacity reduction factor ϕ = 0.9, which would normally be used in this situation.

3. When a column is considerably stiffer than the beams that frame into it, cantilever action will dominate the behavior of the columns, at least in the lower stories. In such cases the column moment at a floor may be larger than the total beam moment input at that floor. Therefore at the floor below which a column point of contraflexure is not indicated by the elastic analysis for lateral code loading, and at all floors below that level, the value of ϕ_o need not be taken larger than 1.4. (For typical values of ϕ_o and their effects on final column design moments for such an example column are shown in Fig. 8.5.)

Step 7: Dynamic magnification of column moments. Determine the appropriate dynamic moment magnification factor ω. The equivalent static load specified by codes is considered to lead to a satisfactory distribution of potential beam strengths throughout the frame. To give columns a high degree of protection against premature yielding, approximate allowance should be made for the departure of the column moment pattern from that which was obtained with an elastic frame analysis for the code static load distribution. This is due to dynamic effects, in particular the higher-mode dynamic responses of the structure. Figure 8.3 compares computed bending moments encountered by a column of a 12-story frame during instants of its response to a severe earthquake with those derived for appropriate lateral static loading. Circles indicate the presence of plastic hinges in adjacent beams or at the base of the column. Dynamic effects may be gauged, for example, by the movement of the column point of contraflexure away from its location, which was determined in the code static load elastic analysis. The higher-mode dynamic responses are assumed to become more prominent in the upper stories and as the fundamental period of vibration of the structure T_1 increases. Therefore the dynamic magnification factor is introduced. For columns of one-way frames it is

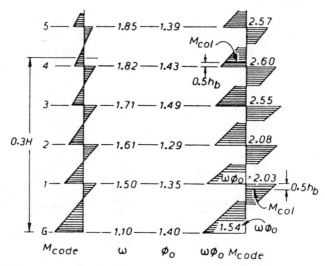

Fig. 8.4 Moment magnification for a column in lower stories of 15-story two-way frame.

$$\omega = 0.6T_1 + 0.85 \qquad (8.5)$$

but not less than 1.3 nor more than 1.8.

The lower limit of $\omega = 1.3$ has been set to minimize the possibility of a story sway mechanism forming in columns that are part of a one-way frame, that is, in which beams frame into a column in one plane only. The columns of two-way frames, in which the lateral load in one direction is resisted entirely by walls, may be designed similarly.

For columns of two-way frames, the effects of concurrent earthquake attack along both principal axes of the structure should be considered. This involves analysis of column sections for biaxial bending and axial load. The concurrent development of plastic hinging in all beams framing into a column should also be taken into account. However, if the dynamic magnification factor is suitably increased, the design process may be simplified by allowing each column section to be designed only for unidirectional earthquake attack, separately in each of the two principal directions of the structure. A column so designed may then be considered to possess adequate flexural strength to resist various combinations of biaxial flexural demands.

Accordingly, for columns of two-way frames,

$$\omega = 0.5T_1 + 1.1 \qquad (8.6)$$

but not less than 1.5 nor more than 1.9.

The minimum value results from the consideration that the columns should be capable of sustaining simultaneous beam hinge moment inputs from two directions, corresponding to the elastic moment pattern which resulted from the analysis for code load. When it is considered that a square column section subjected

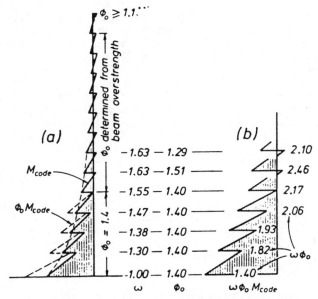

Fig. 8.5   Moment magnification in lower stories of a column of a one-way frame dominated by cantilever action.

to moment along its diagonal is approximately 90% as efficient as for moment action along its principal axes, the approximate minimum value of ω is obtained as follows: $\sqrt{2/0.9} \approx 1.5$.

The likely concurrency of very large orthogonal moments at any one column section due to the occurrence of higher-mode shapes is, however, considered to diminish with lengthening of the fundamental period of the building. Therefore, the allowance for concurrent moment attack gradually decreases with increased fundamental period, that is, with the increase in the number of stories.

Higher-mode responses are not affecting the required strength of the bottom story columns where base restraint exists. At this section, hinging is to be expected, and the column is to be detailed accordingly. To ensure that the flexural capacity of column sections in two-way frames is adequate to sustain at any angle an attack of code load intensity, the unidirectional moment demand should be increased by approximately 10%. Similar considerations apply to column sections at roof level. Accordingly, to allow for this at the roof and at the ground floor or foundation level, the value of ω may be reduced to the following values:

1. 1.0 for columns of one-way frames
2. 1.1 for columns of two-way frames

It is considered that higher-mode dynamic responses are affecting the moments in columns of the upper stories of a frame more significantly than in the lower stories. Accordingly the values of the dynamic magnification factor ω, as given by Eqs. 8.5 and 8.6, are applicable only to levels at and above 0.3 times the height of the structure, measured from the level at which elastic first-story columns are considered to be effectively restrained against rotations. Below this specified level a linear variation of ω should be assumed. However, in no case should the value of ω at first-floor level be taken less than the minimum specified for Eqs. 8.5 and 8.6. Typical values of ω for the lower five stories of a 15-story two-way frame are shown in Fig. 8.4. In this case Eq. 8.6 gave $\omega_{max} = 1.85$.

In many cases where columns are stiff relative to the beams, the column moment pattern in the lower stories of frames, obtained from the analysis of code loading, may be such that no point of contraflexure appears in several stories above the base. As pointed out in step 6, this indicates increased cantilever action of the column which, at these levels, is not likely to be affected significantly by the higher modes of dynamic response. Therefore in the lower stories, in which, according to the analysis for code earthquake loading, no point of contraflexure along a column is indicated, the value of ω at the first floor may be taken not less than 1.3 for one-way and 1.5 for two-way frames, and then linearly increased to the value obtained from Eqs. 8.5 and 8.6, as appropriate, at the floor above which the first point of contraflexure above ground floor is identified. Typical values of ω for such a column in the lower stories of a one-way frame, with $\omega_{max} = 1.63$, are shown in Fig. 8.5.

At the floor immediately below the roof the value of ω may be taken as 1.3 for one-way frames and 1.5 for two-way frames. At the top story of multistory frames the development of story mechanisms is considered to be acceptable, and hence there is no need for a high degree of protection against column yielding. Correspondingly at the floor immediately below roof level these minimum values of the dynamic magnification are applicable.

Step 8: Design axial forces for columns. The derivation of the earthquake-induced axial forces is based on the assumption that with the increasing number of stories above the specified level, the relative number of beam hinges at which the flexural overstrength may be developed simultaneously is reduced. To allow for this, 1.5% reduction per floor in the maximum feasible earthquake-induced column axial load at any level has been considered, up to a maximum of 30% for 20 floors or more above the level to be considered. Hence the axial force P_{eq} induced at any level by earthquake loading only, and used together with the appropriately factored gravity forces and the moments derived in accordance with step 9 to determine the column section strength, should not be less than

$$P_{eq} = R_v \Sigma V_{oe} \qquad (8.7)$$

where V_{oe} is the sum of the earthquake-induced beam shear forces at all floors above the level considered, developed at all sides of the column, taking into account the beam overstrengths and the appropriate sense of the forces. The value of the reduction factor R_v is given in Table 8.1.

In obtaining R_v, the dynamic magnification factor ω, given by Eqs. 8.5 and 8.6, should be as appropriate to the floor considered (see Figs. 8.4 and 8.5). It is considered that the maximum earthquake-induced axial forces are not likely to coincide with the maximum column design moments which result from magnification, in accordance with step 7, to allow for higher-mode responses. Consequently, larger axial load reductions are considered to be appropriate when ω is greater than 1.4. The maximum reduction, when $\omega = 1.9$, is an additional 0.83% per floor, as is seen in Table 8.1.

In summing the shear forces at the column faces, all beams in both directions need to be considered. In general this procedure will not significantly affect the axial load on interior columns. However, for outer columns and corner columns in particular, significant increases in axial load will result, and this should be considered as a consequence of a skew earthquake attack. When the dynamic magnification in the two principal directions of the structure is different, the larger of the ω values, relevant to the level under consideration, may be taken when determining R_v to evaluate the axial load due to concurrent actions.

Step 9: Column design moments.   The design column moments at the intersections of the reference axes of beams and columns are obtained by multiplying at each end of a column the corresponding moments, obtained for the code loading

Table 8.1   Axial load reduction factor R_v

ω	$P_e/f_c' A_g$										
	−0.150	−0.125	−0.100	−0.075	−0.050	−0.025	0.00	0.025	0.050	0.075	0.100
1.0	1.00	1.00	1.00	1.00	1.00	1.00	1.00	1.00	1.00	1.00	1.00
1.1	0.85	0.86	0.88	0.89	0.91	0.92	0.94	0.95	0.97	0.98	1.00
1.2	0.72	0.75	0.78	0.81	0.83	0.86	0.89	0.92	0.94	0.97	1.00
1.3	0.62	0.65	0.69	0.73	0.77	0.81	0.85	0.88	0.92	0.96	1.00
1.4	0.52	0.57	0.62	0.67	0.71	0.76	0.81	0.86	0.90	0.95	1.00
1.5	0.44	0.50	0.56	0.61	0.67	0.72	0.78	0.83	0.89	0.94	1.00
1.6	0.37	0.44	0.50	0.56	0.62	0.69	0.75	0.81	0.88	0.94	1.00
1.7	0.31	0.38	0.45	0.52	0.59	0.66	0.73	0.79	0.86	0.93	1.00
1.8	0.30	0.33	0.41	0.48	0.56	0.63	0.70	0.78	0.85	0.93	1.00
1.9	0.30	0.30	0.37	0.45	0.53	0.61	0.68	0.76	0.84	0.92	1.00
			Tension						Compression		

M_{code}, by the product of the ϕ_o and ω values appropriate to that floor. The moment magnification applies to the end moments only and not to the moment pattern. The two end design moments so obtained for a column in a story are not expected to occur simultaneously. An example is shown in Fig. 8.4, where it is seen that the required ideal (nominal) flexural strength of the column may be 2 to 2.6 times larger than the moment M_{code} indicated by the initial elastic analysis. A comparative value from strength design approach (SEAOC, 1975; ACI 318, 1989) used in the United States would be $1.25/\phi \cong 1.8$, where $\phi = 0.7$. Figure 8.6 shows, as a summary, the individual steps which have led to the critical design moments for one column.

The critical column section is assumed to be at the top or the soffit of the beams, and accordingly the centerline column moment $\phi_o\omega M_{code}$ may be reduced. In this only 60% of the moment gradient used for determining the column shear is considered. Hence the centerline column moment, as shown in Figs. 8.4 and 8.6, is reduced by $0.6 \times 0.5h_bV_{col}$, where the column design shear force V_{col} is in accordance with step 10. Consequently, the design moment M_{col} to be used, together with the appropriate axial load P_e, for the determination of the ideal strengths of the critical column section, separately in each of the two principal directions of the structure, should not be less than

$$M_{col} = \phi_o\omega M_{code} - 0.3h_bV_{col} \tag{8.8}$$

where the value of V_{col} is given by Eq. 8.10 or Eq. 8.12. The application of moment magnification for the moment pattern in the lower stories of a column of a two-way example frame with specific values of ϕ_o and ω is illustrated in Fig. 8.4.

When a column is subjected to small axial compression or to net tension, yielding is more acceptable. For such cases the design moment may be reduced. The larger the axial tension load and the value of the dynamic magnification factor ω, the larger the acceptable moment reduction. Accordingly when the total design axial compression P_e on a column does not exceed $0.1f'_c A_g$, the design column moment may be reduced as follows:

$$M_{col,reduced} = R_m(\phi_o\omega M_{code} - 0.3h_bV_{col}) \tag{8.9}$$

where R_m is given in Table 8.2 and P_e is to be taken as negative if causing tension and provided that the following are considered:

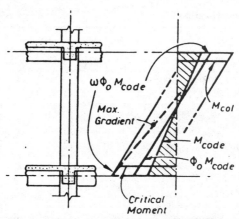

Fig. 8.6 Stages of moment magnification in one column.

1. The value of $P_e/f'_c A_g$ should not be taken less than -0.15 nor less than $-0.5\rho_t f_y/f'_c$.

2. The value of R_m taken for any one column should not be less than 0.3.

3. The moment reduction used for columns of a bent should not be more than 10% of the sum of the unreduced design moments as obtained from Eq. 8.8, for all columns of the bent taken at the same level.

In these specifications h_b is the overall depth of the beam, P_e is the design axial load including earthquake effect, as determined in step 8, f'_c is the specified compression strength of concrete (in MPa), A_g is the gross area of the column, and ρ_t is the ratio of the vertical column reinforcement area to the gross area of the column section. Other symbols were defined previously.

Requirements 1 and 2 are intended to ensure that the reduction of the magnified moments is not excessive. The reduction of column design moments in a bent may result in a loss of lateral load-carrying capacity in that bent. Usually there will be only one column in the bent that will qualify for reduction of the design moment. Because of the possible strength loss, when hinge overstrengths are being developed, according to requirement 3, the moment reduction allowed should not exceed 10% of the sum of the column design moments, taken before the application of moment reduction at the same level for all columns, that is, immediately above or below the beam of the affected bent. For example, the reduction of the design moment in column 1 of Fig. 8.7, $\Delta M_1 = (1 - R_m)M_1$, should not exceed $0.1(M_1 + M_2 + M_3 + M_4)$.

Table 8.2 Moment reduction factor R_m

Number of floors above the level considered	Dynamic magnification factor ω					
	1.4 or less	1.5	1.6	1.7	1.8	1.9
2	0.97	0.97	0.96	0.96	0.96	0.95
4	0.94	0.94	0.93	0.92	0.91	0.91
6	0.91	0.90	0.89	0.88	0.87	0.86
8	0.88	0.87	0.86	0.84	0.83	0.81
10	0.86	0.84	0.82	0.80	0.79	0.77
12	0.83	0.81	0.78	0.76	0.74	0.72
14	0.80	0.77	0.75	0.72	0.70	0.67
16	0.77	0.74	0.71	0.68	0.66	0.63
18	0.74	0.71	0.68	0.64	0.61	0.58
20 or more	0.71	0.68	0.64	0.61	0.57	0.54

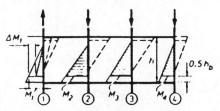

Fig. 8.7   Reduction of design moments in tension columns.

Step 10: Column shear forces.   The design shear forces across a column of one-way frames V_{col} given below are evaluated from the column end moments as follows:

1. In upper-story columns of one-way frames

$$V_{col} = 1.3\phi_o V_{code} \tag{8.10}$$

   should be used. The shear force is estimated from a probable and critical moment gradient along the column. For upper-story columns it is assumed that a shear force 20% in excess of that generated by ϕ_o times the column end moments due to code load may be developed. To provide for additional reserve strength, a reduction factor of 0.85 is incorporated, and hence the ideal column shear strength required will be close to that given by Eq. 8.10. In estimating the maximum value for the design shear, it has been assumed that at the development of all beam hinges above and below a story, an increase in story shear, that is, in moment gradient as shown in Fig. 8.6, in excess of 20% is not possible during the earthquake.

2. In first-story columns, in addition to satisfying requirement 1, the shear forces given by

$$V_{col} = \frac{M_{o,col} + 1.3\phi_o M_{code,top}}{\ell_n + 0.5h_b} \tag{8.11}$$

   should be considered. At the base of a first-story column, hinging with considerable plastic rotations is to be expected. Consequently, for these columns $M_{o,col}$, the flexural overstrength of the base section, with allowance for the axial load on the column that is consistent with the direction of the loading considered, must be evaluated.

The design shear forces across columns of two-way frames should be not less than the following values:

1. In columns of upper stories,

$$V_{col} = 1.6\phi_o V_{code} \tag{8.12}$$

2. In first-story columns of two-way frames,

$$V_{col} = \frac{M_{o,col} + 1.5\phi_o M_{code,min}}{\ell_n + 0.5h_b} \tag{8.13}$$

   but not less than that value given by Eq. 8.12.

In columns of the top story, where columns may hinge before the top floor beams would, the column shear should be evaluated in the same manner as for first-story columns.

3   Detailing of frame components for ductility

Detailing of beams.   Having completed the computations for the necessary flexural reinforcement at various sections of beams, attention must be paid to the detailing of these regions to ensure that these major energy-dissipating components can perform as expected.

Extent of plastic hinges. The length of plastic regions, over which special detailing must be provided, should be assumed as twice the depth h, of the member, as shown in Fig. 8.1.

Transverse reinforcement in plastic hinge regions. Where moment reversals may cause the longitudinal bars to yield both in tension and in compression at each face of a beam (for example, at the left-hand end of the beam in Fig. 8.1), the maximum center-to-center spacing of stirrup ties should not exceed 150 mm (6 in.) $d/4$, or six longitudinal bar diameters, where d is the effective depth of the beam.

In potential plastic hinge regions, where yielding of the longitudinal bars can occur in only one direction (for example, in region C in Fig. 8.1), the spacing of stirrup ties may be increased to 200 mm (8 in.), $d/3$, or 12 longitudinal bar diameters. These requirements are necessary to ensure that premature buckling of compression bars will not occur after the cover concrete may have spalled and the tangent modulus of elasticity of the steel has been reduced. This amount of transverse reinforcement also provides adequate confinement of the concrete in the flexural compression zone.

To ensure that an adequate quantity of transverse reinforcement is provided, it is recommended that ties at 100-mm (4-in.) spacing should be capable of resisting one-sixteenth of the compression force developed in a restrained compression bar (SANZ 3101, 1982). Accordingly the area of one tie A_{te} should not be less than

$$A_{te} = \frac{1}{16} \frac{\sum A_b f_y}{f_{yt}} \frac{s}{100} \quad (\text{mm}^2) \tag{8.14}$$

where $\sum A_b$ is the sum of areas of longitudinal bars reliant on the tie, f_y is the yield strength of longitudinal reinforcement, f_{yt} is the yield strength of transverse reinforcement, and s is the center-to-center spacing of ties. Longitudinal bars without lateral support should not be placed further than 200 mm (8 in.) apart. The application of these rules is illustrated in Fig. 8.8. This simple rule also applies when vertical bars in potential plastic regions of columns of walls need to be restrained.

Outside plastic hinge regions, the detailing requirements are as for gravity-loaded beams.

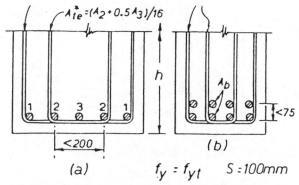

Fig. 8.8   Arrangement and size of stirrup ties in potential plastic hinge regions of beams.

Sectional dimensions of beams.   To prevent premature instability of ductile beams, particularly after a reduction of stiffness resulting from cyclic flexure in the inelastic range, and to ensure efficient interaction with columns at beam-column joints, certain dimensional limitations must be imposed.

The dimensions of beam members to which moments are applied at both ends should be such that

$$\frac{\ell_n}{b_w} \leq 37 \qquad (8.15)$$

and

$$\frac{\ell_n h}{b_w^{\,2}} \leq 150 \qquad (8.16)$$

where ℓ_n is the clear span, h the overall depth, and b_w the width of the web. For beams with rectangular cross sections, that is, without flanges, only two-thirds of the ratios given above should be used.

It is also important that a beam not be too wide, so that the bulk of the flexural reinforcement in a beam may be anchored or pass within the column core. To keep the longitudinal beam reinforcement, required for seismic loading, reasonably close to the column core, the effective width of a beam b_w should be limited as shown in Fig. 8.9. Notwithstanding these recommendations, at least 75% of the effective longitudinal beam reinforcement should pass through or be anchored within the core of a column.

Shear resistance.   With Eq. 8.4, an upper estimate for the beam shear forces V_u has been made in step 5. In the potential plastic hinge regions, as shown at the ends of the beam in Fig. 8.1, the contribution of shear-resisting mechanisms, such as aggregate interlock and dowel action (Park and Paulay, 1975), should not be relied on. Therefore the entire shear force should be assigned to web reinforcement, such as stirrups with area

$$A_v \frac{V_u s}{d f_y} \qquad (8.17)$$

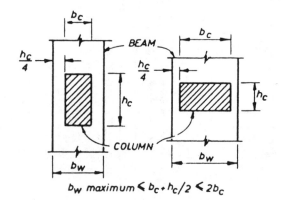

$$b_w \; maximum \leq b_c + h_c/2 \leq 2b_c$$

A PLAN VIEW OF BEAMS

Fig. 8.9 Suggested maximum beam widths.

where s is the horizontal spacing of stirrup sets, d the effective depth of the beam, and f_y the field strength of stirrups.

Tests have shown that wide flexural cracks in the plastic hinge region may develop into a few continuous wide cracks across the entire depth of the beam. Therefore, as Fig. 8.10 shows, eventually the shear force must be transmitted primarily by dowel action of the flexural reinforcement. Because of the flexibility of this mechanism, large sliding displacement can occur, as illustrated in Fig. 8.10d, which in turn may lead to a significant reduction in energy dissipation. To avoid a sliding shear failure and to improve energy dissipation in the plastic hinge, inclined shear reinforcement (as shown in Fig. 8.17a) should be provided whenever the shear stress is large, namely,

$$\frac{V_u}{b_w d} \geq 0.3(2 + r)\sqrt{f'_c} \quad \text{(MPa)} \tag{8.18}$$

where b_w is the web width of the beam and r the ratio at the plastic hinge region of the maximum shear force developing with positive moment hinging to the maximum shear force developing with negative moment hinging, always taken as negative.

The diagonal reinforcement, bent across the beam at approximately 45° in one or both directions, should be capable of resisting a shear force

$$V_{di} = 0.7\left(\frac{V_u}{b_w d\sqrt{f'_c}} + 0.4\right)(-r)V_u \tag{8.19}$$

where, by taking into account the sense of shear forces resulting from the two directions of earthquake attack, V_{di} need only be considered when $-1 < r < -0.2$. In Eq. 8.19 V_{di} is simply the sum of the vertical components of the diagonal steel forces at yield strength. The need for diagonal shear reinforcement, to control sliding shear, arises only when heavily reinforced short-span beams are used.

Outside plastic hinge regions, shear reinforcement should be provided using standard design procedures (ACI 318, 1989).

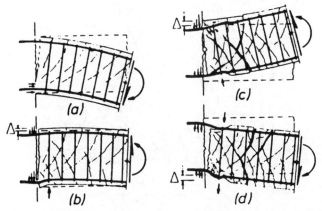

Fig. 8.10   Significant stages of development of a plastic beam hinge under reversed cyclic flexural and shear loading.

Detailing of columns

Potential plastic hinge regions.   The length of the potential hinge region ℓ_o in the ends of columns to be confined, shown in Fig. 8.11, depends on the magnitude of the axial compression force P_e as expressed by the ratio $P_e/f'_c A_g$. When $P_e \leq 0.3f'_c A_g$, the potential plastic hinge region should be assumed as the longer of the column section dimensions in case of a rectangular section or the diameter in the case of a circular section, or where the moment exceeds 0.8 of the maximum moment at the end of the member, whichever is larger. In view of the dynamic effects, as shown in Fig. 8.3, it is prudent to assume a moment gradient as shown by the line $M_{\text{earthquake}}$ in Fig. 8.11. Hence $\ell_o \geq 0.2\ell$.

When $P_e > 0.3f'_c A_g$, the potential plastic hinge region should be increased by 50%. This increase is necessary because tests (Mander et al. 1984) have shown that at high axial load levels the plastic hinge region tends to spread. This is because the flexural strength at the critical section, shown as M_o in Fig. 8.11 is enhanced by the larger confining steel content. Thus flexural failure could occur in the less heavily confined adjacent regions of the column unless the heavy confining steel is spread over a longer length.

Longitudinal reinforcement.   While satisfying code requirements for minimum and maximum vertical reinforcement contents, it is important that, to ensure efficient confinement in potential plastic hinge regions, longitudinal column bars be not spaced further apart than 200 mm (8 in.) between centers.

Lapped splices should be within the middle quarter of the column height, unless it is shown, as in Subsection 2 of this section, that plastic hinges cannot develop at the column end.

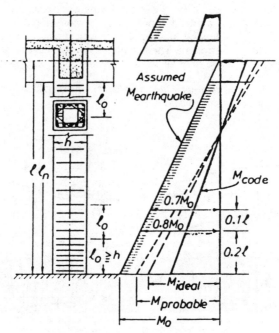

Fig. 8.11   Definition of end regions in first story of a column where special transverse reinforcement is required.

Provided that a significant amount of transverse reinforcement around each pair of lapped bars is available, it is possible to develop the yield strength of lapped bars. Nevertheless, lapped splices should not be placed in plastic hinge regions because an undesirable concentration of inelastic curvature occurs (Paulay, 1981a) at the ends of the splice. This may lead to low cycle fatigue of the longitudinal reinforcement. When columns are designed in accordance with Subsection 2 of this section, lapped splices, subjected to reversed stresses up to nominal yield stress, may be placed in the end region provided that the end region is confined by stirrup ties so that

$$\frac{A_{tr}}{s} \ge \frac{8d_b}{f_{yt}} \qquad (8.20)$$

where A_{tr} is the total area of transverse reinforcement within spacing s normal to the layer of spliced bars (in mm^2), d_b is the diameter of spliced bars (in mm), and f_{yt} is the yield strength of transverse ties (in MPa).

In the end regions of columns, the longitudinal bars must be confined to prevent their buckling. This is achieved with Eq. 8.14 the same way as in the case of beam bars outlined at the beginning of this subsection under detailing of beams.

Transverse reinforcement to confined compressed concrete. The primary purpose of confinement of compressed concrete is to sustain its ability to carry large stresses while strains well in excess of the maximum strain sustained by unconfined concrete are imposed. At this stage the cover concrete has spalled. To achieve this in columns, relatively rigid lateral support must be provided all around the confined core. The mechanisms of confinement with ties, traditionally used in rectangular columns, is often assumed to be that of circular spirals. Because tie legs were assumed to span between supports, as shown in Fig. 8.12a, while subjected to lateral pressure, they were considered to be half as efficient as

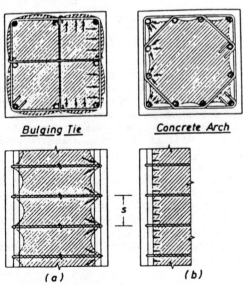

Bulging Tie   **Concrete Arch**

(a)   **(b)**

Fig. 8.12   Contribution of overlapping ties in confinement of compressed concrete in columns.

spirals. The core concrete was assumed to arch vertically between such sets of ties spaced at a sufficiently close distance s, as seen in Fig. 8.12a. It should be appreciated that ties, normally consisting of small [10- to 16-mm (0.4- to 0.6-in.)] bars, are extremely flexible in bending. Consequently they are inefficient in confinement while acting as small beams.

More effective confinement of the core concrete can be achieved by utilizing the main vertical column bars, which normally have larger diameters. These bars can act as relatively stiff continuous vertical beams when they are supported against lateral movement by ties. This mechanism is shown in Fig. 8.12b. It necessitates relatively close spacing (Sheikh and Uzumeri, 1979) of both tie legs and longitudinal bars.

Therefore the center-to-center spacing s of circular or rectangular shaped transverse reinforcing in potential plastic hinge regions should not exceed the smaller of one-fifth of the least lateral dimension of the cross section, six longitudinal bar diameters, or 200 mm (8 in.). For rectangular hoops the center-to-center horizontal spacing between legs across a section should not exceed 200 mm (8 in.). Figure 8.13 (SANZ 3101, 1982) shows typical arrangements of transverse reinforcement. The confinement of longitudinal bars must also be assured as outlined for beams at the beginning of this subsection under detailing of beams.

Legs of transverse ties should be anchored by at least a 135° hook extending into the confined concrete core or by welding. No reliance should be placed on anchorage within the cover concrete, such as by 90° hooks or lapped splices, as the cover is expected to spall off. The disastrous consequences of the unwinding of spiral or circular hoops, because of the failure of lapped splices in the cover concrete, has been observed in recent earthquakes.

The quantity of transverse reinforcement of circular shape for confinement is expressed in terms of ρ_s, which is the ratio of the volume of spiral or circular hoop reinforcement to the volume of the concrete core. Therefore

$$\rho_s = \frac{A_{sp}\pi d_s}{s\pi(d_s/2)^2} = \frac{4A_{sp}}{d_s s} \tag{8.21}$$

where A_{sp} is the area of the spirals, d_s the diameter, and s the center-to-center spacing of spiral bars. For transverse-confining reinforcement with rectangular shapes, with or without cross ties, the quantity is more conveniently expressed in terms of A_{sh}, which is the total area of transverse reinforcement, including all effective legs, in the direction under consideration within longitudinal spacing s_h.

The quantity of confining reinforcement must ensure adequate rotational ductility of the potential plastic hinge region rather than compensate for the reduction of axial load-carrying capacity because of the loss of cover concrete. The necessary volume of confining reinforcement will increase as the neutral axis depth and curvature ductility demands increase. Hence ρ_s will be a function of the axial compression load P_e, derived in step 8 of Subsection 2 of this section. Based on extensive research in New Zealand (Park and Sampson, 1972; Park and Leslie, 1977; Park, 1977; Priestley and Park, 1984; Mander et al., 1984), the following procedure is recommended (SANZ 3101, 1982).

In potential plastic hinge regions with spirals or circular hoops, the volumetric ratio ρ_s should not be less than

$$\rho_s = 0.45\left(\frac{A_g}{A_c} - 1\right)\frac{f_c'}{f_{yh}}\left(0.5 + 1.25\frac{P_e}{f_c'A_g}\right) \tag{8.22a}$$

or
$$\rho_s = 0.12\frac{f'_c}{f_{yh}}\left(0.5 + 1.25\frac{P_e}{f'_c A_g}\right) \qquad (8.22b)$$

whichever is greater. Here A_c is the area of the concrete core of the section measured to the outside of peripheral transverse reinforcement, f_{yh} is the yield strength of transverse steel, and P_e is the axial load on the column as derived in

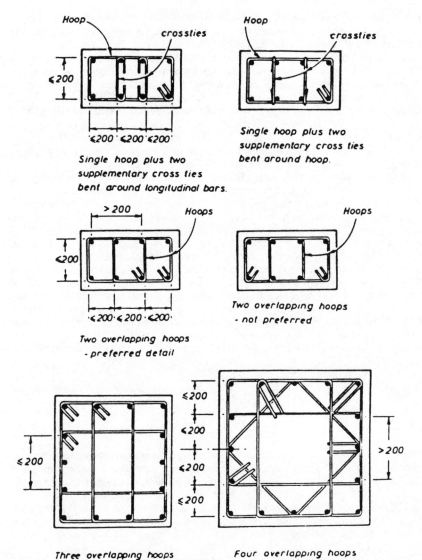

Fig. 8.13 Arrangements of transverse reinforcement in rectangular column sections. (Dimensions in mm)

step 8, with the other symbols having been defined previously. When rectangular hoops with or without cross ties are used (Fig. 8.13),

$$A_{sh} = 0.3s_h h'' \left(\frac{A_g}{A_c} - 1 \right) \frac{f'_c}{f_{yh}} \left(0.5 + 1.25 \frac{P_e}{f'_c A_g} \right) \qquad (8.23a)$$

or

$$A_{sh} = 0.12 s_h h'' \frac{f'_c}{f_{yh}} \left(0.5 + 1.25 \frac{P_e}{f'_c A_g} \right) \qquad (8.23b)$$

whichever is greater. Here h'' is the dimension of the concrete core of the section measured perpendicular to the direction of the hoop bars to the outside of the perimeter hoop, and s_h is the center-to-center spacing of the hoop sets.

In the end region of columns in the upper stories of frames, designed in accordance with the principles outlined in Subsection 2 of this section, whereby the development of plastic hinges is not expected, the volume of confining transverse reinforcement need only be one-half that required by Eqs. 8.22 and 8.23. However, the spacing and anchorage requirements, as outlined, should be maintained.

Columns so detailed will exhibit very stable hysteretic response with imposed displacement ductilities of at least 6. When axial compression is significant ($P_e > 0.3f'_c A_g$), a considerable increase in flexural resistance will also result in spite of the spalling of the cover concrete (Priestley and Park, 1984).

Shear resistance in columns. Because a shear failure due to both diagonal tension and compression may be brittle, every effort must be made to suppress it. It is for this reason that the rather conservative, but not necessarily uneconomical, approach in the derivation of the column design shear force V_{col}, in step 10 of Subsection 2 of this section was developed. As in the case of beams, a different approach should be used for elastically responding columns and potential plastic hinge regions, such as occur at the base of first-story columns.

Established procedures for shear design (ACI 318, 1989) are appropriate for all regions which are expected to remain elastic. These include the full length of upper-story columns designed in accordance with Subsection 2 of this section. Where a plastic hinge is expected to develop, allowance should be made for the deterioration of shear-resisting mechanisms (Park and Paulay, 1975), other than that of the shear reinforcement, during the high intensity of cyclic loading. Accordingly the nominal shear stress carried by the concrete may be assumed to be

$$v_c = 4v_b \sqrt{\frac{P_e}{f'_c A_g}} - 0.1 \quad \text{(MPa)} \qquad (8.24)$$

where

$$v_b = (0.07 + 10\rho_w)\sqrt{f'_c} \quad \text{(MPa)} \qquad (8.25)$$

is the basic shear stress assigned to beams subject to gravity loads only. In these expressions P_e is the minimum axial compression load on the column during the earthquake, A_g is the gross area of the column section, and ρ_w is the ratio of the tension reinforcement to the shear area of the column section (normally one-half of the total reinforcement ratio A_{st}/A_g). Equation 8.24 assumes that the concrete makes no contribution to the shear resistance of the plastic hinge when P_e $0.1f'_c A_g$. The determination of shear reinforcement follows routine procedures (ACI 318, 1989).

The reason for specifying larger dynamic magnifications in Subsection 2 of this section for both bending moments and shear forces in columns of two-way frames was to make in a simple way allowance for concurrent earthquake attack from the two orthogonal directions. With these larger factors the designer needs to consider only an artificially increased unidirectional earthquake attack separately in each of the two directions.

Because of the presence of reasonably closely spaced vertical bars all around the column section, significant dowel shear resistance in the potential plastic hinge region may be relied on. For this reason the use of diagonal shear reinforcement in columns is not warranted. Short columns in low-rise buildings, which may be the weak links in the chain of resistance, are not considered here. In those, diagonal bars will greatly improve the hysteretic response (Wakabayashi, 1986).

4 Beam-column joints

Up until recently designers tended to give little, if any, attention to the detailing of beam-column joints. Recent experimental work, particularly in the United States (Meinheit and Jirsa, 1983) and New Zealand (Paulay et al., 1978), has shown that joints, if not reinforced properly, can become the weakest links in the chain of resistance. Shear resistance and anchorage of beam reinforcement are the two most critical features of behavior. It is difficult to develop satisfactory energy dissipation in joints. Therefore the strength of joints should not be less than the strength of the weakest member they connect. In general this will be a beam. The capacity of a column should not be jeopardized by possible strength degradation of a joint, which must be also considered as an integral part of the column. Joint deformations should not significantly increase story drift. During moderate earthquakes joints should remain elastic, as they are difficult to repair. In developing design criteria, one of the important tasks is to ensure that the necessary joint reinforcement does not lead to congestion and hence construction difficulties. The recommendations which follow were developed in New Zealand (SANZ 3101, 1982; Paulay and Park, 1984).

Types of beam-column joints. In terms of geometry, location within the framework, and hence loading, the major classes of joints shown in Fig. 8.14 should be considered. In terms of behavior, distinct differences exist in elastic and inelastic joints. In elastic joints strains in all types of reinforcement within the joint and at its boundaries are expected to remain within elastic limits, even while the frames are subjected to large seismic displacements, involving numerous plastic hinges developing overstrength. The criterion for elastic joints is that no plastic hinges, either in beams or in columns, should develop at the boundaries of the joint. When plastic hinges immediately adjacent to a joint can develop, for example at the faces of the column shown in Fig. 8.15, inevitably yield penetration along beam bars into the joint core will occur. This commonly encountered situation will seriously affect the anchorage conditions for beam bars, and hence the functioning of joint mechanisms. Consequently such "inelastic" joints require a slightly different treatment.

From the precepts of the capacity design philosophy, it follows that locating any potential plastic hinge within the frame must be a design decision. To overcome difficulties which may arise in "inelastic" joints, the designer may deliberately relocate beam plastic hinges away from beam faces. Practical alternatives are shown in Fig. 8.16. In prismatic beams a deliberate weak section may be introduced by suitable curtailment of the flexural reinforcement, as shown in Fig. 8.17a. Alternatively haunches may be used as in Fig. 8.17b. To ensure that steel strains in beam bars do not exceed yield strain at the column face, critical sections ×, shown in Fig. 8.17, should be at least 500 mm (20 in.), or a distance equal to the beam's depth h, away from column faces. The assumed lengths of plastic hinges 2h, over which special detailing is required, are also shown in Fig.

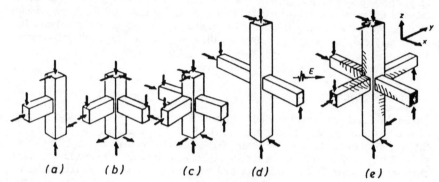

Fig. 8.14   Types of beam-column joints. (a) Exterior joints of one-way frames. (b) Corner joints. (c) Exterior joints of two-way frames. (d) Interior joints of one-way frames. (e) Interior joints of two-way frames.

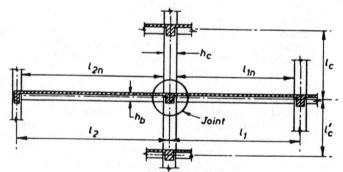

Fig. 8.15   Interior beam-column assemblage.

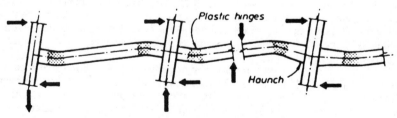

Fig. 8.16   Beams with relocated plastic hinges.

8.17. In frames designed in accordance with Subsection 2 of this section, columns are expected to remain elastic at all times. Therefore beam hinge positions will be decisive in controlling elastic or inelastic joint response. When plastic hinges in columns are admitted, the role of beams and columns in the following sections is simply to be interchanged.

Joint forces. The external actions in equilibrium, acting on a typical interior joint, such as seen in Fig. 8.15, are shown in Fig. 8.18a. For the given direction of earthquake attack, joint shear forces may cause a corner-to-corner diagonal tension failure as shown. After diagonal cracking, a part or all the joint shear force need to be transferred across this potential failure plane by horizontal and vertical or possibly diagonal reinforcement. The major task of the design is to determine the required amount of shear reinforcement for this joint.

By considering the horizontal stress resultants shown in Fig. 8.18b, with the notation defined there, the simple equilibrium statement is established:

$$V_{jh} = C_c + C_s + T' - V'_{col} = -(C'_c + C'_s + T - V_{col}) \qquad (8.26a)$$

However, $C_c + C_s = T$ and $C'_c + C'_s = T'$, and therefore the horizontal joint shear force is

$$V_{jh} \simeq T + T' - V_{col} \qquad (8.26b)$$

when it is assumed that $V_{col} \cong V'_{col}$.

Because joints are not suitable for energy dissipation (Paulay et al., 1978), their proportioning should be based on capacity design principles. Accordingly the joint core should remain essentially elastic while flexural overstrengths $M_{1,o}$ and $M_{2,o}$ might be developed in adjacent beam plastic hinges. Hence the corresponding column shear force V_{col}, to be used in Eq. (8.26b), can be estimated from

$$V_{col} \cong 2\left(\frac{\ell_1}{\ell_{1n}}M_{1,o} + \frac{\ell_2}{\ell_{2n}}M_{2,o}\right)(\ell_c + \ell'_c) \qquad (8.27)$$

where the terms are defined in Figs. 8.15 and 8.17.

Similar consideration would lead to the establishment of the vertical joint shear force V_{jv}. However, for design purposes this can be closely approximated as

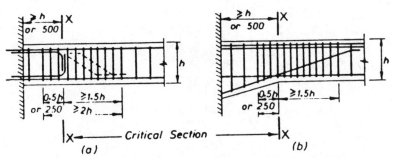

Fig. 8.17   Details of beam plastic hinges relocated away from column faces.

$$V_{jv} \simeq \frac{h_b}{h_c} V_{jh} \tag{8.28}$$

The same expressions could have been arrived at by consideration of the stress resultants of an elastic joint, as shown in Fig. 8.18c.

For external joints, where only one beam frames into a column,

$$V_{jh} \simeq T - V_{col} \tag{8.29}$$

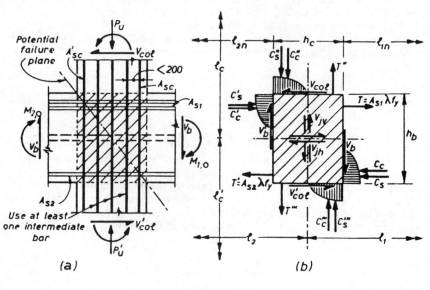

(a)   (b)

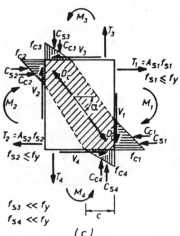

(c)

Fig. 8.18   (a) External actions and internal stress resultants introduced at interior joint. (b) Inelastic joint. (c) Elastic joint.

Joint shear stresses. To evaluate the severity of joint shear forces, it is convenient to introduce, as an index, the average horizontal joint shear stress

$$v_{jh} = \frac{V_{jh}}{b_j h_c} \quad (MPa) \tag{8.30}$$

where h_c is the overall depth of the column in the direction being considered (Fig. 8.18b) and b_j is the effective joint width. This is defined in Fig. 8.19. It is preferable to use beams with width b_w less than the width of the column b_c to enable all main beam bars to pass through or being anchored in the column core. The limitations of Fig. 8.9 need also be observed.

To avoid diagonal compression failure of the concrete within the joint core, the horizontal joint shear stress v_{jh} in either principal direction should be limited to $1.5\sqrt{f_c'}$ MPa.

Mechanisms of shear resistance. The design of beam-column joints may be based on the proposition (Park and Paulay, 1975) that there are two significant mechanisms which can transfer shear forces in the joint core. One consists of a single diagonal concrete strut, such as shown in Fig. 8.18c. The mechanism is primarily sustained by horizontal and vertical concrete stress resultants C_{ci}. The strut is particularly effective in elastic joints. The horizontal and vertical components of this diagonal compression force are V_{ch} and V_{cv}.

The other mechanisms, shown in Fig. 8.20, consist of horizontal and vertical tensile forces and a diagonal compression field. The horizontal and vertical shear forces V_{sh} and V_{sv} are introduced to this truss mechanism by bond forces from the longitudinal beam and column bars, respectively. The interplay between these two mechanisms is significantly affected by the yield penetration into the joint from the adjacent plastic hinges (Paulay and Park, 1984).

Horizontal joint shear reinforcement. The total area of horizontal shear reinforcement, placed between the innermost layers of top and bottom beam bars, should not be less than

$$A_{jh} = \frac{V_{jh} - V_{ch}}{f_{yh}} \tag{8.31}$$

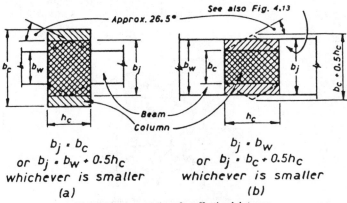

Fig. 8.19 Assumptions for effective joint area.

where V_{ch} is the joint shear carried by the diagonal strut and f_{yh} the yield strength of the shear reinforcement used.

The contribution of the diagonal concrete strut, shown in Fig. 8.17c, to the shear strength may be estimated as follows:

1. When the minimum average compression stress on the gross concrete area of the column above the joint exceeds $0.1 f'_c / C_j$,

$$V_{ch} = \frac{2}{3} \sqrt{\frac{C_j P_e}{A_g} - \frac{f'_c}{10}} (b_j h_c) \quad (\text{N}) \tag{8.32}$$

where
$$C_j = \frac{V_{jh}}{V_{jx} + V_{jy}}$$

Here V_{jx} and V_{jy} are the horizontal design joint shear forces in the principal directions x and y. $C_j = 1$ for one-way frames and 0.5 for symmetrical two-way frames. Other symbols have been defined previously.

Equation 8.32 recognizes the observed facts that with very small or no axial compression load on the column, the contribution of the diagonal strut gradually diminishes with reversed cyclic loading and with the penetration of yield into the joint core along beam bars. This is largely due to the disappearance of the horizontal concrete stress resultants, shown as C_c and C'_c in Fig. 8.17b. At this stage the entire or the major part of the internal flexural compression forces in the beam are transmitted to the joint core by the beam reinforcement. The transfer relies on the bond in the joint core.

2. When the critical section of the plastic hinge is deliberately relocated from the column force, as shown in the examples of Figs. 8.16 and 8.17, yielding of the beam reinforcement should not occur at column faces. Thereby permanently open flexural cracks in the beam will not occur and the horizontal compression stress resultants, shown in Fig. 8.18b and c, will sustain the diagonal compression strut across the core of the joint. Its resistance to horizontal joint shear may be conservatively estimated as

$$V_{ch} = 0.5 \frac{A'_s}{A_s} V_{jh} \left(1 + \frac{C_j P_e}{0.4 A_g f'_c} \right) \tag{8.33}$$

where A'_s is the area of compression reinforcement in the beam and A_s the area of tension reinforcement in the beam; the other notations are as for Eq. 8.32.

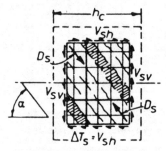

Fig. 8.20   Truss mechanism of joint core.

A'_s/A_s should not be taken larger than 1.0. When the axial column load results in tensile stresses over the gross concrete area exceeding $0.2f'_c$, then $V_{ch} = 0$. For axial tension between these limits, V_{ch} may be obtained by linear interpolation between zero and the value given by Eq. 8.33 when P_e is taken as zero.

3. When joints are formed in wide elastic columns, where h_c/h_b is greater than 2.0, V_{ch} need not be taken less than

$$V_{ch} = 0.2b_jh_c\sqrt{f'_c} \quad (N) \qquad (8.34)$$

4. The horizontal reinforcement in the joint should not be less than what is required in the adjacent end regions of the columns (see Subsection 2 of this section).

5. There are significant differences between the recommendations presented here (SANZ 3101, 1982) and those used in the United States (ACI 318, 1989; ACI-ASCE 352, 1984), where emphasis is placed on the contribution of the confining reinforcement to joint strength. In these recommendations it is required that, irrespective of the level of joint shear stress, the horizontal joint reinforcement should be equal to that used for the confinement of the potential plastic hinge end regions of adjacent columns. However, when beams from all four sides frame into a column, this horizontal joint reinforcement may be reduced to one-half in recognition of the confinement offered to the joint core by four beams of sufficient width. This approach was not adopted in New Zealand, where it was considered that beams with plastic hinges on all four sides of a column, as shown in Fig. 8.14e, do not provide any confinement.

   A comparison of the two approaches, with respect to a specific example, is shown in Fig. 8.21. Here the horizontal joint reinforcement content $\rho_h = A_{sh}/hs_h$ is expressed as a function of the axial compression load intensity in terms of P_n/f'_cA_g, where P_n is the nominal axial compression load. It is seen that the ACI requirements specify 1.2% transverse reinforcement for both confinement of the column (Fig. 8.21b) and shear resistance of the joint in a one-way frame (Fig. 8.21c), while half of this amount is considered sufficient for the joint if it is part of a two-way frame (Fig. 8.21d). The recommendations presented earlier in this chapter are shown by shaded bands in Fig. 8.21. The influence of increasing axial load intensity on the confinement of columns, as expressed by Eq. 8.23, with potential plastic hinges (top line) or on those that are to remain elastic according to Subsection 2 of this section (bottom 50% line) is seen in Fig. 8.21b. The beneficial effect of axial compression on the demand for horizontal joint shear reinforcement, in accordance with Eqs. 8.31 and 8.32, is shown for different joint shear stress levels in Fig. 8.21c and d. A very significant difference between the two approaches exists in the case of columns of two-way frames which are subjected, for example in the top stories, to low axial compression and yet have to sustain large joint shear forces in both directions of earthquake attack.

6. When an insufficient amount of joint shear reinforcement is provided, failure of the joint will be progressive, because with cyclic loading more and more load will need to be resisted by the truss mechanism of Fig. 8.20. After yielding of the entire joint shear reinforcement, corner-to-corner failure cracks will develop, as seen in Fig. 8.22. It may be noted in this figure that adjacent beams could not develop their full flexural strength.

Vertical joint shear reinforcement.   The truss model in Fig. 8.20 shows that at the top and bottom boundaries of the joint core, external compression is required to sustain the diagonal compression field. This can be achieved by axial compression load from the column above and by vertical tension reinforcement within the joint. By analogy to Eq. 8.31, the area of this should be

$$A_{vj} = \frac{V_{jv} - V_{cv}}{f_y} \tag{8.35}$$

where V_{jv} is the vertical joint shear force estimated with Eq. 8.28, f_y is the yield strength of vertical joint shear reinforcement, and V_{cv} is the shear carried by the diagonal strut of Fig. 8.18c, which is estimated for columns in which plastic hinges are not expected to develop from

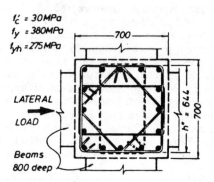

$f'_c = 30 MPa$
$f_y = 380 MPa$
$f_{yh} = 275 MPa$

LATERAL

LOAD

Beams
800 deep

(a) *Section of Example Column*

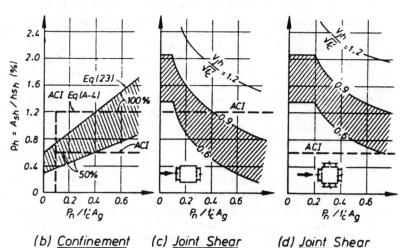

(b) *Confinement*   (c) *Joint Shear*   (d) *Joint Shear*

Fig. 8.21   Comparison of requirement for transverse reinforcement to provide confinement in columns and shear resistance in beam-column joints.

$$V_{cv} = \frac{A_{sc}'}{A_{sc}} V_{jv} \left(0.6 + \frac{C_j P_e}{A_g f_c'} \right) \tag{8.36}$$

where A_{sc}' and A_{sc} are the areas of compression and tension reinforcement, respectively, in one face of the column, and the other symbols are as for Eq. 8.33. When the axial force P_e produces tension, the value of V_{cv} is interpolated linearly between values given by Eq. 8.36 when P_e is taken as zero and zero when the average tensile stress over the gross concrete area reaches $0.2 f_c'$. The vertical joint shear reinforcement normally consists of intermediate column bars which pass continuously through the joint, as shown in Fig. 8.18a.

Exterior beam-column joints. The disposition of internal forces in exterior beam-column joints is similar to that in interior joints. External actions, internal stress resultants, and typical crack patterns for such a joint are shown in Fig. 8.23.

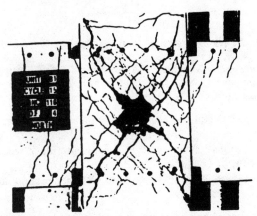

Fig. 8.22 Diagonal tension failure of interior beam-column joint due to insufficient horizontal joint shear reinforcement.

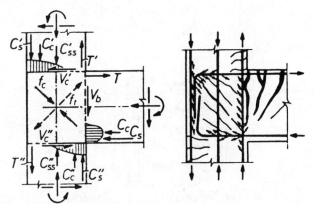

Fig. 8.23 Forces acting on exterior beam-column joint during severe seismic loading.

Apart from the smaller shear input at exterior joints, conditions are less critical provided that beam bars are anchored by standard 90° hooks or equivalent, as shown in Fig. 8.23. These hooks enable a diagonal compression strut to be sustained. Its contribution to horizontal shear resistance V_{ch} can also be approximated with Eq. 8.32. To avoid having to anchor hooked bars in the core concrete of the joint, which may have thoroughly cracked in both diagonal directions, it is advantageous, if possible, to provide a beam stub as shown in Fig. 8.24. This greatly improved anchorage enables Eq. 8.33 to be used in this case to evaluate V_{ch}.

Often the intermediate vertical reinforcement in exterior columns is in excess of that required for vertical joint shear reinforcement by Eq. 8.35. This excess vertical steel improves somewhat the joint shear strength. Also the inclination of the diagonal strut (Fig. 8.18c) influences the value of V_{ch}. In recognition of these beneficial factors, Eq. 8.33 may also be used for exterior joints, when the beam bars are anchored as shown in Fig. 8.23, when multiplied by the factor

$$\frac{3h_c\, A_{jv,\text{provided}}}{4h_b\, A_{jv,\text{required}}} \tag{8.37}$$

which should not be taken as greater than 1.0.

Anchorage of beam and column bars.   As Figs. 8.18 and 8.23 suggest, bond conditions for the longitudinal beam and column bars at the boundaries of the joint cores are unfavorable for the following reasons:

1. Large steel forces need to be transferred to the concrete over relatively short lengths of bar.
2. Flexural and diagonal tension cracks are present, which will alternate in direction during cyclic loading.
3. Bond deterioration will occur due to both yield penetration and reversed cyclic loading.

For interior joints, when plastic hinges form in the beams at the column faces, a beam bar will be yielding in tension on one side of the joint core and in compression on the other side of the core, and hence twice the yield force of the bar

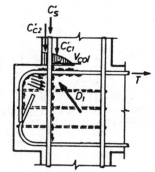

Fig. 8.24   Anchorage of beam bars in beam stub.

will need to be transferred by bond to the joint core. This may require extremely high bond stresses. Hence the bar diameters need to be limited to prevent excessive slip of bars through the joint core.

For exterior joints, a degradation of bond strength will also cause yielding of longitudinal beam bars to penetrate into the joint core, thus reducing the effective anchorage length and possibly resulting in loss of anchorage. Therefore, it is recommended that at exterior beam-column joints in which plastic hinging occurs in the beam at the column face, the anchorage of beam bars should be considered to commence within the joint core. Also for exterior joints, the outer longitudinal column bars will be subjected to high bond stresses, which can result in vertical splitting of concrete along those bars.

Bond in the joint core is not so critical when plastic hinges form some distance away from the joint core, since yield penetration into the joint core does not then occur.

Bar anchorage at exterior joints. The basic development length of a deformed bar with diameter d_b in tension terminating with a standard 90° hook is (SANZ 3101, 1982)

$$\ell_{dh} = \frac{66d_b}{\sqrt{f_c'}} \frac{f_y}{275} \quad \text{(mm)} \tag{8.38}$$

If the bar diameter is 32 mm (1.3 in.) or smaller, with side cover not less than 60 mm (2.4 in.) and the cover on the tail extension not less than 40 mm (1.6 in.), the value may be reduced by a factor of 0.7, and where the concrete is suitably confined, the value may be reduced by a factor of 0.8.

The basic development length for a deformed bar in compression is

$$\ell_{db} = \frac{0.24d_b f_y}{\sqrt{f_c'}} \quad \text{(mm)} \tag{8.39}$$

but not less than $0.044d_b f_y$. Where the concrete is suitably confined, the value may be reduced to $0.75\ell_{db}$ (SANZ 3101, 1982).

The anchorage is considered to commence within the column at a distance $0.5h_c$ or $10d_b$ from the column face, whichever is less (Fig. 8.25) except that when the plastic hinge is located sufficiently far away from the column face, anchorage may be considered to commence at the column face (see Fig. 8.17), where h_c is the column overall depth.

When the column depth is not great enough to accommodate the required development length for beam bars, a beam stub at the far face of the column, such as shown in Figs. 8.24 and 8.26, may be used to increase the available concrete length for anchorage. The presence of such a stub has been shown to result in considerable improvement in joint performance, and they are being used by some designers in New Zealand. Alternatively, short, tightly fitted bearing bars may be placed within the bend of a standard hook, as shown in Fig. 8.25, to reduce bearing stresses against the concrete. Thereby bends with smaller radii may also be used.

To enable diagonal concrete compression forces, which are vital components of joint shear resistance (Fig. 8.23), to develop, it is important that standard hooks of beam bars be bent into the joint, as shown in Fig. 8.25a, rather than into columns below or above the joint.

Bar anchorage in interior joints. To keep bond stresses to an acceptable level, the diameters of longitudinal bars d_b passing through a joint core should be limited as follows:

1. *Beam bars.* When yielding can occur at the face of the column,

$$d_b \leq \frac{11h_c}{f_y} \qquad\qquad (8.40a)$$

When yielding cannot occur at the column face,

$$d_b \leq \frac{14h_c}{f_y} \qquad\qquad (8.40b)$$

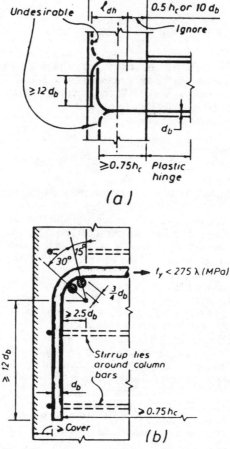

Fig. 8.25 Anchorage of beam bars at exterior joints.

For beam bars which are placed in the adjacent slab with thickness h_s,

$$d_b \leq \frac{h_s}{5} \qquad (8.40c)$$

When there is a reliable and significant axial compression present in the column ($P_{e,min} > 0.4f'_c A_g$) the beam bar diameter can be increased due to the beneficial effects of compression transverse to the bar.

2. *Column bars.*   When yielding can be expected to occur,

$$d_b \leq \frac{14h_b}{f_y} \qquad (8.41a)$$

When yielding is not expected to occur,

$$d_b \leq \frac{18h_b}{f_y} \qquad (8.41b)$$

When it can be shown that stresses in extreme columns bars remain either in tension or in compression during an earthquake over the entire length of the bars contained within the joint, in other words over the overall depth of the beam h_b, no limitation on bar size seems warranted. This situation will arise only in columns dominated by cantilever action (Fig. 8.5).

Joints with special features.   There are as numerous alternatives in joint configurations as there are possibilities for imaginative detailing (Paulay and Park, 1984), and those are not described here. Only two examples, not uncommon in two-way ductile frames, are briefly reviewed.

  Eccentric joints.   Because of architectural requirements, eccentric connections, such as those shown in Fig. 8.27a, may result. To avoid the necessity to consider additional complications, for example, those due to torsion, it is suggested that the effective joint area, shown shaded in Fig. 8.27b, should be estimated as outlined in Subsection 4 of this section under joint shear stresses. Subsequently all joint shear reinforcement necessary to resist the shear forces

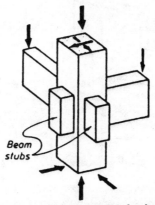

Fig. 8.26   Beam stubs at corner joint to accommodate beam bar anchorages.

introduced by the continuous eccentrically placed beams, should be placed within this assumed joint core area. Similarly, vertical intermediate column bars, to resist the required part of the vertical joint shear force V_{jv}, should be within this joint area, as shown in Fig. 8.27*b*.

Interior joints with horizontal haunches.   Unless the content of flexural reinforcement in beams is less than approximately 1.5%, horizontal joint shear reinforcement in interior joints, which receive load from adjacent beam plastic hinges at flexural overstrength, becomes excessive. The use of standard hoop types, such as those shown in Fig. 8.21*a,* leads then to congestion of reinforcement in the joint core. One way to overcome this difficulty is to use horizontal haunches, as illustrated in Fig. 8.28. A plan and an elevation of such a specific joint are seen in Fig. 8.29 (Paulay and Park, 1984). Conventional ties and hoops can be omitted

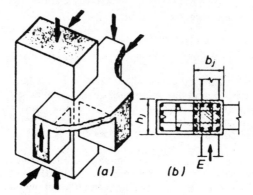

Fig. 8.27   Eccentric beam-column joint.

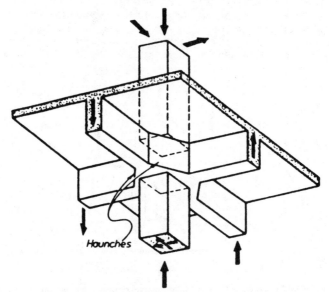

Fig. 8.28   Interior joint formed by horizontal beam haunches.

altogether. Instead larger-diameter deformed bars (f_y = 400 MPa) may be used to form circumferential and intermediate hoops with lapped hooks or welded connections, to provide the necessary horizontal joint shear reinforcement. This way, considerably more space can be made available for placing and compacting the fresh concrete in the joint area.

8.3 DUCTILE STRUCTURAL WALLS

The purpose of this section is to provide an update in developments of design procedures for buildings in which the entire seismic resistance has been assigned

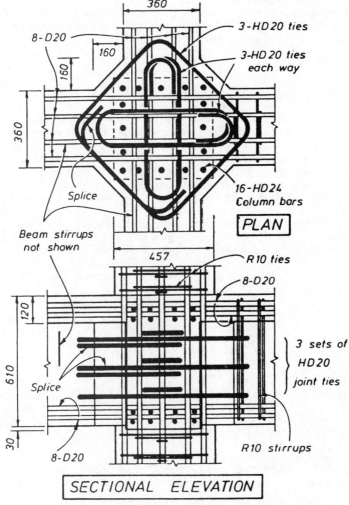

Fig. 8.29   Reinforcement in joint formed within horizontal beam haunches.

to structural walls. A brief classification of walls and their roles was given in Monograph Volume CB, Section 3.3.4, while methods of elastic analyses were reviewed in Volume CB, Sections 5.5.4 and 5.5.5. In the review of nonlinear behavior and analyses (Volume CB, Section 5.5.4) it was pointed out that criteria for the redistribution of forces and for the effects of axial load on the ductility of walls have, as yet, not been proposed (Council on Tall Buildings, 1978). The following sections report on significant advances in these areas. The major issues of the inelastic response and design of cantilever and coupled walls were outlined in some detail in Volume CB, Section 6.4. Further research in this area has since enabled certain design procedures to be formalized and codified. Also, experimental work enabled improved and more specific recommendations for the detailing of structural walls to be formulated.

As an extension to Volume CB, Section 6.4, this section reviews in some detail some new developments in the understanding of the behavior of walls and in relevant design procedures and detailing practices. The underlying deterministic philosophy for the design of ductile walls, which must provide seismic resistance, is the same as that outlined in Section 8.1 and used in the design of ductile multistory frames.

1   Failure modes in structural walls

A prerequisite in the design of ductile structural walls is that flexural yielding in clearly defined plastic hinge zones should control the strength, inelastic deformations, and, hence, energy dissipation in the entire structural system. As a corollary to this fundamental requirement, brittle failure mechanisms, or even those with limited ductility, should not be permitted to occur. This is achieved either by designing for fully elastic response or, when relying on inelastic behavior, by establishing a desirable hierarchy in the failure mechanisms, as outlined in Section 8.1.

The principal source of energy dissipation in a laterally loaded cantilever wall (Fig. 8.30a) should be the yielding of the flexural reinforcement in the plastic hinge regions, normally at the base of the wall, as shown in Fig. 8.30b and e.

Failure modes to be prevented are those due to diagonal tension (Fig. 8.30c) or

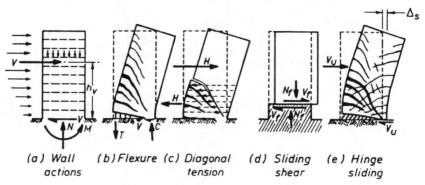

| (a) Wall actions | (b) Flexure | (c) Diagonal tension | (d) Sliding shear | (e) Hinge sliding |

Fig. 8.30   Failure modes in cantilever walls.

diagonal compression caused by shear, instability of thin-walled sections or of the principal compression reinforcement, sliding shear along construction joints (Fig. 8.30d), and shear or bond failure along lapped splices or anchorages. Attempts must be made to control effects, particularly those due to shear, which lead to both premature stiffness and strength degradation and consequently to reduced ability for energy dissipation.

An example of the undesirable response of a structural wall to reversed cyclic loading is shown in Fig. 8.31. Particularly severe is the steady reduction of strength and ability to dissipate energy.

Numerous theoretical studies have been conducted recently, particularly in the United States and Japan, to establish suitable mathematical models for such degrading hysteresis relationships in order to predict more realistically nonlinear structural response to various earthquake records. These studies sometimes imply that responses, such as those shown in Fig. 8.31, are inevitable due to the nature of reinforced concrete. However, this need not be the case. With foresight and judicious detailing of the reinforcement in critical areas of structural walls, greatly improved and sometimes optimal response can be readily achieved. Figure 8.32 shows such a response, which was obtained from the test of a one-third full-size cantilever structural wall with rectangular cross section. It is seen that a displacement ductility of approximately 4 has been attained in a very stable manner (Paulay and Goodsir, 1985). Failure due to inelastic instability, to be examined subsequently, occurred only after two cycles to a displacement ductility of 6, when the lateral deflection was 3.5% of the height of the wall.

2 Flexural strength and ductility

Flexural response. The evaluation of flexural strength is based on well-established principles. These are identical to those used in the analysis of beams. The effects of axial loads on flexure are conveniently expressed by moment–axial load interaction curves (Volume CB, Section 6.4.1).

The development of the ideal (nominal) flexural strength of a wall section, as shown in Fig. 8.32, is associated with a particular strain pattern. This is defined by the failure strain ε_c of the concrete and the neutral axis depth c. With moment only, or moment with small axial compression and, even more, with axial tension, the neutral axis depth c_1 of the rectangular section in Fig. 8.33 will be small relative to the length of the wall ℓ_w. Consequently the curvature ductility will be large and usually adequate to accommodate the plastic hinge rotations imposed

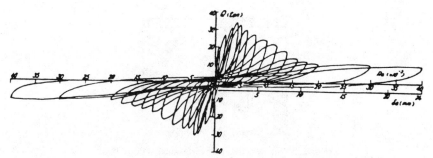

Fig. 8.31 Hysteretic response of structural wall controlled by shear mechanics.

on the structure during a large earthquake. However, when the wall is simultaneously subjected to moment and large axial compression, a large flexural compression zone may be required, resulting in a relatively large neutral axis depth, such as c_2 in Fig. 8.33. The resulting strain profile, shown by line 2, indicates clearly very small curvature ductility. If these two walls are part of an interconnected wall system, similar curvatures will be required to develop in all walls. This means that the wall with large compression load will have to develop the strain profile shown by line 2' in Fig. 8.33. This would imply concrete compression strains in the extreme fiber ε_u considerably in excess of the critical value ε_c. Clearly such curvature could not be sustained unless the concrete subjected to

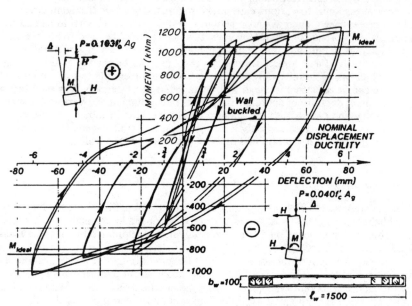

Fig. 8.32 Stable hysteretic response of ductile cantilever wall.

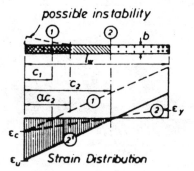

Fig. 8.33 Strain patterns for rectangular wall sections.

excessive compressive strains is confined. This is examined later in this section under confinement of structural walls.

The effect of sectional configuration on the ductility potential of a wall section can be studied with the example of a channel-shaped wall in Fig. 8.34. In the case of wall A, subjected to earthquake loading in the direction shown, all the internal tension forces resulting from the yielding of the bars in the flanges of the channel, and also some considerable axial compression load on the wall, could be equili-brated by the long but narrow compression zone in the web part of the section. The associated theoretical neutral axis c_1 is very small, and hence the ensuing curvature, shown by the dashed line, is extremely large. This large curvature is not likely to be required, and possibly the one shown by the full line would be adequate. Thus concrete compression strains might remain subcritical at all times.

Wall B of Fig. 8.34, on the other hand, requires a large neutral axis depth c_2 to develop a compression zone large enough to balance the tension forces generated in the web part of the section. Even specified minimum wall reinforcement placed in a long wall, as in Fig. 8.34, can develop a significant tension force when yield-ing. As the dashed-line strain profile indicates, the curvature developed with the ideal strength will not be sufficient if the same ductility demand as in wall A, shown by the full-lien strain profiles, is imposed. The excessive concrete com-pression strain in the vicinity of the tip of the flanges of wall B will require con-finement to be provided if a brittle failure is to be avoided.

It is thus seen that the depth of the neutral axis c relative to the length of the wall ℓ_w is a critical quantity. If a certain curvature ductility is to be attained, the ratio c/ℓ_w will need to be limited, and thus is examined in a following section on limitations on curvature ductility.

As in the case of beams and columns, shown in Subsection 2 of Section 8.2, the ideal flexural strength of wall sections is based on specified material proper-ties f'_c and f_y. During large inelastic displacement pulses, particularly when large-curvature ductility demands arise, such as shown for wall A in Fig. 8.34, much larger moments may be developed at the critical wall section. This strength en-

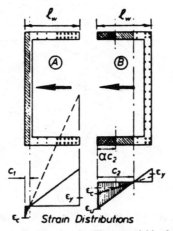

Fig. 8.34 Strain profiles showing ductility potential in channel-shaped walls.

hancement needs to be taken into account. This can be quantified with the flexural overstrength factor $\phi_{o,w}$ which in the case of cantilever walls is the ratio of the overstrength moment of resistance to the moment resulting from the code-specified lateral loading, where both moments refer to the base section of the wall. This is defined by Eq. 8.56 later in this section.

Ductility relationships in walls.   Whether a structural wall is capable of sustaining plastic deformations consistent with an expected displacement ductility ratio will depend on the ability of its plastic hinge, normally at the base of the wall, to sustain the corresponding plastic rotations. These hinge rotations will in turn depend on the available curvature ductility and the expected length of the plastic hinge (Park and Paulay, 1975). It is important to appreciate that curvature ductility and displacement ductility ratios are not equal. The plastic hinge length ℓ_p is primarily a function of the wall length ℓ_w. Typical values are such that $0.5 < \ell_p/\ell_w < 1.0$. The yield deflection, normally measured at the top of the wall and used in defining the displacement ductility ratio, rapidly increases with the height of the wall h_w. Hence the curvature ductility demand $\mu_\Delta = \phi_u/\phi_y$ corresponding to an imposed displacement ductility ratio $\mu_\Delta = \Delta_u/\Delta_y$ is also influenced by the aspect ratio of the wall h_w/ℓ_w. These relationships are shown graphically (Paulay and Uzumeri, 1975) in Fig. 8.35. The shaded bands result from two different suggestions for estimating the length of the plastic hinge ℓ_p. It is seen that for a rather slender wall with an aspect ratio of 10, a curvature ductility of approximately 12 is required to sustain a top deflection, which is four times that at yield; in other words, $\mu_\Delta = 4$. With this knowledge, recommendations may be made with re-

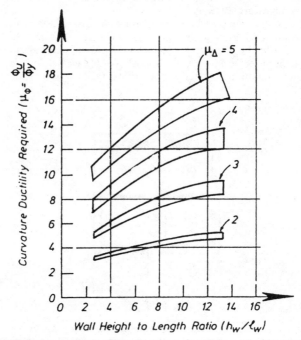

Fig. 8.35   Variation of curvature ductility ratio at base of cantilever wall with aspect ratio and displacement ductility demand.

spect to the c/ℓ_w ratio to ensure adequate curvature ductility in any wall section. It is evident that rather large curvature ductility demands would arise in slender walls when $\mu_\Delta > 5$.

Wall stability. When part of a thin wall section is subjected to large compression strains, the danger of premature failure by instability arises. This is the case when a large neutral axis depth is required in the plastic hinge zone of the wall, as shown in Fig. 8.33, while the length of the plastic hinge ℓ_p is large, such as one story high or more. The problem is compounded when cyclic inelastic deformations occur. Instability should not govern the seismic response of ductile walls.

The problem of the inelastic out-of-plane buckling of thin-walled reinforced concrete sections does not lend itself to meaningful analytical assessment. However, an appreciation of the mechanisms involved should assist the designer in inhibiting the influence of instability on overall ductile wall response. For this reason the perceived major factors of out-of-plane buckling, as well as its consequences, are briefly described in the following.

At large curvature ductilities, large tensile strains will be imposed on vertical bars placed at the extreme tension edge of a wall section, as shown in Fig. 8.32. At this stage approximately uniformly spaced large cracks will have developed in the tension zone of the plastic hinge. During the subsequent reversal of wall displacement, and hence unloading, the tensile stresses will reduce to zero. Further reversed lateral load will cause compression in the bars previously subjected to tensile yield. While the large cracks will gradually close, these bars will be subjected to inelastic compression strains. Due to the Bauschinger effect, the modulus of elasticity of the steel is reduced. When it reaches a critically small value, while cracks are still open, out-of-plane buckling may commence. When cracks across the thickness of the wall close before this stage is reached, the section will stiffen and instability at this level of loading will be arrested. It is important to recognize that the critical stage for out-of-plane buckling is reached at relatively small lateral loads, which follow a very large displacement excursion and consequent tension in this part of the wall, rather than at peak loads. Out-of-plane displacement before crack closure may also be triggered by internal discontinuities caused by dislocated aggregate particles and a misfit between crack forces caused by shear displacements.

An important consequence of out-of-plane displacements in relatively thin walls is the skewing of compression strains across the thickness of the wall section. This causes the migration of large compression stresses away from the extreme compression fiber toward the center of the wall. This may then lead to premature compression failure of unconfined regions adjacent to the confined edges of a wall.

In the absence of more accurate information on the "compactness" of reinforced concrete wall sections, existing code rules (ACI 318, 1989) relevant to short columns are best considered as guides. For such columns, the effective height-to-width ratio ℓ_n/b should not exceed 10. In walls, ℓ_n is the clear height of the wall in the critical story. Therefore, intuitive judgment was used (SANZ 3101, 1982) to recommend that, with the exceptions to be set out subsequently, in the outer half of the conventionally computed compression zone, thickness b of ductile walls should not be less than one-tenth of the clear vertical distance between floors or other effective lines of lateral support ℓ_n.

When the computed neutral axis depth is small, as shown by strain distribution 1 in Fig. 8.33, the compressed area may be so small that adjacent vertical strips of the wall will stabilize it. Accordingly, when the fiber at $0.5c$ is within a distance of the lesser of $2b$ or $0.15\ell_w$ from the compressed edge, the $b > \ell_n/10$ limit should not need to be complied with. In terms of neutral axis depth, these criteria are met when $c < 4b$ or $c < 0.3\ell_w$, whichever is less. The strain profile 1 in Fig. 8.33, which occurs commonly in lightly reinforced walls with small gravity load, clearly satisfies this condition.

These recommendations are intended for structural walls in which displacement ductilities on the order of 4 are expected. It has been suggested (Vallenas et al., 1979; Bertero, 1980) that the expected ductility demand should also be considered in slenderness limitation. The smaller the inelastic excursion, the less critical will instability be. Hence it is suggested that for walls with a wide range of lateral load resistance, the discussed thickness limit may be controlled by

$$b \le \frac{\ell_n}{10\sqrt{\phi_{o,w}K - 0.2}} \tag{8.42a}$$

or

$$b \ge \frac{\ell_n}{22\sqrt{\phi_{o,w}/R - 0.05}} \tag{8.42b}$$

where K is the horizontal force factor defined in the Uniform Building Code (UBC, 1982) and R is the response modification coefficient in the tentative provisions of the Applied Technology Council (ATC 3-06, 1978). It was assumed that $K = 0.8$ and $R = 5.5$ approximate an expected displacement ductility demand on the order of 4.

It may be assumed that only in buildings three stories high or higher would the plastic hinge length at the base, extending toward the first floor, be large enough to warrant an examination of the instability criteria.

Certain components of walls, as shown in Fig. 8.36, provide continuous lateral support to adjacent compressed elements. Therefore, it is considered that parts of a wall along its length ℓ_w, within $c/2$ from the compression edge, which is within a distance of $3b$ of such a line of lateral support, should be exempted from

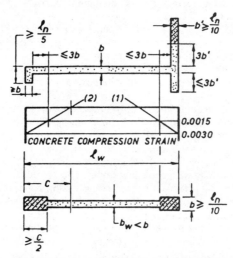

Fig. 8.36 Dimensional limitations on wall sections to prevent premature instability.

slenderness limitations. Figure 8.36 shows a number of such locations. The shaded part of the thin flange is considered to be too remote to be effectively restrained by the web portion of the wall, and hence it should comply with the requirement of Eq. 8.42. In the absence of a flange, the width of which is at least $\ell_n/5$, a boundary element may be formed which satisfies the slenderness limit. This latter case is shown at the bottom of Fig. 8.36. Similar recommendations have been adopted in Canada (CSA, 1984).

It is preferable to use walls with boundary elements (such as shown in Figs. 8.34 and 8.38). Substantial boundary elements provide protection against instability of the flexural compression region (Bertero, 1980). Also such elements are easier to confine.

Limitations on curvature ductility. Because of the variety of cross-sectional shapes and arrangements of reinforcement which can be used, and the presence of some axial load, the availability of ductility in walls cannot be checked by the simple rules suggested by codes. In the analysis of wall sections for flexure and axial load, as shown in Fig. 8.33, the neutral axis depth c is always determined. Hence the ratio c/ℓ_w, an indicator of the curvature ductility required at the development of the ideal strength, can be readily found.

The curvature ductility demand in the plastic hinge zone of cantilever walls was related to the displacement ductility in the subsection on ductility relationships in walls. Typical relationships are shown in Fig. 8.35, where it is seen that in a relatively slender wall with $h_w/\ell_w = 8$, for example, a curvature ductility of approximately 11 is required if the displacement ductility is to be 4. It may be shown from first principles that the yield curvature in a wall with length ℓ_w is approximately $\phi_y = 0.0025/\ell_w$. Hence the expected ultimate curvature for this example wall would need to be on the order of $\phi_u = 0.0275/\ell_w$, a value also observed in tests (Vallenas et al., 1979). By assuming that the maximum compression strain attained in the unconfined concrete during an earthquake may reach the value of 0.004, it is found that the neutral axis depth at the development of $\phi_u = 11\phi_y$ needs to be $c \cong \ell_w/7$.

This approach was based on cantilever walls in which the flexural overstrength at the base, corresponding to an overstrength factor of $\phi_{o,w} = 1.4$, is associated with a displacement ductility demand of 4. When the flexural overstrength is larger, or when larger K and lower R factors are used in the design, curvature ductility demand is expected to decrease, and hence the acceptable neutral axis depth may be increased. Consequently this critical depth c_c can be conservatively estimated (SANZ 3101, 1982) from

$$c_c = \frac{\phi_{o,w} K \ell_w}{8} \quad \text{or} \quad c_c = \frac{0.55 \phi_{o,w} \ell_w}{R} \tag{8.43}$$

the symbols having been defined previously.

In view of the approximations involved in the assessment of seismic design loads, a more elaborate curvature estimate is hardly warranted. Whenever the computed neutral axis depth c in the critical section of the wall at its base exceeds the critical value c_c given by Eq. 8.43, it is necessary to assume that the required ductility can be attained only at the expense of concrete compression strains in excess of 0.004.

Confinement of structural walls. When the neutral axis depth is too large, some part of the flexural compression zone of the wall will need to be confined in order to enable concrete strains in excess of 0.004 to be sustained without significant loss of flexural resistance. In this context three aspects need to be addressed:

Area of wall section within which compressed concrete is to be confined. The strain gradient associated with previous assumptions and the critical neutral axis depth are shown by the shaded line 1 in Fig. 8.37. When the neutral axis becomes larger, as shown by line 2, a length $\alpha'c$ will be subjected to strains larger than 0.004 if the same curvature is to be attained. Hence it is suggested that by taking previously mentioned factors, particularly those relevant to effects of out-of-plane displacements, into account, the length of wall section to be confined should be αc, where

$$\alpha = \left(1 - \frac{0.7c_c}{c}\right) \geq 0.5 \qquad (8.44)$$

whenever $c/c_c > 1$. When c is only a little larger than c_c, a very small and impractical value of α is obtained. In such cases at least one-half of the theoretical compression zone (SANZ 3101, 1982) should be confined. The length of the confined region is independent of the configuration of a possible boundary element which may be present. Naturally a boundary element will significantly affect the magnitude of the neutral axis depth c.

Quantity of confining reinforcement. The principles of concrete confinement to be used are those relevant to columns, as outlined in Subsection 3 of Section 8.2 under detailing of columns. However, very rarely will the need arise to confine the entire wall section. The governing principle is, that as the compressed area in a wall section increases, concrete strains associated with the necessary ductility also increase proportionally, and hence the amount of confining reinforcement must also increase. Accordingly it is recommended that rectangular or polygonal hoops and supplementary ties surrounding the longitudinal bars in the region to be confined should be used so that

$$A_{sh} = 0.3s_h h'' m \frac{f'_c}{f_{yh}}\left(0.5 + 0.9\frac{c}{\ell_w}\right) \qquad (8.45)$$

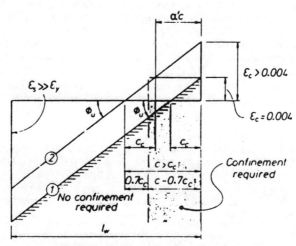

Fig. 8.37 Strain patterns for wall sections.

$$\text{where} \qquad 0.4 \le m \le \left(\frac{A_g^*}{A_c^* - 1} \right) \qquad (8.46)$$

In practice the ratio c/ℓ_w will seldom exceed 0.3. In these equations, A_{sh} is the total effective area of hoops and supplementary cross ties in the direction under consideration within spacing s_h (in mm^2), s_h in the vertical center-to-center spacing of hoop sets (in mm), A_g^* is the gross area of the wall section which is to be confined in accordance with Eq. 8.44 (in mm^2), A_c^* is the area of the concrete core within area A_g^*, measured to outside of peripheral hoop legs (in mm^2), f_c' is the specified compression strength of concrete (in MPa), f_{yh} is the specified yield strength of hoop or supplementary cross tie reinforcement (in MPa), and h'' is the dimension of the concrete core of the section measured perpendicular to the direction of the effective legs of hoop bars (in mm).

These equations are similar to and are based on those developed for columns, such as Eqs. 8.23. The area to be confined is thus extending to αc_2 from the compressed edge, as shown by cross-hatching in the examples of Figs. 8.34 and 8.36.

For the confinement to be effective, the vertical spacing of hoops or supplementary ties s_h should not exceed six times the diameter of vertical bars in the confined part of the wall section, one-half of the thickness of the confined part of the wall, or 150 mm (6 in.), whichever is least. When confinement is required, walls with a single layer of reinforcement should not be used for obvious reasons. This confining transverse reinforcement should extend vertically over the probable plastic hinge length of the wall, which for this purpose should be assumed to be equal to ℓ_w or $h_w/6$, whichever is greater, but need not exceed $2\ell_w$, where ℓ_w and h_w are the length and height of the wall, respectively.

Confinement of longitudinal bars. A secondary purpose of confinement is to prevent the buckling of the principal vertical wall reinforcement where this may be subjected to yielding in compression. It is therefore recommended that in the regions of potential yielding of the longitudinal reinforcement within a wall with two layers of reinforcement, where the longitudinal reinforcement ratio ρ_ℓ computed from

$$\rho_\ell = \frac{\Sigma A_b}{b s_v} \qquad (8.47)$$

exceeds $2/f_y$ (f_y in MPa), transverse reinforcement should be provided as for beams and columns, described in Subsection 3 of Section 8.2 under detailing of beams—transverse reinforcement in plastic hinge regions, and satisfying the requirements of Eq. 8.14. In Eq. 8.47 ΣA_b is the area of the bars within horizontal spacing s_v and b is the thickness of the wall section being considered.

The interpretation of Eq. 8.47 with reference to the wall return at the left of Fig. 8.38 is $\rho_\ell = 2A_b/bs_v$. Figure 8.38 summarizes the previous recommendations with respect to transverse reinforcement. When low local reinforcement content, typically $\rho_\ell \le 0.005$, is used in part of the wall, the contribution of the bars to the compression strength of the area is negligible, and hence the loss of this contribution due to possible buckling of the bars is of no consequence in terms of overall strength.

Curtailment of flexural reinforcement. With the use of code-specified lateral loads, bending moment diagrams of the types shown in Fig. 8.39 are obtained. If the flexural reinforcement were to be curtailed exactly in accordance with the moment so indicated, instantaneous plastic hinges could form anywhere along the height of such walls during a strong earthquake. This would be undesirable from a design point of view because potential plastic hinges require special, and necessarily more expensive, detailing. Some of these special requirements were examined in the previous sections. Moreover, as in the case of beams (discussed in Subsection 3 of Section 8.2 under detailing of beams—shear resistance), the shear strength of reinforced concrete walls will diminish in regions where yielding of the flexural reinforcement occurs. This would then necessitate additional hor-

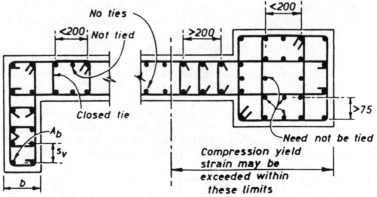

Fig. 8.38   Transverse reinforcement in potential yield zones of wall section.

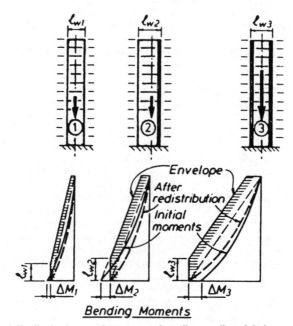

Fig. 8.39   Load distribution between interconnected cantilever walls and design moment envelopes.

izontal shear reinforcement at all levels. It is preferable to ensure that plastic hinges can develop only in predetermined locations, logically at the base of walls, by providing over the remainder of the wall flexural strength that is in excess of the likely maximum demands.

Bending moment envelopes, covering moment demands which arise during the dynamic response, are different from bending moment diagrams resulting from static loading. This may be readily shown with modal superposition techniques or from time history analyses of wall structures using a variety of earthquake records (Fintel et al., 1975; Iqbal and Derecho, 1980). It was found that there is an approximate linear variation of maximum moment demands during the inelastic as well as elastic dynamic response of the walls to ground shaking.

For the reasons enumerated, the flexural reinforcement in cantilever walls (SANZ 3101, 1982) should be curtailed so as to give a linear variation of the moment of resistance with height, as shown in Fig. 8.39. Once the critical wall section at the base has been designed and the exact size and number as well as the positions of flexural bars have been established, the ideal flexural strengths of this section, to be developed in the presence of realistic axial loads on the wall, can be evaluated. It is this ideal (nominal) flexural strength rather than the maximum moment derived from the specified lateral load, which is to be used at the bases when constructing the linear moment envelope.

3   Interacting cantilever walls

Determination of design actions.   Often the entire lateral load resistance is assigned to a number of strategically positioned full-height cantilever walls. Assuming, as is generally done, that floor slabs act as infinitely rigid diaphragms, and using standard techniques of elastic analyses, the lateral load is readily allocated to each wall (Park and Paulay, 1975). In this, allowance should be made for various effects on wall stiffness, as outlined in the next subsection.

In recognition of the fact that during a severe earthquake, all walls of such a system will need to develop plastic hinges with significant rotational ductility, some redistribution of resistance between walls should be considered. In this the designer will, among other aspects, need to consider the potential flexural strength of a wall and the resistance of foundations with respect to plastic hinge development at the wall base. For example, wall 3 in Fig. 8.39 may carry significantly larger gravity loads than the other two walls. Thereby its potential for flexural and, hence, lateral load resistance is enhanced. Hence the designer may decide to reduce the initial load demands on walls 1 and 2 and correspondingly assign more resistance to wall 3. This may be seen in Fig. 8.39 when moments for elastic analysis, shown by full lines, are compared with those after load redistribution, shown by dashed lines. To ensure that no reduction in the total resistance occurs, the condition

$$\Delta M_1 + \Delta M_2 \leq \Delta M_3 \tag{8.48}$$

must be satisfied. Such load redistribution has negligible effects on the ductility potential of a well-detailed wall if the reduction of flexural resistance does not exceed 30% of the initial value.

Modeling of member properties.   When, for the purpose of either a static or a dynamic elastic analysis, stiffness properties of various elements of reinforced concrete wall structures need to be evaluated, some approximate allowance for the effects of cracking should be made. An approximate allowance for shear and anchorage deformations may also be made.

It should be appreciated that the stiffness of reinforced concrete components depends on the level of loading or amplitude of displacement and hence on the extent of cracking imposed previously. Therefore any assumption made is necessarily a compromise. Within the limits of conventional assumptions, the stiffness of walls may vary by a factor of 4 (Freeman et al., 1980). Whatever assumption is made, it should be used consistently in estimating both periods of vibration and drifts due to lateral loading (Gates, 1978).

Accordingly, for cantilever walls subjected predominantly to flexural deformations, the equivalent second moment of area I_e may be taken as 60% of the value I_g based on the uncracked gross concrete area of the cross section, with the contribution of reinforcement being ignored:

$$I_e = 0.6I_g \qquad (8.49)$$

When elastic coupled walls are considered where, in addition to flexural deformation, extensional distortions due to axial loads are also being considered, the equivalent moment of inertia I_e and area A_e may be estimated as follows. For a wall subjected to axial tension,

$$I_e = 0.5I_g \qquad (8.50a)$$

$$A_e = 0.5A_g \qquad (8.50b)$$

for a wall subjected to compression,

$$I_e = 0.8I_g \qquad (8.51a)$$

$$A_e = A_g \qquad (8.51b)$$

If a more refined analysis is preferred, axial load effects may be allowed for. Thus,

$$I_e = \left(0.6 + \frac{P_e}{A_g f_c'}\right)I_g \leq I_g \qquad (8.52)$$

where P_e is the axial load considered to act on the wall during an earthquake, taken negative when causing tension.

For diagonally reinforced coupling beams (Paulay and Santhakumar, 1976), to be examined in Subsection 5 of this section under design of components—coupling beams, with depth h and clear span ℓ_n,

$$I_e = \frac{0.4I_g}{1 + 3(h/\ell_n)^2} \qquad (8.53a)$$

For conventionally reinforced coupling beams,

$$I_e = \frac{0.2I_g}{1 + 3(h/\ell_n)^2} \qquad (8.53b)$$

In these expressions the subscripts e and g refer to the equivalent and gross sectional properties, respectively.

For cantilever walls with aspect ratios h_w/ℓ_w larger than 4, the effect of shear deformations upon stiffness may be neglected. When a combination of slender and squat structural walls provides the seismic resistance, the latter may be allocated an excessive proportion of the total load if shear distortions are not accounted for. For such cases, that is, when $h_w/\ell_w < 4$, it may be assumed that

$$I_w = \frac{I_e}{1.2 + F} \tag{8.54}$$

where

$$F = \frac{30I_e}{h_w^2 b_w \ell_w} \tag{8.55}$$

and where b_w is the web thickness of the wall section, ℓ_w the horizontal length of the wall, and h_w the height of the wall.

In Eq. 8.54 some allowance has also been made for deflections due to anchorage (pull-out) deformations at the base of a wall, and therefore these deformations do not need to be calculated separately. Deflections due to code-specified lateral static loading may be estimated with the use of the properties of equivalent sections, as discussed.

4　Control of shear

Determination of shear load.　To ensure that shear forces will not interfere with the ductile behavior of wall systems and that shear effects will not significantly reduce energy dissipation during hysteretic response, they must not be allowed to control strength. Therefore an estimate must be made for the maximum shear intensity that may be encountered by a structural wall during a very large earthquake. This is another typical situation where the principles of capacity design, as outlined in Section 8.1, need be applied.

The design shear must not be less than that associated with the development of the flexural overstrength M^o. For a wall that has been designed, this can be readily evaluated by means of the overstrength factor $\phi_{o,w}$, which is defined as

$$\phi_{o,w} = \frac{\text{flexural overstrength}}{\text{moment resulting from code loading}} = \frac{M^o}{M_{o,\text{code}}} \tag{8.56}$$

where both moments refer to the base section of the wall. Thus the corresponding shear force would be $\phi_{o,w} V_{\text{code}}$.

As outlined in Sections 8.1 and 8.2, the optimum values of $\phi_{o,w}$ are affected by the grade of steel used and the relevant strength reduction factor ϕ. The actual value of the overstrength factor encountered during the design will be modified by the excess or deficiency of strength provided by the designer and the changes in the use of M_{code} resulting from moment redistribution which may have been carried out within a wall system.

Further increase of shear demand may result from dynamic effects. During a predominantly first-mode response of the structure, the distribution of inertial story forces will be as shown in Fig. 8.40a. This force pattern is similar to that used in standard code-specified static loadings. The center of inertial forces is typically located at approximately $0.7h_w$ above the base. When the response is strongly influenced by the second and third modes of vibration, the story forces may be distributed as seen in Fig. 8.40b, with the resultant force being located much lower than in the previous case. If a plastic hinge at overstrength M^o develops at the base in both of these cases, then the induced shear in the second case is obviously much larger. The contribution of the higher modes to shear will increase as the fundamental period of the structure increases. From a specific study of this problem (Blakeley et al., 1975), the following recommendation (SANZ 3101, 1982) has been deduced (Eq. 8.3) for estimating the total design shear:

$$V_{\text{wall}} = \omega_v \phi_{o,w} V_{\text{code}} \tag{8.57}$$

Here V_{code} is the horizontal shear demand derived from code-specified lateral static loads, $\phi_{o,w}$ is as defined by Eq. 8.56, and ω_v is the dynamic shear magnification factor, to be taken as

$$\omega_v = 0.9 + \frac{n}{10} \tag{8.58a}$$

for buildings up to six stories, and as

$$\omega_v = 1.3 + \frac{n}{30} \tag{8.58b}$$

for buildings over six stories, where n is the number of stories, which in Eqs. 8.58 need not be taken larger than 15.

An application of this approach will show that the design shear force at the base of a structural wall can become a critical quantity. When the potential flexural strength of the wall at its base is very large and much in excess of that required, the values of $\phi_{o,w}$ and, hence, V_{wall} may also become excessively large. Obviously a wall need not be designed for shear forces larger than those corresponding to the elastic response of the building. As the shear given by Eq. 8.57 is considered to be an upper-bound estimate, the strength reduction factor associated with this capacity design procedure is $\phi = 1.0$, rather than 0.85.

Control of shear failure mechanisms

Inelastic regions. The approach to the design for shear resistance may be based on established practice (ACI 318, 1989), whereby it is assumed that some of the shear in a wall is resisted by only concrete mechanisms and the remainder is assigned to shear reinforcement. In recognition of the inevitable deterioration of the concrete in the potential plastic hinge regions, the contribution of the con-

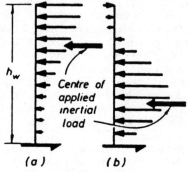

(a)   (b)

Fig. 8.40 Modal lateral story forces.

crete, in terms of shear stress, may be conservatively estimated (SANZ 3101, 1982) as

$$v_c = 0.6 \sqrt{\frac{P_e}{A_g}} \quad \text{(MPa)} \tag{8.59}$$

where P_e is the design axial compression force on the wall derived from appropriately factored loads or capacity design considerations, and A_g is the gross concrete sectional wall area, including flanges or boundary elements.

To simplify computations, the average shear stress, serving as an index, is estimated (ACI 318, 1989) as

$$v_i = \frac{V_{\text{wall}}}{0.8 b_w \ell_w} \quad \text{(MPa)} \tag{8.60}$$

The web reinforcement, consisting of reasonably closely spaced and adequately anchored horizontal bars, is then readily determined from

$$A_v = \frac{(v_i - v_c) b_w s}{f_y} \tag{8.61}$$

and thereby diagonal tension failure can be precluded. It should be recognized, however, that after reversed cycles of large displacements, wide flexural cracks interconnect with shear cracks. This in turn may develop at angles larger than 45° to the axis of a member. Thus eventually some yielding of the web reinforcement may also occur.

To prevent the web from prematurely crashing because of large diagonal compression forces, it is recommended that in the plastic hinge regions the total shear stress be limited to

$$v_{i,\text{max}} \le 0.9 \sqrt{f_c'} \quad \text{(MPa)} \tag{8.62}$$

Tests have shown, however, that when imposed displacement ductilities are in excess of approximately 4, such high shear stresses may lead to web crushing (Oesterle et al., 1980; Vallenas et al., 1979; Bertero et al., 1977). When boundary elements with a well-confined group of vertical bars were provided, significant shear could be carried after the failure of the web panel, because the boundary elements acted as short columns. It is considered, however, that it is more efficient to rely on the shear strength of the web, by preventing diagonal compression failure, rather than on the second line of defense offered by the boundary elements. To ensure this, either the ductility demand on a wall with large shear stresses must be reduced, or if this is not done, the shear stress, used as a measure of diagonal compression, should be limited to

$$v_{i,\text{max}} \le (0.37\phi_{o,w}K + 0.16)\sqrt{f_c'} < 0.9\sqrt{f_c'} \quad \text{(MPa)} \tag{8.63a}$$

or

$$v_{i,\text{max}} \le \left(\frac{1.65\phi_{o,w}}{R} + 0.16\right)\sqrt{f_c'} < 0.9\sqrt{f_c'} \quad \text{(MPa)} \tag{8.63b}$$

These equations recognize that the use of larger K or smaller R factors and excess flexural strength provided in the wall as built (when $\phi_{o,w} > 1.4$) will reduce ductility demands and hence allow larger maximum shear stresses to be used in the design. Equations 8.63 often control the wall thickness at the base.

Elastic regions. The strategy adopted in Subsection 2 of this section under curtailment of flexural reinforcement, whereby flexural yielding outside the potential plastic hinge region is inhibited (Fig. 8.39), will enable the design for shear in these regions to be based on the same principles as those routinely used for gravity-loaded structures. As a consequence wall thicknesses and shear reinforcement contents can be reduced significantly in upper stories of ductile walls.

Sliding shear. Excessive sliding displacements along construction joints or near horizontal flexural cracks, which, after inelastic load reversals, may form a plane of potential weakness in the plastic region, may diminish energy dissipation in structural walls. In walls with aspect ratios h_w/ℓ_w larger than 3, sliding displacements can be readily controlled by an adequate quantity A_{vf} of distributed vertical reinforcement, which will provide the necessary clamping force for the shear friction mechanism,

$$A_{vf} = \frac{V_{\text{wall}} - \mu P_e}{\mu f_y} \tag{8.64}$$

where V_{wall} is the maximum shear force given by Eq. 8.57 (in newtons), μ is the coefficient of friction, the value of which may be between 1.0 and 1.4, depending on the surface roughness provided (ACI 318, 1989), P_e is the maximum axial compression that can be relied on during an earthquake (in newtons), and f_y is the yield strength of the steel (in MPa). Commonly the designer simply checks that the total vertical reinforcement provided in the shear area (web) satisfies Eq. 8.64.

Sliding shear is more critical in squat walls, which are not examined here. Depending on the shear stress intensity and the likely demand for ductility, expressed by the K or R factors, it may be necessary to provide diagonal reinforcement to resist a significant fraction of the shear force across a potential sliding plane (Paulay et al., 1982).

5 Capacity design principles as applied to coupled walls

Having examined several features of the behavior, analysis, and detailing of structural walls for seismic regions, in the following subsections the main conclusions are summarized. For this purpose the specific example of a coupled wall structure, as shown in Fig. 8.41b and c, is used. The highlights of modeling and response to lateral static load, both in the elastic and inelastic domains, were reviewed in Monograph Volume CB, Sections 5.4.2 and 6.4.3 (Council on Tall Buildings, 1978). Because of their large stiffness, coupled structural walls provided protection against all forms of damage in moderate earthquakes while, when carefully detailed, they also possess excellent energy-dissipating properties, to be utilized in large earthquakes (Park and Paulay, 1975).

Preliminary studies. Before any analysis is undertaken, the geometry of the structure must be reviewed to ensure that in critical regions compact sections, suitable for energy dissipation, will be used (see Subsection 2 of this section under wall stability). From the relative stiffness of coupling beams, their contribution to overturning moments must be established to determine the appropriate value of the structural response factor, such as K and R (Eqs. 8.42 and 8.63).

From Fig. 8.41, which compares the modes of flexural resistance in cantilever and coupled walls, it is seen that the total overturning moment at the base M_o is resisted in the latter by wall moments M_1 and M_2 and axial force T, so that

$$M_o = M_1 + M_2 + \ell T \tag{8.65}$$

The contribution of the coupling beams to flexural resistance may be expressed by the parameter

$$A = \frac{\ell T}{M_o} \tag{8.66}$$

where the lateral load-induced axial force T is the accumulation of shear forces across all the coupling beams. When $A > \frac{2}{3}$, the behavior of coupled walls is similar to that of a ductile frame examined in Section 8.2. On the other hand, when $A < \frac{1}{3}$, the contribution of the coupling system to the overturning moment, or in the plastic state to energy dissipation, is not significant. In this case reliance should be placed on the two walls, primarily acting as cantilevers (Subsection 3 of this section). A typical structure of this type is shown in Fig. 8.41c. Slab coupling is inefficient in terms of shear transfer, and it deteriorates rapidly under inelastic reversed cyclic loading (Paulay and Taylor, 1981).

To allow for the significant difference in dependable energy dissipation, resulting from the contribution of a very ductile coupling system (Fig. 8.42d), it is suggested that the appropriate response factor, such as K (UBC, 1982), should be taken as

$$0.67 \leq K = 1.33 - A \leq 1.0 \tag{8.67a}$$

where
$$\frac{2}{3} \geq A \geq \frac{1}{3} \tag{8.67b}$$

Having established the value of the overturning moment M_o at the base of the coupled wall (Eq. 8.65), the foundation structure must be examined to ensure that

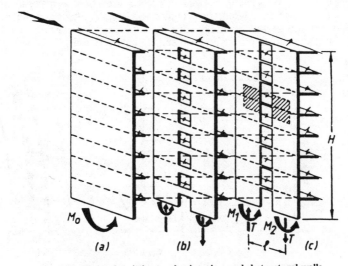

Fig. 8.41 Flexural resisting mechanisms in coupled structural walls.

it will be capable of absorbing moments developed with the overstrength of the superstrength, $M^o = \phi_{o,w} M_o$. Otherwise the intended energy dissipation in the ductile superstructure may not be mobilized.

The aim in the design of coupled structural walls is to enable, when necessary, plastic hinges to develop in the coupling system and at the base of the two walls, as implied in Fig. 8.42c.

The elastic analysis for such a symmetrical structure, based on the modeling by laminar coupling (Beck, 1962; Rosman, 1964; Coull and Choudhury, 1967), may have resulted in bending moments M_1 and M_2 for the tension and compression walls, respectively, as shown by solid lines in Fig. 8.42a and b. In this analysis, the elastic redistribution of moments from the tension to the compression wall, due to the effects of cracking, as outlined in Subsection 3 of this section under modeling of member properties, has already been considered. In spite of M_1 being smaller than M_2, more tension reinforcement is likely to be required in wall 1 because it may be subjected to large lateral load-induced axial tension. The moment of resistance of wall 2, on the other hand, will normally be enhanced by the increased axial compression. It is therefore suggested that, if desirable and practical, the moments in the tension wall be reduced by up to 30%, and that these moments be redistributed to the compression wall. This range of maximum redistributable moments is shown in Fig. 8.42a and b. Ductile walls would be quite capable of much larger inelastic moment redistribution. The limit of 30% is considered to be a prudent measure to protect walls against excessive cracking during moderate earthquakes. Moment redistribution from one wall to another, as outlined in Subsection 3 of this section under determination of design actions, also implies redistribution of wall shear forces of approximately the same proportions.

Similar considerations lead to the intentional redistribution of vertical shear forces in the coupling system. It has been shown (Volume CB, Section 6.4.3) that considerable ductility demands may be imposed on the coupling beams. Hence they will need to be designed and detailed, as shown in the following section for very large plastic deformations. A typical elastic distribution of shear forces q in coupling beams is shown in Fig. 8.42c. For practical reasons, as many identically reinforced coupling beams would be provided as possible. Shear and, hence, moment redistribution vertically among coupling beams can be utilized, and the application of this is shown by the stepped shaded line in Fig. 8.42c. It is suggested

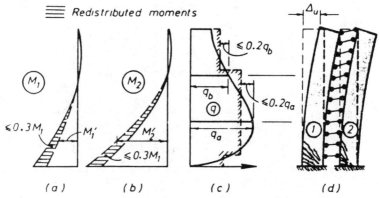

Fig. 8.42   Load redistribution between components of coupled walls.

that the reduction of design shear in any coupling beam should not exceed 20% of the shear predicted for this beam by elastic analysis. It is seen that with this technique a large number of beams can be made identical over the height of the building.

When shear is redistributed in the coupling system, it is important to ensure that no shear is "lost," that is, the total axial load introduced to the walls, supplying the T component of the moment resistance, as seen in Fig. 8.41c, should not be reduced. Therefore the area under the stepped and shaded lines of Fig. 8.42c must not be allowed to be less than the area under the curve giving the theoretical elastic beam shear q.

Design of components

Coupling beams. Allowing for some moment redistribution between coupling beams, as shown in the previous section and in Fig. 8.42c, design shear forces for groups of beams are established. When coupling beams, also referred to as wall segments, are short and relatively deep, conventional design procedures and detailing (ACI 318, 1989) will almost certainly lead to a diagonal tension failure, as shown in Fig. 8.43a. When excess stirrup reinforcement is provided, so that diagonal tension failure cannot occur, sliding shear, as shown in Fig. 8.43b, will inhibit the development of satisfactory hysteretic response (Volume CB, Section 6.4.3). Therefore, whenever the ideal (nominal) shear stress exceeds

$$v_i = 0.1\frac{\ell_n}{h}\sqrt{f_c'} \quad \text{(MPa)} \tag{8.68}$$

diagonal reinforcement to resist both shear and moments should be used, as shown in Figs. 8.43c and 8.44. In Eq. 8.68 ℓ_n and h are the clear span and overall depth of the beam, respectively. In determining the diagonal forces T_b and C_b in Fig. 8.44, only first principles are used (Park and Paulay, 1975).

Specific requirements for the detailing of the reinforcement for coupling beams, as shown in Fig. 8.44, include provisions of the following:

1. Transverse ties, around the cage of diagonal bars, in accordance with Eq. 8.14, spaced no further than 100 mm (4 in.)

2. Increase of development length specified for individual bars by 50%, extending into the adjacent walls

3. "Basketing" nominal mesh reinforcement in the remainder of the beam

Coupled walls. As the moments at the base have been established from the code-specified factored lateral loading, they may now be considered together

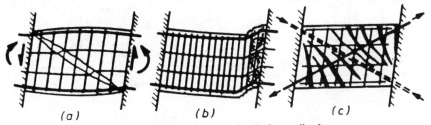

Fig. 8.43 Mechanisms of shear resistance in coupling beams.

with the appropriate combination of axial load due to factored gravity and lateral loads. It will often be found that considerably more flexural reinforcement is required in the tension than in the compression wall. For this or other reasons, moment redistribution from the tension to the compression wall, as outlined in the previous section, should be undertaken. As Fig. 8.42a and b shows, the design moments M_1 and M_2 are adjusted to give moments M_1' and M_2'. In determining the amount of flexural reinforcement for both directions of lateral loading, a strength reduction factor $\phi = 0.9$ may be used.

Considerations of the necessary shear strength of walls. In accordance with the principles of capacity design, the design shear forces across the walls should be those developed with the flexural overstrength of the coupled wall structure rather than those derived from the specified and factored lateral loading. Therefore the following sources of flexural overstrength need to be studied.

1. *Overstrength of coupling beams.* As the design of the beams has been finalized, their overstrength in terms of shear force Q^o, based on $\rho_o f_y$, can be readily evaluated. The role of the strength enhancement was described in Section 8.1 (Eq. 8.1). The value of ρ_o should be confirmed by the designer for the type of steel used in the structure.

2. *Earthquake-induced axial force.* The maximum feasible axial load on a wall would occur when all coupling beams above the level considered would develop their overstrength Q_i^o. For multistory coupled walls it is recommended that the earthquake-induced axial force at overstrength be estimated as

$$P_{eq,i}^o = \left(1 - \frac{n}{80}\right)\sum_i^n Q_i^o \tag{8.69}$$

where n is the number of floors above level i, the value of which should not be taken larger than 20. The approach is similar to that outlined in step 8 of Subsection 2 in Section 8.2 for columns of ductile frames.

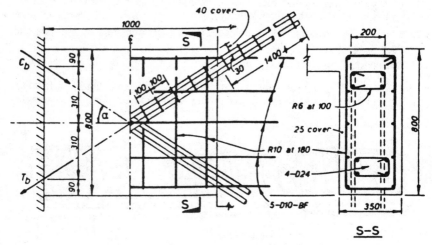

Fig. 8.44 Details of typical coupling beams.

3. *Flexural overstrength of walls.* As every detail of the wall base sections is known at this stage of the design, the flexural overstrengths, based on $\rho_o f_y$, may be readily estimated. For this purpose a rational estimate for the concurrent axial load on each wall need also be made. For this extreme event, effects of live load may be neglected, so that the extreme axial loads become, for the tension wall,

$$P_1^o = P_{eq}^o - P_D$$

and for the compression wall,

$$P_2^o = P_{eq}^o + P_D$$

where P_D is the axial load at the base due to dead load only. With these axial forces the flexural overstrengths for the walls become M_1^o and M_2^o, respectively, from which the overstrength factor for the system is simply

$$\phi_{o,w} = \frac{M_1^o + M_2^o + P_{eq}^o \ell}{M_{o,\text{code}}} \tag{8.70}$$

where $M_{o,\text{code}}$ is the total overturning moment at the base due to code-specified lateral load.

To sustain the energy-dissipating mechanisms of coupled wall structure, the foundation system must be capable of absorbing an overturning moment $\phi_{o,w} M_{o,\text{code}}$.

4. *Estimation of wall shear forces.* Using the concepts of load redistribution among interacting inelastic walls, outlined in the preliminary studies in Subsection 5 of this section, the maximum shear force for each wall can be estimated, as for cantilever walls (Subsection 4 of this section and Eq. 8.57), from

$$V_{i,\text{wall}} = \omega_v \phi_{o,w} \left(\frac{M_i^o}{M_1^o + M_2^o} \right) V_{\text{code}}, \qquad i = 1, 2 \tag{8.71}$$

where ω_v is the dynamic shear magnification factor given by Eq. 8.58.

Detailing of coupled walls. As outlined for cantilever walls in Subsections 2 and 4 of this section, the requirements for detailing are significantly different in the elastic and potential plastic regions of the walls. These were defined with the use of the linear moment envelopes shown in Fig. 8.39. In every respect the detailing of one of the coupled walls rests on the principles applicable to cantilever walls.

8.4 CONCLUSIONS

Design procedures were outlined for reinforced concrete buildings in which earthquake resistance is provided entirely by ductile frames or structural walls. Emphasis was placed on those design features which were developed in New Zealand and in parts adopted elsewhere. The design strategy described evolved from the following precepts:

1. Current predictions of the characteristics of large earthquakes are crude. Therefore an aim to achieve a high degree of precision in analytical techniques, to predict both earthquake-induced actions and deformations within the structure, is not justified.

2. Provided that a reasonable level of resistance to lateral forces, such as prescribed for seismic zones by relevant national building codes, is chosen, the errors arising from an inability to provide good predictions for the effects of future earthquakes will manifest themselves only in erroneous predictions of structural displacements, such as ductility demands.

3. Types and localities of energy-dissipating mechanisms chosen as part of the "capacity design procedure," in which a unique hierarchy of strengths has been established, are not affected by erroneous structural displacements. Ductility demands during an earthquake may, however, differ significantly from values anticipated by building codes.

4. With few exceptions, rationally detailed inelastic regions can be made very ductile with relative ease and at little additional cost. Hence reinforced concrete buildings, designed in accordance with described deterministic principles, are made very tolerant to earthquakes in terms of inelastic displacements. This tolerance compensates for an ability to estimate the desired level of earthquake resistance only crudely.

5. Another class of structural systems, very common in tall buildings, in which earthquake resistance is provided by ductile frames interacting with ductile structural walls, was not examined in these pages. Such structures, when suitably designed, may combine all the desirable properties of both frames and walls. A detailed capacity design procedure has also been formulated for this system (Paulay and Goodsir, 1986). As expected, this combines the features presented for frames in Subsection 2 of Section 8.2 and those for walls in Subsections 3 and 5 of Section 8.3. It should be noted, however, that in certain regions the deviation of design actions derived from routine analyses for such elastic systems, subjected to lateral static loading, from those encountered during the elastoplastic dynamic response to earthquakes is much greater than in either frames or walls alone.

Various steps in the description of the design procedure were intended to emphasize the designer's determination to "tell the structure what to do." This simple approach should ensure excellent inelastic response provided that, as a complementary task, all critical regions are judiciously detailed. The numerous detailed recommendations presented manifested attempts to quantify unambiguously the goodness of detailing. Thereby reinforced concrete buildings can be made extremely tolerant to a wide range of ductility demands. Hence they can be expected to perform "as they were told to."

8.5 CONDENSED REFERENCES / BIBLIOGRAPHY

ACI 318 1989, *Building Code Requirements for Reinforced Concrete*
ACI-ASCE Committee 352 1984, *Revised Recommendations for the Design of Beam-*
ATC 3-06 1978, *Tentative Provisions for the Development of Seismic Regulation for Build-*

Beck 1952, *Contribution to the Analysis of Coupled Shear Walls*
Bertero 1977, *Seismic Design Implications of Hysteretic Behaviour of Reinforced Concrete*

Bertero 1980, *Seismic Behaviour of Reinforced Concrete Wall Structural Systems*
Blakeley 1975, *Seismic Shear Loading at Flexural Capacity in Cantilever Wall Structures*

CEB 1983, *Model Code for Seismic Design of Concrete Structures*
Coull 1967, *Analysis of Coupled Shear Walls*
Council on Tall Buildings 1978, *Structural Design of Tall Concrete and Masonry Buildings*
CSA 1984, *Design of Concrete Structures for Buildings* (CAN-A23.3)

Fintel 1975, *Structural Walls in Earthquake Resistant Structures*
Freeman 1980, *Significance of Stiffness Assumptions on Lateral Force Criteria*

Gates 1978, *The Art of Modeling Buildings for Dynamic Seismic Analysis*

IAEE 1984, *Earthquake Resistant Regulations—A World List*
Iqbal 1980, *Inertial Forces Over Height of Reinforced Concrete Structural Walls during*

Ma 1976, *Experimental and Analytical Studies on the Hysteretic Behaviour of Reinforced*
Mander 1984, *Seismic Design of Bridge Piers*
Meinheit 1983, *Shear Strength of Reinforced Concrete Beam-Column Connections*

Oesterle 1980, *Reinforcement Details for Earthquake-Resistant Structural Walls*

Park 1972, *Ductility of Reinforced Concrete Column Sections in Seismic Design*
Park 1975, *Reinforced Concrete Structures*
Park 1977, *Columns Subjected to Flexure and Axial Load*
Park 1977, *Curvature Ductility of Circular Reinforced Concrete Columns Confined by the*
Paulay 1975, *A Critical Review of the Seismic Design Provisions for Ductile Shear Walls of*
Paulay 1976, *Ductile Behaviour of Coupled Shear Walls*
Paulay 1978, *Reinforced Concrete Beam-Column Joints under Seismic Actions*
Paulay 1980, *Deterministic Design Procedure for Ductile Frames in Seismic Areas*
Paulay 1981a, *Lapped Splices in Earthquake-Resisting Columns*
Paulay 1981b, *Slab Coupling of Earthquake Resisting Shear Walls*
Paulay 1982, *Ductility in Earthquake Resisting Squat Shearwalls*
Paulay 1984, *Joints in Reinforced Concrete Frames Designed for Earthquake Resistance*
Paulay 1985, *The Ductility of Structural Walls*
Paulay 1986, *The Capacity Design of Reinforced Concrete Hybrid Structures for Multi-*
Priestley 1984, *Strength and Ductility of Bridge Substructures*

Rosman 1964, *Approximate Analysis of Shear Walls Subjected to Lateral Loads*

SANZ 3101 1982, *Code of Practice for the Design of Concrete Structures*
SEAOC 1975, *Recommended Lateral Force Requirements and Commentary*
Sheikh 1979, *Properties of Concrete Confined by Rectangular Ties*

UBC 1982, *Uniform Building Code*

Vallenas 1979, *Hysteretic Behaviour of Reinforced Concrete Structural Walls*

Wakabayashi 1986, *Design of Earthquake Resistant Buildings*

Yoshimura 1985, *Inelastic Behaviour of the Building, Earthquake Effects on Reinforced*

9

Connections

Connections in a reinforced concrete structure are potentially the most critical part of the system. The main role of connections is to maintain the integrity of the structure under the applied loads. Because usually several elements meet at a connection, the combination of these forces results in a complex behavior of the connection. Lower-strength concrete and steel in structures subjected to relatively simple loading produce connection forces which are relatively small. These forces can usually be accommodated by satisfying the anchorage requirements for the steel. When higher-strength materials are used or the loading is complex, connections become a point of special concern. The current trend in high-rise reinforced concrete structures is toward using smaller sections, building taller structures, and utilizing reinforced concrete as a ductile material in seismic regions. As a result, connections become increasingly important.

Having realized the importance of connections in new reinforced concrete structures, researchers and engineers have studied the behavior of connections extensively during the past 20 years. While many more studies are in progress, based on what has been learned thus far, guidelines and codes have been prepared to assist the practicing engineer in a more rational design of connections.

Many types of connections are encountered in structures. The bulk of knowledge about the behavior of some of these types is more extensive than about others. Cast-in-place monolithic beam-column and slab-column connections are two types for which much has been learned. Nevertheless, experimental and analytical research is continuing even on these types.

The purpose of this chapter is to review the behavior of monolithic beam-column and slab-column connections under monotonic and cyclic loadings, and to discuss the important parameters. Only rigid (moment-resisting) joints are considered. A summary of important design considerations with reference to more detailed guidelines is also included. Finally, the areas in which there is still a considerable amount of uncertainty are listed for the benefit of researchers. To be compatible with the current state of the art, joints are grouped into two general categories: type 1 joints in structures where no special ductility is required under overloads, and type 2 joints expected to undergo deformation reversals well beyond the yield deformation. For example, when gravity loads control the design of the adjoining structural members, the joint is considered to be of type 1. A joint in areas with severe seismic activities is considered to be of type 2. A de-

tailed description of the two joint types was presented by ACI-ASCE Committee
352 (1985).

9.1   TYPES OF FAILURE

Figure 9.1 shows typical beam-column and slab-column joints. Field and laboratory observations have indicated that the behavior of beam-column joints is generally different from that of slab-column joints. In the following subsections, a
summary of the observed failures in each joint group is presented.

1   Beam-column joints

Past destructive earthquakes have demonstrated that there are two major factors
which influence the seismic behavior of beam-column joints: anchorage of reinforcement and confinement of concrete. [Forell and Nicoletti, 1980; National Research Council Committee on Natural Disasters (NRCCND), 1983]. These factors have shown to be critical even for nonseismic loading of connections,
although to a lesser degree, for reasons to be described (Park and Paulay, 1975;
Holmes and Martin, 1983).

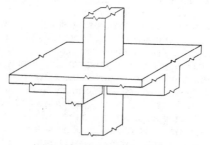

(a) Beam–Column Connection

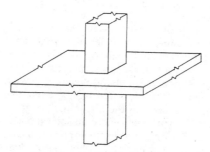

(b) Slab–Column Connection

Fig. 9.1   Beam-column and slab-column specimens.

Anchorage of reinforcement. The type of problems created by the lack of sufficient anchorage depends on the primary source of the loads and on whether the
joint is of an exterior or an interior type.

Figure 9.2 shows exterior and interior joints which are subjected to gravity
loads. In corner and exterior joints, the tension due to negative moment has to be
resisted by a hooked bar, as illustrated. The critical section is taken at the column
face, and the bar forces are calculated. Even with sufficient anchorage, the top
bars will have some elongation, which produces a concentrated rotation at the
face of the column. As a result, the joint stiffness is reduced. Failure tests of corner joints (Fig. 9.2a) have confirmed that unless a relatively low percentage of
steel (1 to 1.5%) is used in the beam, the beam moment capacity cannot be developed at connections with common reinforcement details (Kemp and Mukherjee,
1968; Mayfield et al., 1971), the primary reason being the diagonal forces, which
are created by the moments. Improved detailing techniques were recommended
by Swann (1969). The extensions in hooked bars at exterior joints (Fig. 9.2b)
need to be positioned near the outer edge of the column to provide for the largest
possible anchorage length. However, if the concrete cover on the tail is not sufficiently thick, failure of concrete will result near the extension.

Interior joints (Fig. 9.2c) are generally immune to anchorage failure when the
primary load is due to gravity. This is true in connections with relatively small
beam-moment imbalance at the joint region.

The anchorage problem becomes particularly important when seismic loads
are dominant and when the joint is likely to undergo several cycles of postelastic
deformations. Figure 9.3 gives elevation views for an interior and an exterior connection. Test results have shown that the critical section for the calculation of
anchorage requirements needs to be taken at the outer surface of column bars

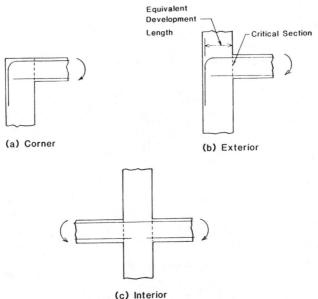

(a) Corner   (b) Exterior

(c) Interior

Fig. 9.2   Joints subjected to gravity loads.

and not at the column face. This is due to the spalling of concrete covers on column bars, caused by cycling of the loads. With the critical section for anchorage taken at the column core, the available effective development length for the hook becomes smaller, thus making the anchorage requirements more difficult to satisfy. A proper solution, which also reduces steel congestion, is the addition of a short beam stub at the exterior edge of the column, as shown in Fig. 9.4. (Park and Paulay, 1975).

Unlike the cases in which gravity loads are dominant, the anchorage of beam bars passing through the column in interior joints can be critical when seismic forces are dominant. These bars are pulled from one side while pushed from the other. The only force resisting these forces is the bond force provided by concrete in the column core. Tests have shown that the concrete "shell" in the column becomes rapidly ineffective as cyclic loads are applied (Ehsani and Wight, 1982; Durrani and Wight, 1982). Tests have also indicated that when the bond

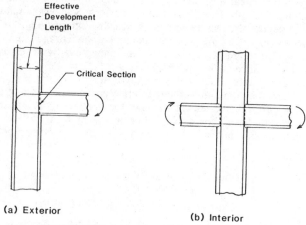

(a) Exterior

(b) Interior

Fig. 9.3   Joints in structure subjected to lateral loads.

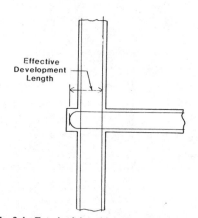

Fig. 9.4   Exterior joint with improved anchorage.

strength provided by the column core is insufficient, significant pinching occurs in hysteresis loops due to the slippage of the reinforcement. As a result, the energy absorption capacity of the joint is severely reduced. The joint behavior improves when a relatively thick column (in the direction of beam bars) or smaller beam bars are used. Insufficient anchorage for column bars has also resulted in the loss of energy absorption capacity of the joint. More detailed reviews of the effect of anchorage on the seismic behavior of reinforced concrete joints can be found in ATC (1983) and Paulay and Park (1984).

Confinement of concrete.   Confinement of concrete in the joint core is provided by adjoining beams or transverse ties in the core, or both. For columns in which bars are distributed around the perimeter, the cage effect, provided by the combination of column longitudinal bars and core ties, produces additional confinement.

The primary advantages of confinement are the increases in the shear and axial load strength of the joint core. In addition the bond strength between concrete and steel increases. The magnitude of shear in interior joints subjected to gravity loads (Fig. 9.2c) is relatively small and is usually not critical. In exterior connections (Fig. 9.2a and b), however, shear can be relatively large. Tests have shown that diagonal cracks may develop in the core if sufficient shear reinforcement is not provided and if the core concrete is not confined (Park and Paulay, 1975). The problem is intensified when a large moment imbalance is present in the orthogonal direction.

Figure 9.5 shows an interior connection in a structure subjected to horizontal loads. The floor slab is not shown for the purpose of clarity. When the load is caused by ground motion, the direction of the forces oscillates. The combined loads produce stresses in the joint core which are relatively complex. Tests data have indicated that the confinement of concrete provides for a better shear behavior at the joint (Uzumeri, 1977). Unconfined cores have also been found to be weak in resisting the column axial forces. The spacing and size of the confining steel have been found to be major factors. Tests have shown that, to maintain the integrity of the connection after large forces have been developed, it is necessary

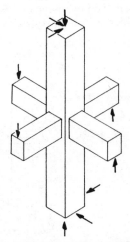

Fig. 9.5   Space frame joint in structure subjected to lateral loads.

to use tie bars which show strain hardening as soon as yielding occurs (Sekin and Uzumeri, 1980). This provision allows for an increase in the confinement stresses even after the ties yield.

2 Slab-column joints

Figure 9.6 shows the stresses at an interior and an exterior slab-column connection when the uniaxial bending of the column is considered. The stresses shown are caused by the direct shear force V and the moment M. The nonuniform stresses in the figure may be viewed as the twisting effect of the moment. In addition to the shear stresses, normal stresses due to moment act on the slab. These stresses are not shown for clarity. Failure testings of slab-column connections have indicated that the unbalanced moment is transferred through a combination of shear and flexure. The mechanism of moment transfer is basically the same regardless of whether the forces are due to gravity or to lateral loading. Tests have indicated that when the unbalanced moment is relatively small (less than 20% of the product of the ultimate shear and the effective depth of the slab), the shear stresses due to moment may be neglected (ACI-ASCE Committee 426, 1977). Generally, however, the shear stresses due to moment are significant, and when combined with the direct shear stresses, they result in critical values which can cause punching failure.

The poor shear performance of slab-column connections has been their weakest point. In seismic zones, this characteristic results in insufficient energy-dissipating capacity, thus making flat-plate structures inappropriate for resisting earthquake loads. Shake-table tests of slab-column subassemblages and flat-plate structures have indicated rapid deterioration of the strength and stiffness of slab-column connections (Morrison and Sozen, 1981; Moehle et al., 1984).

Another weakness of slab-column structures is their vulnerability to progressive collapse initiated by failure at one or more joints during construction (Lew et al., 1982; Galeotti et al., 1983). Test data to study the parameters affecting the behavior of slab-column connections are relatively scarce. Nonetheless, it has been demonstrated that the addition of continuous bottom reinforcement in slab-column connections can inhibit the problem (Hawkins and Mitchell, 1979; Mitchell and Cook, 1984).

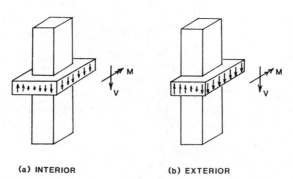

(a) INTERIOR   (b) EXTERIOR

Fig. 9.6   Joint failure mechanisms due to shear.   (*From Birss, Paulay and Park, 1978*)

9.2 RECOMMENDATIONS FOR DESIGN OF BEAM-COLUMN JOINTS

The ACI code (ACI 318, 1989) and the guidelines on beam-column design prepared by the ACI-ASCE Committee 352 (1985) are perhaps the most comprehensive documents for the design of connections in the United States. The basic philosophy used in these documents is to satisfy strength and ductility requirements at connections. Other codes used in countries actively involved in research on reinforced concrete joints (such as Japan and New Zealand) use the same basic philosophy (SANZ 3101, 1982). A detailed comparison of different codes is made in ATC 11 (1983).

The current design codes and guidelines in effect categorize reinforced concrete joints into two types, as described at the beginning of this chapter, and present specific recommendations for each type. The design provisions address the anchorage, shear, and confinement problems. In addition, provisions are made for the relative strength of beam and columns at a joint.

1 Design for anchorage

The basic intent of anchorage requirements is to ensure that the steel bar will transmit the maximum expected stress to concrete without losing bond. In joints where the capability to develop large inelastic deformations is not required (type 1 joints), the maximum stress is expected to be the yield stress f_y. On the other hand, if large inelastic deformations are caused by the loads (type 2 joints), the strain hardening may result in stresses exceeding the yield stress.

Large inelastic deformations are expected in type 2 joints. As a result, the ACI Committee 352 design document (1985) calls for a steel stress of $1.25f_y$ or higher to compute the anchorage requirements. The f_y value used is the specified yield stress for steel. It should be noted that the actual yield stress is generally higher than the specified value, thus increasing the anchorage length requirement. However, the increase may be offset by the additional bond strength that concrete may provide over and above the bond strength calculated using the specified strength of concrete.

The anchorage of beam longitudinal bars at exterior connections has been a difficult task. Typically, hooked bars are used. Smaller bars and wider columns have had to be used to satisfy the development length requirements. The ACI code (ACI 318, 1989) has simplified the design and has reduced the anchorage length demand in hooked bars. The critical section for anchorage should be taken as shown in Fig. 9.2 for type 1 joints and in Fig. 9.3 for type 2 joints.

The design recommendations for the anchorage of longitudinal bars in interior type 2 joints call for a minimum element-depth-to-bar-diameter ratio to avoid slippage of reinforcement (ACI-ASCE Committee 352, 1985). For example, to properly anchor the beam bars passing through the joint, the ratio of column dimension over beam bar diameter has to be at least 20.

2 Design for shear

Large shear values are known to be the principal cause of joint failures. Three methods of design, based on three failure mechanisms for shear, have been used.

Zhang and Jirsa (1982) describe and compare the three methods. The failure mechanisms are shown in Fig. 9.7. Depending on the particular mechanism used in design, different tie bar designs are obtained. A comparison of different designs has shown that the compression strut mechanism (Fig. 9.7c) results in the least amount of tie bars, while the panel truss mechanism (Fig. 9.7b) leads to the largest. The latter mechanism is used in the New Zealand code. ACI Committee 352 recommends the beam shear mechanism to compute the shear and sets maximum limits on the joint shear stress, ranging from $12\sqrt{f'_c}$ (in type 2 corner joints) to $24\sqrt{f'_c}$ (in type 1 interior joints), in which f'_c is the 28-day compressive strength of concrete in psi. Limits are set on the spacing of the tie bars to provide sufficient confinement.

3 Control of plastic hinge location

Researchers and practitioners agree that to avoid the potential for the total collapse of the structure under overloads, it is necessary to limit the plastic hinges to beams in the connection region. This approach, of course, requires an overdesign of columns, which may lead to unusually large column dimensions. Because the problem is less severe when vertical loads control the design, the requirement may be waived for type 1 joints. However, when lateral loads dominate, plastic hinges in columns can create large drifts, which amplify the overturning moments caused by the gravity loads. Therefore it is critical to limit plastic hinging to beams in type 2 connections. New Zealand researchers have gone one step further by forcing the plastic hinge away from the connection region to keep the joint elastic even under overloads (ACI-ASCE Committee 426, 1977). The joint is kept elastic by providing a relatively large amount of steel in and near the joint.

The codes and guidelines used in the United States have sufficed by specifying limits on the flexural strength ratio of columns to beams connected at a joint. Appendix A in the ACI code (1989) calls for a factor of 1.2, while ACI Committee 352 (1985) specifies a minimum ratio of 1.4. It should be noted that these ratios are usually calculated for "bare" beams (the floor slab excluded). Actual reinforced concrete structures include slabs, the reinforcement of which increases the beam negative moment capacity and, hence, reduces the effective column–beam strength ratio.

9.3 RECOMMENDATIONS FOR DESIGN OF SLAB-COLUMN JOINTS

The primary slab-column design document used in the United States is the ACI code 318 (1989). ACI-ASCE Committee 426 (1977), which includes recommendations on shear design, is also a relevant document used by designers. A more detailed design document was prepared by ACI-ASCE Committee 352 (1988).

The main concern in the design of slab-column joints is the resistance against shear stresses, which are generally produced by a combination of direct shear, moment, and torque. The general approach in design provisions has been to limit concrete shear stress below certain values. To accomplish this objective, a sufficient slab thickness is used. In many cases, column capitals and drop panels are incorporated into the joints to satisfy the design requirements for shear. Where

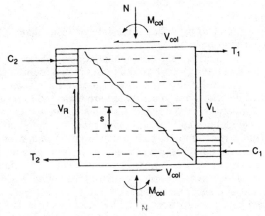

(a) Beam Shear Mechanism of Joint Shear Resistance

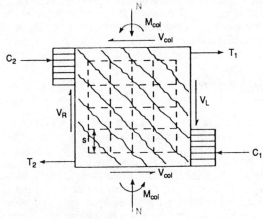

(b) True Mechanism of Joint Shear Resistance

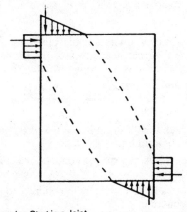

(c) Compression Strut in a Joint

Fig. 9.7 Idealized shear stress distribution in slab-column joints.

these solutions are found to be either infeasible or inadequate, shear heads or shear reinforcement may be used.

In the ACI-ASCE Committee 352 recommendations (1988), slab-column joints are categorized into two types: type 1 are joints subjected to primarily nonseismic loads in which the implicit ductility demands of the ACI code can be met with no special detailing, while type 2 are joints which are expected to possess sustained strength under relatively large deformations caused by, for example, extreme seismic loads. The guidelines call for sufficient shear strength and axial strength of the joint core (the part common to slab and column). The concern for the latter arises in cases where the compressive strength of the concrete in the slab is less than that of the concrete in the columns. For type 2 joints, special requirements on the longitudinal and transverse reinforcement in the columns are stated to provide for confinement and shear strength.

The longitudinal bars in slabs need to be sufficiently anchored and should be of such an amount as to provide for the continuity of slab elements. Both the ACI 318 and ACI-ASCE 352 Committees have requirements on the detailing of longitudinal bars. In addition, the Committee 352 recommendations include a requirement for minimum continuous bottom steel in the slab at the connection to avoid progressive failure of the slab.

9.4 DETAILING PRACTICES

The Council on Tall Building's Monograph Volume CB (1978) states that, "the single most important factor regarding good practice is that details be worked out by the structural engineer and not relegated to subprofessional personnel." This statement remains valid. Improper detailing has led to many problems in the construction of reinforced concrete connections (Saiidi, 1986). Construction delays have resulted in many cases in order to resolve steel congestion at joints. In some cases, quick alternative details have been devised without appropriate scrutiny to determine whether the new detail satisfies the design requirements.

While detailing is as much an art as it is engineering and, therefore, is subjective to some extent, there are some general rules that may be followed to alleviate detailing problems:

1. In sizing structural elements, minimum acceptable dimensions should not necessarily be used. The designer needs to size the elements in such a way that the steel is anchored and the concrete is placed with relative ease.

2. Use beam widths which are different from the column width so that the beam bars can pass through the column cage. In seismic regions, a beam width that is less than the column width is appropriate.

3. Use beam depths which are different in the two orthogonal directions to avoid interference of beam bottom bars.

4. If possible, use beam stubs at exterior connections (Fig. 9.4) to facilitate the anchorage of beam bars.

5. When appropriate, use superplasticizers in concrete to facilitate the placement and compaction of concrete.

An added consideration is the use of split ties and cross ties in the joint regions. Provisions for permissible hook detail and anchorage for these ties may be found in ACI 318 (1989) and ENR (1973).

9.5 RESEARCH NEEDS

Many of the research needs in the previous version of this document have been addressed by the numerous investigations conducted during the past decade. Many more topics remain to be investigated. These may be grouped into three categories. The first comparison is the relatively common, but irregular, connection types, which have not been considered by researchers. The opinion of many practicing engineers is that the focus of future research should be on a second category, namely, developing methods of reducing steel congestion at joints. The third category relates to a move toward a more realistic modeling of test specimens. Some researchers and practitioners believe that with the availability of advanced testing and data acquisition systems, the focus of future research needs to be on simulating real-life loading.

It may be impractical to try to obtain unanimity among the designers and researchers involved in different aspects of reinforced concrete joints on a priority list of research needs. The following list presents topics from the different categories described. The list was primarily based on the opinions of the ACI-ASCE 352 committee members (1985) and input from interested practicing engineers.

1. *Behavior of unsymmetric connections.* In many connections, especially at exterior frames, the beam axis does not intersect the column axis. The lack of symmetry can result in combinations of stresses which are drastically different from what is observed in symmetric connections. In the case of significant earthquake loads, the lack of symmetry has resulted in the torsional failure of columns.

2. *Effect of biaxial bending.* Corner columns are subjected to biaxial bending due to vertical and lateral loads. The effects of the combined stresses on joint behavior have not been studied in any appreciable detail.

3. *Connections with high-strength concrete.* The majority of the available experimental data are for normal-weight concrete. Experimental data and design guidelines are needed on joints built with high-strength concrete.

4. *Behavior of interior joints with beam on one side only.* In many multistory structures, beams are terminated at the joint while the slab extends to the next column line. No information is available on the behavior of this type of connections.

5. *Use of wire mesh in connection region.* The steel congestion problem may be alleviated by using wire mesh. The reliability of connections utilizing wire mesh needs to be investigated.

6. *Large-scale testing of total structure.* Most reported experimental research has been on isolated beam-column joints. The behavior may be different in joints of an actual structure where redistribution of forces among connections is expected.

7. *Slab-wall connections.* This class of connections is common in multistory residential buildings. Specifically, the seismic behavior of this type of connection needs to be investigated.

8. *Strong beam–weak column connections.* In many of the existing structures, the girders are stronger than the columns. In areas with severe seismic activities, such joints are undesirable and are no longer designed for new buildings. Nonetheless, the behavior of the existing joints needs to be studied, and retrofitting guidelines need to be developed.

9.6 CONDENSED REFERENCES / BIBLIOGRAPHY

ACI 318 1989, *Building Code Requirements for Reinforced Concrete*
ACI-ASCE Committee 426 1977, *Suggested Revisions to Shear Provisions for Building*
ACI-ASCE Committee 352 1985, *Recommendations for Design of Beam-Column Joints in*
ACI-ASCE Committee 352 1988, *Recommendations for Design of Slab-Column Connec-*
ATC 11 1983, *Seismic Resistance of Reinforced Concrete Shear Walls and Frame*

Birss 1978, *The Elastic Behavior of Earthquake Resistant Reinforced Concrete*

Council on Tall Buildings Group CB 1978, *Structural Design of Tall Concrete and Masonry*

Durrani 1982, *Experimental and Analytical Study of Internal Beam to Column*

Ehsani 1982, *Behavior of External Reinforced Concrete Beam to Column Connections*
ENR 1973, *Collapse Kills Five and Destroys Large Portion of 26-Story Apartment*

Forell 1980, *Mexico Earthquakes, Oaxaca—November 29, 1978, Guerrero—March 14*

Galeotti 1983, *Discussion in ACI Concrete International*

Hawkins 1979, *Progressive Collapse of Flat-Plate Structures*
Holmes 1983, *Analysis and Design of Structural Connections, Reinforced Concrete*

Kemp 1968, *Inelastic Behavior of Corner Knee Joints*

Lew 1982, *Cause of the Condominium Collapse in Cocoa Beach, Florida*

Mayfield 1971, *Corner Joint Details in Structural Lightweight Concrete*
Mitchell 1984, *Preventing Progressive Collapse of Slab Structures*
Moehle 1984, *Experimental Study of a Flat-Plate Building Model*
Morrison 1981, *Response of Reinforced Concrete Plate-Column Connections to*

NRCCND 1983, *El-Asnam, Algeria Earthquake of October 10, 1980*

SANZ 1982, NZS 3101 *Code of Practice for the Design of Concrete Structures*

Park 1975, *Reinforced Concrete Structures*
Paulay 1984, *Joints in Reinforced Concrete Frames Designed for Earthquake*

Saiidi 1986, *Constructability of Reinforced Concrete Joints*
Sekin 1980, *Exterior Beam-Column Joints in Reinforced Concrete Frames*
Swann 1969, *Flexural Strength of Corners of Reinforced Concrete Portal Frames*

Uzumeri 1977, *Strength and Ductility of Cast-in-Place Beam-Column Joints*

Zhang 1982, *A Study of Shear Behavior of Reinforced Concrete Beam-Column*

10

Foundations

10.1 SHALLOW FOUNDATIONS

In shallow foundations the load transfer is mostly by end bearing and occurs close to the ground surface. Such foundations can be divided into spread footings, which support isolated loads of a structure (Figs. 10.1 and 10.2), and mat or raft foundations, which receive the loads of all columns and walls of a building.

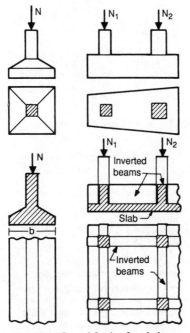

Fig. 10.1 Spread footing foundations.

Although it is a well-known fact that the stress distribution under a footing is not linear, it is generally assumed, for practical reasons, that it is so (Fig. 10.3).

1 Centrally loaded spread footings

Centrally loaded spread footings may be wall footings (Fig. 10.4) with, essentially, one-way action or column footings with two-way action (Fig. 10.5). In either case the footing may fail in shear, flexure, or bond.

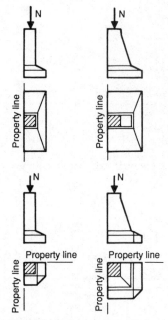

Fig. 10.2 Perimeter column footings.

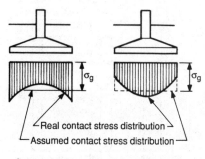

Cohesive soil   Cohesionless soil

Fig. 10.3 Real and assumed distributions of contact stress reaction in cohesive and cohesionless soils.

Shear is checked at a distance $d/2$ from the face of the wall or column. The maximum bending moment and bond stress occur at the face of the wall or column. Bond strength is an important factor in footing behavior, which can generally be controlled by using small-diameter bars. Very seldom is a spread footing centrally loaded, since a small eccentricity is nearly always present.

2 Eccentrically loaded spread footings

Design generally follows the procedure outlined for centrally loaded footings, taking into account that the soil stress distribution is not uniform but varies linearly across the footing, and no tension stresses can develop at the contact face. The stress distribution is calculated from

$$\sigma_s = \frac{N}{A_f} \pm \frac{M}{R} \qquad (10.1)$$

in which N is the normal load, M is the moment, and A_f and R are the area and the section modulus of the contact face, respectively.

For perimeter footings, structural features are introduced to prevent column and footing rotation. Usually a uniform stress distribution is assumed, but any

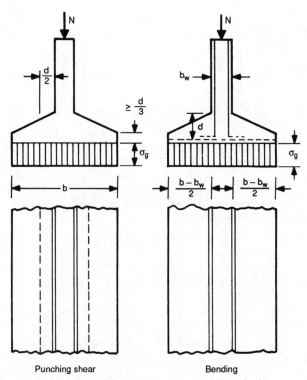

Punching shear   Bending

Fig. 10.4 Centrally loaded one-way continuous footing.

other may be adopted. One method to inhibit footing rotation is to provide a column of sufficient rigidity. This solution is only applicable to foundations on soils with a small modulus of deformation relative to the rigidity of the column. The column must be enlarged to absorb the moment Ne with only small deformations (Fig. 10.6). This moment is balanced by the moment resulting from the frictional force, which develops at the contact face,

$$N \cdot e = \frac{Fh\zeta}{\gamma_g} \tag{10.2}$$

For cohesive soils the adhesion may also be considered. It is advisable to assume that only half of the adhesion is effective, because the water absorption from the wet concrete frequently softens this soil layer at the contact face. Substituting for F, including the adhesion, and rearranging Eq. 10.2 results in

$$\frac{N\tan\phi + C_a b_a b_y}{\gamma_g} \geq \frac{Ne_{max}}{h\zeta} \tag{10.3}$$

in which $F = N \tan \phi$, and ϕ may be taken as the angle of internal friction. For articulated columns $\zeta = 1$, while for a fixed-end column $\zeta = \frac{2}{3}$. (For partial fixity the value is somewhere in between.) γ_g is a safety factor ($\gamma_g \geq 1.5$), and e_{max} is the maximum permissible eccentricity.

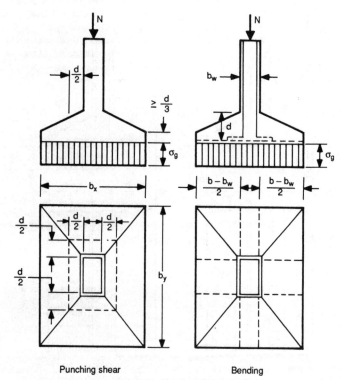

Punching shear   Bending

Fig. 10.5 Centrally loaded rectangular footing.

Thus once the footing size has been selected for the appropriate stress distribution, e is determined corresponding to this distribution, with $e \leq e_{max}$. The footing design follows and, subsequently, the redesign of the column, taking into account the moment induced by the footing reaction.

Another method by which footing rotation can be controlled is to join the column to an adjacent one with a rigid beam (Fig. 10.7). The size of the footing, which acts one way because of the beam, is generally determined by assuming a uniform stress distribution.

3 Combined footing

Combined footings support the load of two or more columns. With or without linked beams (Fig. 10.1), they are assumed rigid. The contact stress distribution is uniform or varies linearly, and the design follows that outlined for centrally loaded footings.

4 Footings on elastic foundations

In a flexible footing the contact stress distribution derives not only from its displacement and rotation as a rigid unit, but also from its bending deflection. The

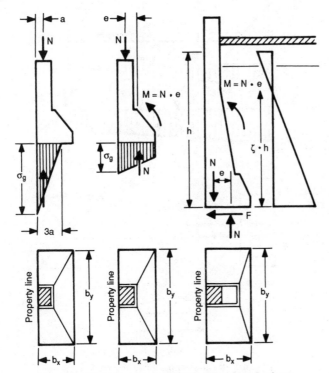

Fig. 10.6   Perimeter column footings with enlarged column.

theory of beams on an elastic foundation, based on the assumption that the soil reaction of each point is proportional to the vertical displacement of the contact face at that point, is used to solve this problem. Solutions have been obtained for many practical cases using the well-known differential equation

$$\frac{EI}{b}\frac{d^4y}{dx^4} = -ky \qquad (10.4)$$

in which k is the coefficient of vertical subgrade reaction, y is the deflection, b is the width, EI is the stiffness, and x is the coordinate parallel to the length of the footing (Timoshenko, 1965; Hetenyi, 1946). When the subgrade or subsoil is variable or stratified, Eq. 10.4 may be solved by numerical methods.

Although this theory is currently the most elaborate procedure available for the design of flexible footings, it does have several drawbacks. There is no proportionality between deflection and ground reaction, and the value of k depends also upon stress level, load repetitions, and duration of load. Furthermore, it is influenced by footing size and shape. Finally, it is difficult and costly to determine (Terzaghi, 1955). The solutions obtained by this theory should only be used as guidelines, unless the coefficient k has been determined with confidence. Real

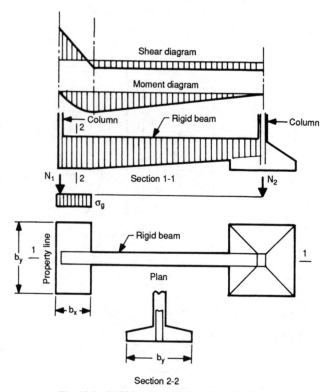

Fig. 10.7   Rigid-beam perimeter column footing.

soil distributions will be between two extremes, which are easy to define (Fig. 10.8).

Except when a sufficiently reliable stress distribution can be assessed, the design should cover the maximum possible moment and shear envelopes located within those resulting from the two extreme stress distributions mentioned. Frequently, however, unique envelopes for moments and shear can be assessed safely from these extremes for design and detailing.

5 Mat foundations

They are the most common foundations used for tall buildings. A mat or raft carries all columns or walls of a building. Either it consists of a single thick slab, with or without base enlargements, or the columns may be joined by beams which receive the ground reaction through the slab.

Although it is well known that the ground stress distribution under a rigid foundation is nonlinear (Fig. 10.3), mat design is generally based on a uniform or linearly varying stress distribution, as it is usually possible to make the mat sufficiently stiff to justify this assumption. For purely cohesive soils the errors in moments and shear are less than 20% and well within the provisions of the safety factor, because no material under a footing behaves purely cohesively. For cohesionless soils the error due to the difference in the stress distribution is on the safe side.

The structural design of a mat follows the same procedure as that for a building floor. The ground reaction provides the distributed load, and the columns act as supports. For a flexible mat foundation the stress distribution at the contact face is also a function of the deflection of the mat itself. A two-dimensional theory has been developed, but it involves all the difficulties pointed out for beams on elastic foundations.

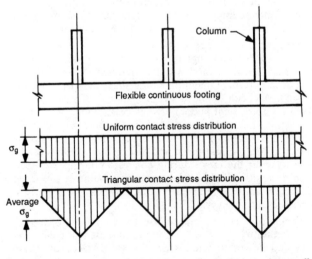

Fig. 10.8　Two extreme ground reactions for long rectangular footing carrying equally loaded columns.

Numerical methods, such as finite-element computer programs, provide readily available solutions to take into account the flexibility of the mat for different subgrade conditions such as soil stratification and soil elastic or nonelastic behavior.

Elevator pits introduce a discontinuity in the thickness of the raft. The usual practice is to build recesses within the mat, a mandatory solution below the water table. Although there is a local loss of rigidity, for concrete elevator shafts it is largely overcome by the rigidity of the walls of the shafts, and the mat as a whole behaves rather similarly to a structural element of uniform thickness. However, the recesses introduce local stress fields in their vicinity, which should be adequately investigated and taken care of with proper reinforcement.

6 Construction of shallow foundations

Most shallow footings can be built by pouring a thin layer of mortar on the bottom of the excavation and placing the reinforcement on top, using suitable spacers. With adequate slope for the top face of the footing and proper mix consistency, no forms are needed. Concrete will not slip, except during vibration, and surface finishing is only necessary for that portion of the top horizontal face that will support the columns or column forms.

Mats pose some problems, for which suitable decisions should be made.

1. The first and most important refers to waterproofing when the mat is located below the water table. There is no safe way of building a waterproof mat by relying only on the low permeability of concrete, whatever the procedure used to pour it. Therefore consideration should be given to the need for installing a continuous impermeable cover surrounding the outside faces of the mat and perimeter walls, up to a level higher than the maximum possible rise of the water table. At present, the most promising solution appears to be the use of weldable plastic impermeable membranes, of the type called geomembranes. Even so, the chances of some groundwater seeping into the building cannot be disregarded. With adequate provisions, this water can be collected into sumps and drawn out with automatic pumps.

2. Most rafts for tall buildings require thick slabs with bottom and top reinforcement to resist positive and negative moments. Usually, diagonal tensile stresses are not important, though punching shear may be, controlling the thickness of the slab. A check of these stresses should be made and whatever their values, a web reinforcement should always be provided to join the bottom and top reinforcements and to serve as main bars for support and spacing. This reinforcement should be made of vertical and horizontal closed stirrups, using adequate bar sizes to form a rigid mesh and having bar spacings large enough to allow a person to enter the mesh during concrete pouring. Consideration should also be given to additional skin reinforcement to control surface cracking. Frequently reinforcement is placed in two or more steps, particularly when concrete pouring is carried out in several lifts.

3. The placing of concrete is based on specifications for massive structures, such as ACI Committee 207 (1986) or the requirements of the *Concrete Manual* of the Water and Power Resources Service (U.S. Department of the Interior, 1981). Essentially two problems condition placing: temperature buildup and shrinkage. Temperature buildup can be controlled by placing concrete precooled to a temperature of less than 10°C. Keeping material in the shade and using finely chipped ice in the mix have proved adequate in hot weather. To avoid concrete damage by excessive shrinkage, it is usually necessary to cast the mat in a chessboard sequence and in several lifts. For the first and last lifts, embedding the main reinforcement, it may prove more appropriate to cast the concrete in one unit, taking proper measures to control shrinkage.

10.2 DEEP FOUNDATIONS

Deep foundations are divided into piles and caissons. A pile is defined here as a solid or hollow structural element with a slenderness ratio greater than 10. Whether installed by driving or by filling an excavation with concrete, provisions are generally made to ensure good contact between the lateral surfaces of the pile and the surrounding soil.

Caissons are hollow, having any cross section and a slenderness ratio of less than 10. A caisson is excavated inside and underneath the edges and sinks into the ground by its own weight or with the aid of additional deadweight.

1 Small-diameter piles

Precast or cast-in-place small-diameter piles have lateral dimensions of 600 mm (23⅝ in.) or less. After installation they are considered short columns because of the confining effect of the surrounding soil (even when buried in soft soil). However, they are weak in bending. Precast piles must also be designed for handling stresses that occur when they are being lifted to the site prior to driving.

Cast-in-place piles can be displacement piles with a driven close-ended shell or bored piles with or without an open-ended driven shell. Bored piles are always placed vertically. The contact between the pile shaft and the surrounding soil is usually less effective than in displacement piles. End bearing is also lower, unless treatment with pressure cement grout is applied as explained for large-diameter piles.

Lateral loads are mostly taken by inclined piles. (Usually there is a maximum inclination of 1:3.) For vertical piles, lateral loads depend on the pile bending resistance, the type of fixation provided by the pile cap, and the soil confinement effect. They may be calculated using Eq. 10.2, in which k is the coefficient of horizontal subgrade reaction (Terzaghi, 1955). For reinforced concrete piles with about 1% steel reinforcement, driven through soft soil, as a first approximation, the load H may be determined as follows (Moretto, 1971). For square piles,

$$H \text{ (kg)} = \frac{b^2}{100 \text{ mm}^2} \qquad (10.5a)$$

and for circular piles,

$$H \text{ (kg)} = \frac{(0.8b)^2}{100 \text{ mm}^2} \qquad (10.5b)$$

in which b is the length of the side of a square pile or the diameter of a circular pile. If a pile group is fully aligned, bracing should be provided to give lateral stability.

Usually at least two piles are required to support a column. The piles are joined with a cap, which serves as a link between columns and piles. The design of the cap should consider the displacement which may occur during driving. In a good installation the distance from the theoretical location usually does not exceed 100 mm (4 in.). The cap may fail by bending, splitting, or bond and is generally designed as a deep beam (Fig. 10.9), assuming a uniform load distribution over all piles for a centrally applied load. For three piles placed in an equilateral-triangle pattern, the maximum moments develop along the medians, and the cap is reinforced parallel to them (Fig. 10.10). The same line of thought is followed for the design of caps with four or more piles (Moretto, 1970).

For an eccentrically loaded pile cap, which allows only rotation and no deflection, the load per pile varies and is determined from

$$P = \frac{N}{n} \pm Ne_y \frac{y}{\varepsilon y^2} \pm Ne_x \frac{x}{\varepsilon x^2} \tag{10.6}$$

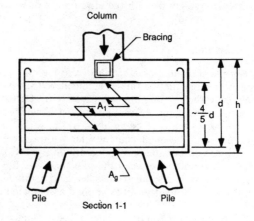

Section 1-1

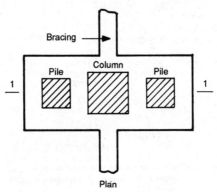

Plan

Fig. 10.9 Pile cap for two piles.

in which n is the number of piles, and the other terms are defined in Fig. 10.11. The design of the cap follows the ideas outlined earlier.

For piles at the perimeter of a building along a property line, a situation similar to the one for spread footings arises, as shown in Fig. 10.12. The design is essentially identical to the previous case.

The design of flexible pile caps requires an assessment of the deformation of the piles under load. The cap is assumed to be supported on elastic columns, and a solution is obtained for the distribution of pile loading. The problem with this approach is that the settlements under load vary erratically from pile to pile, depending on small details in their installation. Consequently a flexible pile cap should be designed for all possible and reasonable pile load distributions.

2 Large-diameter piles

Large-diameter piles, also called caissons in some locations, are always placed vertically. They can carry not only large normal loads, but also substantial hori-

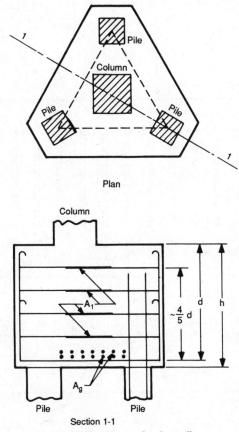

Plan

Section 1-1

Fig. 10.10 Pile cap for three piles.

zontal and eccentric loads. Their lateral and vertical bearing capacities can be increased considerably by lateral pressure grouting with cement along the shaft and by preloading at the base, also with cement pressure grout (Moretto, 1975). Because of their size and the relative precision with which they can be placed, it is possible to use one pile per column. Bracing in two nonaligned directions is required.

Pile caps are placed for load transfer between columns and piles. Everything discussed with regard to small-diameter pile caps is applicable here.

3 Diaphragm walls

A new type of deep foundation introduced recently makes use of the slurry wall technique of excavation to bore rectangular holes which are tremie concreted with adequate reinforcement (Kienberger, 1975). They behave as bored piles and become adequate as foundations of bearing walls and other structural panels for high-rise buildings.

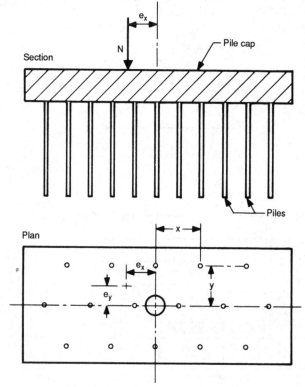

Fig. 10.11   Eccentrically loaded pile cap.

4 Caissons

Typical caissons are used in building construction only where deep basements
are required in soft soils and the caisson itself takes the place of the temporary
and permanent bracing of the excavation. On reaching the final level, the caisson
is closed at the bottom with a concrete floor.

Because a caisson is always a rigid structure, the ground reaction may be
taken as uniform for a centrally loaded caisson, or linearly varying for an eccentrically loaded one.

While a caisson is lowered into the ground, it may be subjected to nonuniform
lateral pressures by the surrounding soil. The distribution of this pressure depends on the soil properties and any deviation of the caisson from the vertical,
which cannot be predicted. The structural design of the caisson is thus an empirical task, in which these effects should be assessed adequately.

10.3 BRACING OF FOUNDATIONS

Whenever horizontal loads produced by wind and seismic action become important, spread footings (except for rafts) and pile foundations are braced in two nor-

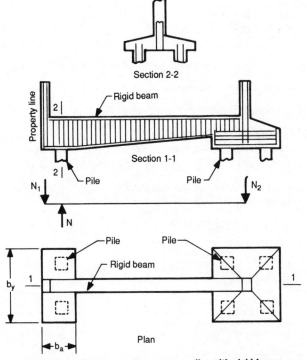

Fig. 10.12 Perimeter column on two piles with rigid beam.

mal, or nearly normal, directions in order to distribute these loads among all foundation elements. The bracing struts are designed in compression and tension to adequately support the forces involved.

10.4 SUGGESTIONS FOR FURTHER RESEARCH

Research should be directed to improve the existing knowledge on soil-structure interaction. Most of this information can only be obtained from field measurements. Only from a large mass of field data that would indicate real general trends in the distribution of contact stresses may the design of footings be improved. Analytical studies may also be made using finite-element analysis for various selected laws of soil reaction, both elastic and inelastic.

Pile foundations appear to lend themselves better to laboratory studies. However, the distribution of the load per pile in a multiple-pile foundation is a function not only of the soil, but also of the shape and rigidity of the pile cap. It also depends on minor construction details, such as variations in the refusal per pile, thus making laboratory studies questionable. Therefore field measurements are of major importance for the improvement of deep foundations. Again, analytical model simulation may provide useful insights.

10.5 CONDENSED REFERENCES / BIBLIOGRAPHY

ACI Committee 207 1986, *ACI Manual of Concrete Practice, Part I*

Hetenyi 1946, *Beams on Elastic Foundations*

Kienberger 1975, *Diaphragm Walls as Load Bearing Foundations*

Moretto 1970, *Reinforced Concrete Course*
Moretto 1971, *Deep Foundations—Selected Synthesis of Present State of the Knowledge*
Moretto 1975, *Foundations of the Bridges over the Parana River in Argentina*

Terzaghi 1955, *Coefficients of Subgrade Reactions*
Timoshenko 1965, *Strength of Materials*

U.S. Dept. of the Interior 1981, *Concrete Manual*

11

Quality Control
by In-Place Testing
at Early Ages

Historically the universal method of checking the strength of concrete placed in a building has been to test specimens cast, cured, and tested to a specific standard procedure. In North America the cylinder test procedure is used, which was first approved in 1921 as ASTM C39 (1921). Elsewhere cubes, prisms, or cylinders of various sizes were tested for the same purpose. These standard cured test specimens established the potential strength of the concrete. Design codes use specified strengths based on such test specimens for all structural design parameters and apply appropriate modifiers.

It has long been known that the compressive strength of a concrete, as measured by standard cured specimens, does not necessarily reflect the strength of the same concrete in place in a structure. Differences in curing and compaction can produce significant differences. Nevertheless it has been assumed that if concrete with the strength specified, as determined by standard cured test specimens, is placed, compacted, and cured to reasonable standards, the structure will perform as designed. In practice this has proved to be true. Where collapses have occurred, the causes have been identified as gross departures from safe design or construction practices. In the past the pace of construction did not warrant the use of any special testing procedures.

Today, however, the pace of construction makes the use of the traditional 28-day cylinder test inappropriate as a construction tool. The test still has relevance as a measure of the quality of concrete delivered to a site, and it is still the legal test for this purpose. But this test does not help speed the building process, nor does it assure safe construction.

Indeed, when rapid construction schedules are used, form removal, post-tensioning, and the cessation of curing as soon after the placing of concrete as in 1 day, make it prudent to have a reliable knowledge of the in-place strength. In cold-weather conditions such data become an essential part of safety.

In January 1971 a 16-story apartment building in Boston collapsed during construction, causing the loss of four lives (Bickley, 1971). Investigations showed that while all relevant standard test cylinders met specification requirements, the in-place strength of the concrete at the time of collapse was not much more than 50% of the specified 28-day strength; and by then it was 2 months old.

Since then there have been a number of spectacular collapses of structures during construction. A cooling tower collapsed in West Virginia in 1978 with the loss of 51 lives (Lew, 1980). *New Civil Engineer International* of December 1979 quotes a U.S. National Bureau of Standard report as indicating that "all the evidence points to the concrete having been loaded before it gained sufficiently in strength." This factor has been cited in other failures.

Safety and economy in construction make knowledge of in-place strength a necessity. The American Concrete Institute (ACI) Committee 228 on Non-Destructive Testing has written a state-of-the-art report which reviews the widely used methods for determining the in-place strength of concrete (ACI Committee 228, 1988). The underlying principles and inherent limitations of the methods and the statistical analysis of in-place test data are discussed. The overall objective of this report is to provide the potential user with a guide to assist in implementing and interpreting the results of in-place testing.

The methods described, and the related ASTM testing standards, are:

Rebound hammer	C805-85
Probe penetration	C803-82
Pullout	C900-87
Ultrasonic pulse velocity	C597-83
Maturity	C1074-87
Cast-in-place cylinder	C873-85

It is now widely recognized that the best in-place method of testing for practical and technical purposes is the pullout test, and this should be supplemented in cold weather by the use of maturity testing.

These procedures are being used on such major transportation projects as the Channel tunnel between France and England and the Storebaelt project in Denmark. They have been extensively used in North America in the construction of high-strength high-rise buildings using specified concrete strengths of up to 85 MPa (12,300 psi).

ASTM C900 *Pullout Strength of Hardened Concrete* (1982) states:

1.1 This method covers determination of the pullout strength of hardened concrete in test specimens or structures by measuring the force required to pull an embedded metal insert and the attached concrete fragment from a concrete mass.

Figure 11.1 shows the basic principles involved.

11.1 SPECIFICATIONS AND INTERPRETATION

Pullout testing has so far been used predominantly to determine form-stripping times. This has invariably been part of an accelerated construction program involving floor form stripping as early as 1 day after casting. Since the introduction of the pullout test on a site has generally followed the issue of contract documents, specification requirements have been developed on each project by discussions with the structural engineer involved.

Generally it has been agreed that form removal can be made at about 75% of the specified 28-day strength for floor slabs, the range being 67 to 80%. For vertical elements, form removal can be carried out at much lower strengths, and on chimneys and cooling towers 7 MPa (1000 psi) has been specified.

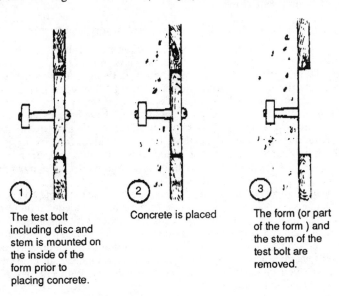

① The test bolt including disc and stem is mounted on the inside of the form prior to placing concrete.

② Concrete is placed

③ The form (or part of the form) and the stem of the test bolt are removed.

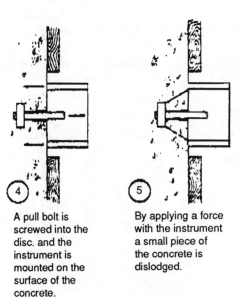

④ A pull bolt is screwed into the disc. and the instrument is mounted on the surface of the concrete.

⑤ By applying a force with the instrument a small piece of the concrete is dislodged.

Figure 11.1   Different stages of pullout strength test (ASTM C900-82).

Codes and specifications do not yet provide guidance in interpretation, and structural engineers generally do not have the experience. If a number of tests are made, is the average strength the strength required for form removal, or does some calculated minimum have to equal or exceed this strength? In practice, a number of approaches have been adopted, one of which follows.

A set of test results is expressed as a mean, a standard deviation, and a calculated minimum, as follows:

$$\text{Specified strength} = \text{mean value of test results} -ks$$

where s is the standard deviation and k is taken from Table 11.1, based on the number of tests performed on the particular class of concrete.

Generally this procedure is followed, but it is thought to be conservative. On some projects the specified form-stripping strength has been interpreted as the value that the average of the pullout tests has to meet, with no result less than 75% of this value. When very early stripping times have been used, the minimum has been increased to 80% of this value for a 2-day cycle and to 90% for a 1-day cycle. Again, this approach is thought to be conservative. On most projects, however, the minimum strength calculated by this procedure has been required to equal or exceed the specified strength for form removal. This is even more conservative.

If in-place testing is to become widely used, it must be both safe and economical. Pullout testing provides an economic way of obtaining an adequate number of tests from which statistically valid calculations can be made. With this number of tests, a minimum strength can be calculated. In the past, where a small number of tests such as field-cured cylinders determined form-removal times at greater ages, no statistically valid minimum was, or could be, determined. As long as all the tests or their averages exceeded a required value, everyone was happy. With a more sophisticated approach possible with pullout testing, a true minimum strength for a pour can be calculated.

The following clauses are from a contract specification. They worked well in practice and are recommended as a model for guidance.

Issue reports of in-place testing to Structural Engineer, Resident Engineer, and Construction Manager immediately after tests are made and checked. Keep file on site.

Table 11.1 k values

n	k	n	k
3	2.50	15	1.58
4	2.13	16	1.57
5	1.96	17	1.55
6	1.86	18	1.54
7	1.79	19	1.54
8	1.74	20	1.53
9	1.70	25	1.50
10	1.67	30	1.47
11	1.65	35	1.46
12	1.62	40	1.44
13	1.61	45	1.43
14	1.59	50	1.43

1. *Concrete tested with pullouts.* Until correlation between 28-day pullout tests and concrete cylinder tests is satisfactory to the Engineer, make two cylinders per 100 m³ (130 yd³) or less of each pour for testing at 28 days.
2. *Where in-place testing is required.* Install at least 15 pullout inserts per 100 m³ (130 yd³) pour of concrete. For pours in excess of 100 m³ (130 yd³) provide at least an additional one insert per 230 m³ (300 yd³). Install two additional pullout inserts per pour for testing at 28 days.

In the substructure install inserts on the top of slabs at random locations agreed by the Engineer. In the superstructure direct the installation of inserts in the soffit of slabs at random locations agreed by the Engineer.

Test inserts just prior to the time it is proposed to remove forms. Generally at least 10 tests shall be made. If the first five results indicate that the concrete is below form-removal strength, discontinue testing and reschedule. If a set of 10 tests indicates results marginally below the required values, recommend further tests then or additional curing time.

After checking, report the results on the approved form as provided in the Terms of Reference.

Where necessary to check exposed areas, make additional tests using either additional inserts or maturity meters.

Test two inserts at 28 days.

During cold-weather concreting make temperature checks within the heated or insulated areas and record.

11.2 CREEP AND CURING FACTORS IN THE EARLY STRIPPING OF FORM WORK

When early stripping of formwork is proposed, there is concern about creep and the adequacy of curing. A review of the literature (Neville, 1970) reveals the following:

1. For a constant stress-strength ratio creep increases with the age of loading. Also, the smaller the fractional strength increases, the greater the creep.
2. Earlier investigation had shown that creep increased with loading at one earlier age, but had failed to take into account the effect of the stress-strength ratio. Since the load had been constant, the stress-strength ratio at earlier ages was higher. At early ages the rate of creep is higher, except for concrete loaded very early, such as after 1 to 2 days.
3. Recent work found that at a given stress-strength ratio, creep decreased with the logarithm of the age of loading between 18 hours and 28 days. Attempts to relate creep to elastic deformation at the time of loading have not been convincing.
4. It appears that the most critical factor affecting creep is the stress-strength ratio. Therefore, if the stress is reduced or the strength is increased, creep will be reduced independent of the age of loading.
5. It is normal for the engineer to require that concrete gain a certain minimum strength or maturity before
   a. Loading, and
   b. Cessation of curing
6. Criteria specified by engineers vary, but values between 0.70 and $0.85f_c'$ are typical of those specified by professional engineering offices.
7. Curing equal to 5 days at 50°F or 3 days at 70°F is normally adopted. This approximates a strength of 0.5 to $0.6f_c'$.

8. At present, acceptable criteria for loading lie between 0.70 and $0.85f'_c$; for cessation of curing approximately 0.5 to $0.6f'_c$ is acceptable.
9. It is therefore concluded that an acceptable stress-strength ratio at the time of loading is obtained at between 0.70 and $0.85f'_c$. If, therefore, concrete is designed to reach these parameters at an early age, creep should not be increased and may be reduced.

11.3 ACCELERATED PROGRAMS

Historically concrete test cylinders have been used to determine the potential quality of concrete delivered to a site. In addition, it has been assumed, with good reason, that if the concrete is installed in accordance with normal accepted practice, the structure will be safe. This procedure has been used since early in this century.

A number of factors now apply which make this standard practice no longer a valid approach in assisting in the construction process.

1. With today's speed of all forms of construction, 28 days are far too long to wait for confirmation of the potential adequacy of the concrete. Using slip forms, 152.4 m (500 vertical feet) is possible in a month. Jump forms can pour a 2.4-m (8-ft) lift every day, and contractors are now achieving two to three floors per week with site-cast concrete on major commercial and residential structures, using flying forms.
2. In cold weather, the safety of the structure has to be of paramount concern.
3. To meet economic realities, early posttensioning, form removal, and termination of cold-weather curing as quickly as possible are desirable.
4. Concrete mixes can now be formulated to give high percentages of f'_c within 1 to 3 days.
5. Reliable test procedures for a rapid determination of the in-place strength of concrete, such as pullout tests, are now available.
6. ASTM-approved procedures for such tests now exist (ASTM C900, 1982).

A policy decision to accelerate the construction program is justified if significant savings can be achieved. With acceleration, savings can be realized in the following areas (Bickley, 1982): reduction in financing costs, earlier rental of facilities, overhead, form-work costs, reshoring costs, cold-weather heating costs, and savings on concrete meeting 91-day requirements.

The maximum benefit will only be realized if all construction activities are rescheduled to the accelerated program. Acceleration may involve the design and use of a wide range of special mixes, from mixes that allow the removal of forms from floor slabs at 24 hours after casting to 63-MPa (9000-psi) cast-in-place concrete, and the use of 56 and 91 days for determining f'_c in order to obtain technical or economic benefits. Experience shows that with the right specifications, preconstruction meetings, and effective supervision and testing, ready-mixed concrete suppliers can deliver these special concretes with consistency and reliability.

The use of special mixes will involve the agreement of the building officials having jurisdiction. This agreement should be obtained prior to the start of the project.

In-place pullout testing methods complying with ASTM C900 (1982) may be used, but the principles could be met by other approved in-place test methods. The criteria for the removal of forms has to be decided by the structural engineer for the project. Generally values in the range of 0.7 to $0.8 f'_c$ are used.

The contractor is responsible for deciding when to remove forms, and the inspection and testing company is responsible for determining that the engineer's criteria for form removal have been met.

Concrete mixes can be formulated to meet any form-removal program. Depending on the form work and the subcontractor's program, the mixes can be designed to achieve strengths that match this program. If, for example, the program calls for a 5-day work week with form stripping at 1 day, concrete placed on Monday through Thursday should be a mix suitable for 1-day stripping. On Friday, however, a mix suitable for 3-day stripping would be used, since it is less expensive and there would be no advantage in gaining strength faster. The use of this approach on a number of projects has been reported in the technical literature (Bickley, 1982).

Control of form-work stripping is achieved by in-place testing. The pullout system used provides about 10 times as many tests as are made to meet standard cylinder testing specifications. All tests are physical tests in place (that is, the test is on the concrete in the element of structure being stripped). A result that is statistically valid can therefore be obtained. The test and the calculation of the results are carried out on site, the apparatus being portable.

A control system is exercised which involves the following steps:

1. Testing on site
2. Calculation of results on site
3. Checking arithmetic and results with an authorized person at head office by telephone (which takes only 2 or 3 minutes, as all authorized personnel have suitably programmed calculators on their desks):
    a. Mean strength, standard deviation, and minimum strength
    b. Levels and limits of the part of the structure tested
    c. Whether the area tested meets or does not meet the structural engineer's requirements for stripping
5. A signature of the owner's authorized site representative obtained on a standard form to confirm receipt of the data for record purposes

For rapid dissemination of the data on site, a color-coded multicopy self-carbon form is used. This is completed manually. Its distribution is limited to those who need it. In the event that a problem arises, the structural engineer is notified as soon as possible.

For a typical pour this procedure takes approximately 30 minutes. If results fail to meet stripping criteria, testing is stopped as soon as this is obvious (usually after five tests), and retesting is scheduled for later. Enough pullout inserts are installed to allow this to be done.

For vertical elements, where rapid strength gain is irrelevant, a different approach is used. The design strength of columns is not required until long after they are cast. Therefore a mix proportioned to meet design requirements 91 days after casting is used. This has been done on a number of major projects, and the results have been reported in the technical literature (Bickley, 1982). The type of mix used for this purpose might contain pozzolanic material to ensure good strength gain at ages later than 28 days.

Adequate curing of the vertical elements is required to ensure strength gain with age. This is easily achieved by spraying all vertical elements designated by the structural engineer with a colorless and fugitive curing compound immediately after stripping, complying with ASTM C309 (1989).

For confirmation of specified strength at 91 days, and of appropriate strength gain earlier, additional pullout inserts may be specified in columns and walls where designated by the structural engineer. For confirmation that reshores may be removed, specified spare inserts, already in place in the slabs, may be used.

11.4 CONDENSED REFERENCES / BIBLIOGRAPHY

ACI 228 1988, *In-Place Methods for Determination of Strength of Concrete*
ASTM C39 1921, *Test Method for Compressive Strength of Cylindrical Concrete Speci-*
ASTM C309 1989, *Specification for Liquid Membrane Forming Compounds for Curing*
ASTM C900 1982, *Pullout Strength of Hardened Concrete*

Bickley 1971, *The Building Collapse at 2000 Commonwealth Ave., Boston, Massachusetts*
Bickley 1982, *Concrete Optimization*

Lew 1980, *West Virginia Cooling Tower Collapse Caused by Inadequate Concrete Strength*

Neville 1970, *Creep of Concrete: Plain, Reinforced and Prestressed*

Nomenclature

GLOSSARY

Actions. Loads and imposed or constrained deformations which cause stresses and deformations in structural members.

Admixtures. Materials other than cement, water, aggregates, or reinforcement that are added to concrete during, or immediately after, batching and mixing.

Allowable stress. Maximum permissible stress used in design of structural members based on a factor of safety against rupture or yielding of any type.

Allowable stress design. *See* Working stress design.

Anchorage. Length of reinforcement, or mechanical anchor, or a hook, or a combination thereof, beyond the point where reinforcing is no longer required to resist calculated stress.

Beam-and-slab floor. A reinforced concrete floor system in which the floor slab is supported by beams of reinforced concrete.

Beam-column. A beam that transmits an axial load along its longitudinal axis in addition to end moments or transverse loads, or both.

Bent. One of a series of parallel plane frame or wall and frame structures that comprise a complete building structure. Bents are usually aligned at right angles to the length of the building.

Bent bar. Longitudinal reinforcement in a beam, bent to pass from one face to the other of a member, anchorage of a bar.

Block. A concrete masonry unit.

Bond. Adhesion and grip of concrete or mortar to reinforcement or to other surfaces against which it is placed; also, the arrangement of units in masonry and brickwork so that vertical joints are discontinuous.

Bond strength. Resistance to separation of mortar and concrete from reinforcing steel and other materials with which they are in contact.

Bundled reinforcement. A group of up to four parallel reinforcing bars in contact with each other and enclosed in stirrups or ties and used as a reinforcing element.

Cast-in-Place. Mortar or concrete that is deposited in the place where it is required to harden as part of the structure, as opposed to precast concrete.

Characteristic strength. A material strength that will be exceeded with an arbitrarily chosen probability (usually 95%).

Coefficient of thermal expansion. The change in length per unit length of an unrestrained member caused by a rise or drop of temperature of one degree Celsius (or Fahrenheit). Its unit is degree^{-1}.

Collapse mechanism.   Sufficient plastic hinges form to create a linkage.

Column, long, slender.   A column whose axial load capacity is reduced because of its slenderness, due to moments induced by deflection of the column.

Column, short.   A column whose axial load capacity need not be reduced because of its slenderness.

Column capital.   An enlargement of the end of a column designed and built to act as an integral unit with the column and flat slab and to increase the shearing resistance or reduce the moments, or both.

Composite construction.   A type of construction made up of different materials (e.g., concrete and structural steel) or of members produced by different methods (e.g., cast-in-place concrete and precast concrete).

Compressive strength.   The measured maximum resistance of a concrete or mortar specimen to axial loading; expressed in stress, or the specified resistance used in design calculations. In the United States it is expressed in lbf per in.^{2} (psi) and designated f'_c.

Concrete.   A composite material that consists essentially of a binding medium within which are embedded particles or fragments of aggregate; in normal portland cement concrete, the binder is a mixture of portland cement and water and the aggregate is sand and gravel.

Concrete, lightweight.   Structural concrete made with lightweight aggregate; the unit density usually is in the range of 1440 kg/m^3 to 1850 kg/m^3 (90 lb/ft^3 to 115 lb/ft^3).

Concrete, normal-weight.   Concrete having a unit density of approximately 2400 kg/m^3 (150 lb/ft^3) made with aggregates of normal weight.

Confinement.   Concrete contained by various structural elements or by closely spaced special transverse reinforcement which restrains the concrete in directions perpendicular to the applied stress.

Connections.   A physical stress-resisting tie between two adjoining or abutting elements. In Chapter CB-12 the following notation is used to describe particular types on connections.

    BB = beam to beam
    BC = beam to column
    CB = column base
    CC = column to column

Construction joint.   The surface where two successive placements of concrete meet.

Construction loads.   Loads applied to a concrete building during construction including the loads supported by temporary structure.

Control joint.   Formed, sawed, or tooled groove in a concrete structure to regulate the location and amount of cracking and separation resulting from the dimensional change of different parts of a structure so as to avoid the development of high stresses.

Core.   An assembly or group of shear walls, usually joined together to form an open or partially closed box structure, often used as a bracing element for a building structure.

Coupled frame–shear wall structure.   A shear wall and frame structure in which the shear walls and the frame are coupled together for analysis purposes to determine the stiffness that the coupled structure provides against lateral movement under lateral loads.

Coupled walls.   Shear walls that are connected together by bending resistant members.

Creep.   The slow, time-dependent change in dimensions of concrete under a sustained load, primarily in the direction in which the load acts. It is a dimensionless quantity having units of strain.

Dead load.   The actual weight of the structural elements. (This is a gravity load.)

Deep beam. A beam in which the elastic distribution of stresses is nonlinear and in which there are significant compressive forces between the loads and reactions.

Deformed bar. Bars with properties or deformations on the surfaces to improve the bond with concrete and reduce the width of tension cracks.

Development length. The length of reinforcement embedment required to develop by bond the design strength of the reinforcement at a critical section.

Diagonal tension crack. Crack in a reinforced concrete member caused primarily by a shear force.

Diaphragm. A thin platelike structural element, whose in-plane rigidity may be used to stiffen the structure; for example, a floor slab which maintains the cross-sectional shape of the building.

Double tee slab. A precast, one-way slab element composed of a horizontal slab and two vertical webs. In cross section the member resembles the letter Π.

Drop panel. The structural portion of a flat slab which is thickened throughout an area surrounding the column, column capital, or bracket.

Drying shrinkage. The shrinkage which takes place due to the loss of water in hardened cement paste.

Ductility. That property of a material by virtue of which the material may undergo large permanent deformation without rupture.

Edge beam. A stiffening beam at the edge of a slab.

Epoxy resin. A thermosetting resin used for model-making. The uncured resin is mixed with a hardener, and the mixture is then cast in a mold.

Expansion joint. A separation between adjoining parts of a concrete structure which is provided to allow small relative movements, such as those caused by thermal changes, to occur independently.

Factor of safety. The ration of the ultimate strength (or yield point) of a material to the working stress assumed in design (stress factor of safety); or the ratio of the ultimate load, moment, or shear of a structural member to the working load, moment, or shear, respectively, assumed in design (load factor of safety).

Factored loads. The specified, working, or characteristic loads multiplied by appropriate load factors.

Falsework. *See* Formwork.

Fiber aspect ratio. Ratio of length to the equivalent fiber diameter. (For noncircular sections the equivalent diameter is that of a circle whose area equals that of the fiber.)

Fiber reinforced concrete. A composite achieved by the incorporation of short discrete fibers (steel, polypropylene, glass, carbon).

Fire resistance. The ability of a material or assembly to withstand fire or give protection from it; the ability to confine a fire or to continue to perform a given structural function, or both.

Flat plate. A flat slab without column capitals or drop panels. (*See* Flat slab.)

Flat slab. A concrete slab with drop panels and with or without column capitals reinforced in two or more directions, generally without beams or girders to transfer the loads to supporting members.

Flexural crack. Crack in a reinforced concrete member caused by bending of the member.

Folded plate. A framing assembly composed of sloping slabs in a hipped or gabled arrangement.

Formwork. The total system of support for freshly placed concrete, including the mold or sheathing which contacts the concrete, as well as all supporting members, hardware, and necessary bracing. *Falsework* and *Shuttering* are also used with essentially the same meaning.

High-strength concrete. Concrete with a 28-day compressive strength of 6000 psi or higher.

High-strength steel. Concrete reinforcing bars generally having a minimum yield strength above 414 MPa (60,000 psi, 4220 kgf/cm^2).

Hook. A bend in the end of a reinforcing bar.

Hooked bar. A reinforcing bar with the end bent into a hook to provide anchorage.

Joint. The interface between adjoining or abutting elements. In monolithic construction, the concrete between the ends of the columns and beams entering the joint.

Joist. One of a series of closely spaced horizontal structural members interacting with or supporting a slab.

Lift slab. A method of concrete construction in which floor and roof slabs are cast on or at ground level and hoisted into position by jacking; also a slab which is a component of such construction.

Limit state. When a structure or structural element becomes unfit for its intended use due to collapse, lack of serviceability, or any other cause, it is said to have reached a limit state.

Limit states design. A design process that involves identification of all potential modes of failure (limit states) and maintaining an acceptable level of safety against their occurrence. The safety level is usually established on a probablistic basis.

Linear creep. The value of creep calculated using the assumption that creep is directly proportional to the applied stress.

Live load. Loads due to the use and occupancy of a structure.

Lost form. A form for cast-in-place concrete often made of precast concrete. The form becomes part of the finished structure.

Masonry. Construction composed of shaped or molded units, usually small enough to be handled by one person and composed of stone, ceramic brick or tile, concrete, glass, adobe, or the like.

Mesh reinforcement. Smooth or deformed wires welded into a two-way mesh in either sheets or rolls, and used to reinforce concrete.

Microconcrete. Concrete suitable for use in an ultimate-strength mode. The concrete may be scaled down by reducing either the size or the unit weight of the aggregate, or both.

Mortar. A mixture of cement paste, lime, and sand, used to bond together masonry elements. The proportions are expressed as a ratio (cement : lime : sand).

One-way construction. A structural system where the arrangement of the steel reinforcement is intended to resist stresses due to bending in one direction only.

Permanent form. Any form that remains in place after the concrete has developed its design strength. The form may or may not become an integral part of the structure.

Plane frame. A framed structure that can be idealized as a two-dimensional structure.

Plastic failure. Formation of plastic mechanism.

Plastic hinge. A yielded zone that forms in a structural member when the plastic moment is attained. The beam rotates as if hinged, except that it is restrained by the plastic moment M_p.

Post. *See* Shore.

Posttensioning. A method of prestressing reinforced concrete in which tendons are tensioned after the concrete has hardened.

Precast concrete. Concrete cast elsewhere than its final position in the structure.

Prestressed concrete. Concrete in which internal stresses of such magnitude and distribution are introduced that the tensile stresses resulting from the service loads are counteracted to a desired degree; in reinforced concrete the prestress is commonly introduced by tensioning the tendons.

Pretensioning. A method of prestressing reinforced concrete, in which the tendons are tensioned between fixed abutments before the concrete is placed, and are released after the concrete has hardened and bonded to the tendons.

Progressive collapse. A situation in which the failure of one element causes failure of adjacent elements which spreads progressively through a large part of the structure. In general, the final amount of damage is many times that expected from the initial failure itself.

Prop. *See* Shore.

Reinforced concrete, masonry. Concrete or masonry containing reinforcement and designed on the assumption that the two materials act together in resisting forces.

Reinforcement. Metal bars, wires, or other slender members which are embedded in concrete in such a manner that the metal and the concrete act together in resisting forces.

Reinforcement ratio. Ratio of the effective area of the reinforcement to the effective area of the concrete at any section of a structural member.

Reshoring. The construction operation in which the original shoring or posting is removed and replaced in such a manner as to avoid damage to the partially cured concrete.

Serviceability requirements. Limitations such as deflection, floor vibration, and cracking.

Shear head. A mechanical device introduced into the slab at a slab-column connection in order to increase the shear capacity of the connection.

Shear reinforcement. Reinforcement designed to resist shear or diagonal tension stresses; dowels are not considered to be shear reinforcement.

Shear wall. A structural wall which in its own plane carries shear forces resulting from lateral loads such as wind, earthquake forces, or explosions.

Shear wall, coupled. Two shear walls connected by beams or slabs which permit the two walls to act together as a load-resisting system.

Shore. Temporary vertical support for formwork and fresh concrete or for recently built structures which have not developed full design strength. Also called *post, prop, strut,* or *tom.*

Shrinkage. Volume decrease caused by drying and chemical changes; a function of time but not of stress due to external load or thermal expansion. It is generally expressed in terms of a linear strain.

Shuttering. *See* Formwork.

Slab. A flat, usually horizontal or nearly so, molded layer of plain or reinforced concrete usually of uniform thickness, but sometimes of variable thickness; as the flat section of floor or roof either on the ground or supported by beams, columns, or other framework. (*See also* Flat slab.)

Slab loads. Loads used to calculate the various load effects such as bending moments and shear forces in the slab.

Slip form. A form which moves, usually continuously, during placing of the concrete. Movement may be either horizontal or vertical. Slip forming is like an extrusion process with the forms acting as moving dies to shape the concrete.

Soffit. The underside of a subordinate part or member of a building, such as a beam, stairway, or arch.

Spandrel. That part of a wall between the head of a window and the sill of the window above it. (An upturned spandrel continues above the roof or floor line.)

Spandrel beam. Floor level beams in the faces of a building, usually supporting the edges of the floor slabs.

Special loads. All loads that can occur during construction and not otherwise included in vertical and lateral loads. Examples are accidental impacts and unsymmetrical placement of heavy material.

Spirally reinforced column. A column in which the vertical bars are enveloped by spiral reinforcement, i.e., closely spaced continuous hooping.

Splice. Connection of one reinforcing bar to another by overlapping, welding, mechanical end connectors, or other means.

Stirrups. Bars bent in a box or U shape in a direction transverse the direction of the main steel.

Strength design. A method of proportioning structures or members to have failure capacities equal to or greater than the elastically computed moments, shears, and axial forces corresponding to a specified multiple of the working loads and assuming a nonlinear distribution of flexural stresses.

Strut. *See* Shore.

Temperature reinforcement. Reinforcement designed to carry stresses resulting from temperature changes, also the minimum reinforcement for areas of members which are not subjected to primary stresses or necessarily to temperature stresses.

Theoretical age. An adjusted age of concrete in days at the time of application of stress, or at the time at which creep or shrinkage are considered. The adjustment accounts for the effect of variation in the average day temperature.

Theoretical thickness. A variable affecting the amount of creep and shrinkage of a concrete member. Its value has the unit of length and is dependent upon the area and perimeter of the cross section and the relative humidity of the ambient medium.

Thin-walled beam. A beam whose cross section consists of platelike elements, whose width-to-thickness and length-to-width ratios are large, say greater than ten to one. Such a section is liable to warp under tension.

Tie. Closed loop of reinforcing bars encircling the longitudinal steel in columns.

Tied column. A column laterally reinforced with ties.

Time-dependent volume changes. The combined effect of creep, shrinkage, and temperature change.

Tom. *See* Shore.

Two-way construction. A structural system intended to resist stresses due to bending in two directions. The reinforcement is placed at right angles to each other.

Tube-in-tube system. A building with an inner core tube system and an exterior perimeter tube system.

Tube system. A building in which columns are closely spaced around the perimeter of the building and interconnected by stiff spandrel beams to optimize stiffness against lateral loads.

Ultimate strength design. *See* Strength design.

Vertical loads. Specified dead loads and live loads acting in the vertical direction.

Volume-to-surface ratio. A variable affecting the amount of creep and shrinkage of a concrete member. Its value has the unit of length and equals the volume of the member divided by its exposed surface are.

Waffle slab. A two-way concrete joist floor construction.

Water-cement ratio. The ratio of the amount of water, exclusive only of that absorbed by the aggregates, to the amount of cementitious material in a concrete or mortar mixture; preferably stated as a decimal by weight.

Working load. The load for which a structure is designed under normal service and conditions.

Working stress. Maximum permissible design stress using working stress design methods.

Working stress design. A method of proportioning structures or members for prescribed working loads at stresses well below the ultimate, and assuming linear distribution of flexural stresses.

Yield point. The point during increasing stress at which the proportion of stress to strain becomes substantially less than it has been at smaller values of stress, below which the stress-strain curve may be assumed to be linear, and above which the curve is usually nonlinear.

Yield strength. The stress corresponding to the yield point.

SYMBOLS

A^{lb}, A^{lt} = area of bottom- and top-chord reinforcement

A_b = area of transverse bar

A_c = area of core of section

A_{cc} = area of concrete core of section measured to center of peripheral

A_d = diagonal steel area

A_f = contact area of footing with ground

A_g = gross area of section

A_g = gross area of concrete

A_{jh} = horizontal shear steel area in the joint

A_{sv} = cross sectional area of two legs of a link

A_{s1} = area of main reinforcement (main tie)

A_{s2} = area of stirrups

A_{sh} = total area of transverse bars in direction under consideration within spacing s_h

A_{sp} = area of spiral reinforcement bar

A_{st} = total area of longitudinal reinforcement

A_{te} = area of one tie

A_{tr} = total transverse steel area

A_v = web steel area

a = distance between load and column face

b	= beam width
b	= width of bracket
b_w	= web width
b_v	= effective web width
b^1	= effective width
C_c	= creep coefficient
c_1	= column (wall) dimension in direction of span considered
c_2	= column (wall) dimension perpendicular to direction of span considered
d	= distance between center of tension force and compressed edge
d	= effective depth of slab
d_b	= bar diameter
d_s	= diameter of spiral
E_c	= modulus of elasticity of concrete
F_c	= compression force in concrete (resultant)
F_s	= tension force in reinforcement (resultant)
F_{s1}	= tension force in main reinforcement
F_{s2}	= tension force in stirrups
f_c	= concrete cylinder strength tested or calculated from cube tests
f'_c	= compressive cylinder strength of concrete
f'_c	= specified strength of concrete
f_{cd}	= design strength of concrete
f_{ps}	= tensile strength of prestressing reinforcement
f_r	= modulus of rupture
f_{sp}	= splitting tensile strength
f_{s1}	= yield strength of main reinforcement
f_{s2}	= yield strength of stirrups
f_{sd}	= design strength of reinforcement
f_{su}	= ultimate strength of steel
f_y	= yield strength of steel
f_y	= yield strength of longitudinal steel reinforcement
f_{yh}	= yield strength of transverse steel reinforcement
f_{yt}	= yield stress for the transverse steel
f_{yv}	= yield stress for the stirrup reinforcement
$_sf_a$	= allowable bond stress
f'_2	= confining pressure
H	= applied horizontal load
h	= overall beam depth
h_c	= cross sectional dimension, measured center to center of confining steel
h''	= width of concrete core of section measured to outside of peripheral hoop

I_{cr}	= moment of inertia for the cracked section
I_e	= effective moment of inertia
I_g	= gross moment of inertia
I_w	= wall moment of inertia
K	= system stiffness matrix
k_{ij}	= stiffness coefficient
l_b	= basic development of a bar in compression
l_{dh}	= basic development length for a hooked bar
l_n	= clear span
l_t	= area of longitudinal column steel divided by gross area of column section
l_x, l_z	= geometric steel ratio
M	= bending moment
M	= moment
M_a	= applied moment at a section
M_a	= cracking moment
M_{bal}	= balancing moment
M_{cr}	= cracking moment
$M_{e\,code}$	= factored moment due to static seismic loads specified by code
M^f	= beam flexural capacity
M_n	= nominal moment capacity
M^0	= beam flexural overstrength
M_{prim}	= primary moment
M_{sec}	= secondary moment
M_u	= factored moment
max V	= maximum vertical load with respect to compression failure
N	= axial load
n	= modular ratio
P	= nodal forces
P	= prestress force
P_c	= buckling load
P_e	= design compressive load on column due to gravity and seismic loading
P_0	= strength of column subjected to concentric loading only
P_{ij}	= element internal forces
R	= modulus of contact area
R	= resultant force from vertical and horizontal reinforcement
S	= section modulus
S_{ed}	= dependable strength
S_i	= required ideal strength

S_v = spacing of the link

s = center-to-center spacing of spirals or circular hoops

s = shear span

s = tie bar spacing

s_h = center-to-center spacing of hoop sets

U = rotation and translation vector

u_{ij} = deformation components

V = applied vertical load

V_a = applied shear at a section

V_a = applied shear force

V_c = shear strength of concrete

V_g = shear due to gravity

V_{jh} = horizontal joint shear

V_t, V_b = top and bottom shear

V' = applied vertical load reduced with vertical force component of inclined stirrups

V_{bal} = balancing shear

V_p = vertical shear component of prestress

V_u = factored shear

V_u = ultimate vertical load (failure load)

W = reinforcement weight

w = unit weight of concrete

w = width of bearing plate

w_{bal} = balancing load

y_0 = elastic deflection

Z = moment arm

α = inclination angle of diagonal bars to the beam axis

α = inclination between vertical and horizontal applied loads

β = inclination of compression member

Δ = horizontal displacement

Δ_y = horizontal displacement at first yield

δ = moment magnification factor

ϵ_{cu} = concrete ultimate strain

ϵ_0 = concrete strain at peak stress

ϵ_s = steel strain

ϵ_y = steel yield strain

η_u = observed ultimate load; calculated capacity

η_y = observed yield load; calculated yield load

θ = inclination of principal compressive stress to the x axis

μ = displacement ductility factor = Δ/Δ_y

ρ_s = ratio of volume of transverse reinforcement to volume of concrete core

ρ_t = area of longitudinal column steel divided by gross area of column section

ρ_w = tensile steel ratio based on web width

ρ_x, ρ_z = geometric steel ratio

σ_s = strength at the bottom of the footing

Φ_0 = overstrength factor

ϕ = strength reduction factor, or curvature

ϕ_u = maximum curvature

ϕ_y = curvature at first yield

ABBREVIATIONS

ACI   American Concrete Institute
AIJ   Architectural Institute of Japan
ANSI   American National Standards Institute
ASCE   American Society of Civil Engineers
ASTM   American Society for Testing and Materials
ATC   Applied Technology Council
BSI   British Standards Institution
CEB-FIP   European Concrete Committee—International Federation of Pre-stressing
CIRIA   Construction Industry Research and Information Association
CSA   Canadian Standards Association
IABSE   International Association of Bridge and Structural Engineers
IAEE   International Association for Earthquake Engineers
NRCCND   National Research Council Committee on Natural Disasters
NZS   New Zealand Standards
OSHA   Occupational Safety and Health Administration
PCA   Portland Cement Association
PCI   Prestressed Concrete Institute
PTI   Post-Tensioning Institute
SANZ   Standards Association of New Zealand
SEAOC   Structural Engineers' Association of California
UBC   Uniform Building Code

UNITS

In the table below are given conversion factors for commonly used units. The numerical values have been rounded off to the values shown. The British (Imperial) System of units is the same as the American System except where noted. Le Système International d'Unités (abbreviated "SI") is the name formally given in 1960 to the system of units partly derived from, and replacing, the old metric system.

SI	American	Old metric
Length		
1 mm	0.03937 in.	1 mm
1 m	3.28083 ft	1 m
	1.093613 yd	
1 km	0.62137 mile	1 km
Area		
1 mm^2	0.00155 in.^{2}	1 mm^2
1 m^2	10.76392 ft^2	1 m^2
	1.19599 yd^2	
1 km^2	247.1043 acres	1 km^2
1 hectare	2.471 acres[1]	1 hectare
Volume		
1 cm^3	0.061023 in.^{3}	1 cc
		1 ml
1 m^3	35.3147 ft^3	1 m^3
	1.30795 yd^3	
	264.172 gal[2] liquid	
Velocity		
1 m/sec	3.28084 ft/sec	1 m/sec
1 km/hr	0.62137 miles/hr	1 km/hr
Acceleration		
1 m/sec^2	3.28084 ft/sec^2	1 m/sec^2
Mass		
1 g	0.035274 oz	1 g

SI	American	Old metric
1 kg	2.2046216 lb[3]	1 kg
	Density	
1 kg/m^3	0.062428 lb/ft^3	1 kg/m^3
	Force, Weight	
1 N	0.224809 lbf	0.101972 kgf
1 kN	0.1124045 tons[4]	
1 MN	224.809 kips	
1 kN/m	0.06853 kips/ft	
1 kN/m^2	20.9 lbf/ft^2	
	Torque, Bending Moment	
1 N-m	0.73756 lbf-ft	0.101972 kgf-m
1 kN-m	0.73756 kip-ft	101.972 kgf-m
	Pressure, Stress	
1 N/m^2 = 1 Pa	0.000145038 psi	0.101972 kgf/m^2
1 kN/m^2 = 1 kPa	20.8855 psf	
1 MN/m^2 = 1 MPa	0.145038 ksi	
	Viscosity (Dynamic)	
1 N-sec/m^2	0.0208854 lbf-sec/ft^2	0.101972 kgf-sec/m^2
	Viscosity (Kinematic)	
1 m^2/sec	10.7639 ft^2/sec	1 m^2/sec
	Energy, Work	
1 J = 1 N-m	0.737562 lbf-ft	0.00027778 w-hr
1 MJ	0.37251 hp-hr	0.27778 kw-hr
	Power	
1 W = 1 J/sec	0.737562 lbf ft/sec	1 w
1 kW	1.34102 hp	1 kw
	Temperature	
K = 273.15 + °C	°F = (°C × 1.8) + 32	°C = (°F − 32)/1.8
K = 273.15 + 5/9(°F − 32)		
K = 273.15 + 5/9(°R − 491.69)		

(1)Hectare as an alternative for km^2 is restricted to land and water areas.
(2)1 m^3 = 219.9693 Imperial gallons.
(3)1 kg = 0.068522 slugs.
(4)1 American ton = 2000 lb.   1kN = 0.1003612 Imperial ton.   1 Imperial ton = 2240 lb.

Abbreviations for Units

Btu	British thermal unit	kW	kilowatt
°C	degree Celsius (centigrade)	lb	pound
cc	cubic centimeters	lbf	pound force
cm	centimeter	lb_m	pound mass
°F	degree Fahrenheit	MJ	megajoule
ft	foot	MPa	megapascal
g	gram	m	meter
gal	gallon	ml	milliliter
hp	horsepower	mm	millimeter
hr	hour	MN	meganewton
Imp	British Imperial	N	newton
in.	inch	oz	ounce
J	joule	Pa	pascal
K	Kelvin	psf	pounds per square foot
kg	kilogram	psi	pounds per square inch
kgf	kilogram-force	°R	degree Rankine
kip	1000 pound force	sec	second
km	kilometer	slug	14.594 kg
kN	kilonewton	U_o	heat transfer coefficient
kPa	kilopascal	W	watt
ksi	kips per square inch	yd	yard

References/Bibliography

ACI Committee 207, 1986
ACI MANUAL OF CONCRETE PRACTICE, PART 1

ACI Committee 209, 1982
PREDICTION OF CREEP, SHRINKAGE, AND TEMPERATURE EFFECTS IN CON-
CRETE STRUCTURES, *Designing for Creep and Shrinkage in Concrete Structures,*
ACI Publication Special SP-76, American Concrete Institute, Detroit, Mich., pp. 139–300

ACI 228, 1988
IN-PLACE METHODS FOR DETERMINATION OF STRENGTH OF CONCRETE,
American Concrete Institute, Mich., *ACI Materials Journal,* vol. 85, no. 5, Sept.–Oct.

ACI, 1983
BUILDING CODE REQUIREMENTS FOR REINFORCED CONCRETE (ACI 318-83),
American Concrete Institute, Detroit

ACI Committee 318, 1983
BUILDING CODE REQUIREMENTS FOR REINFORCED CONCRETE, American
Concrete Institute, Detroit, Mich., 111 pp.

ACI 318, 1989
BUILDING CODE REQUIREMENTS FOR REINFORCED CONCRETE (ACI 318-89)
AND COMMENTARY (ACI 318R-89), American Concrete Institute, Detroit, Mich., 111
pp.

ACI 347, 1978
RECOMMENDED PRACTICE FOR CONCRETE FORMWORK, American Concrete
Institute, Detroit, Mich., 37 pp.

ACI 363, 1984
STATE-OF-THE-ART ON HIGH STRENGTH CONCRETE, *ACI Journal,* July–Aug.,
pp. 364–411

ACI Committee 544, 1973
STATE OF THE ART REPORT ON FIBER REINFORCED CONCRETE, *ACI Journal,*
vol. 70, no. 11, Nov., pp. 729–744

ACI Committee 544, 1978
MEASUREMENTS OF PROPERTIES OF FIBER REINFORCED CONCRETE, *ACI
Journal,* vol. 75, no. 7, July, pp. 283–289

ACI Committee 544, 1988
MEASUREMENTS OF PROPERTIES OF FIBER REINFORCED CONCRETE, *ACI
Journal,* vol. 85, no. 6, Nov.–Dec., pp. 583–593

ACI-ASCE Committee, 352, 1984
REVISED RECOMMENDATIONS FOR THE DESIGN OF BEAM-COLUMN
JOINTS, American Concrete Institute, Detroit, Mich., draft. No. 11, 34 pp.

ACI-ASCE Committee 352, 1985
RECOMMENDATIONS FOR DESIGN OF BEAM-COLUMN JOINTS IN MONO-
LITHIC REINFORCED CONCRETE STRUCTURES, *ACI Journal,* vol. 82, no. 3,
May–June, pp. 266–283

ACI-ASCE Committee 352, 1988
RECOMMENDATIONS FOR DESIGN OF SLAB-COLUMN CONNECTIONS IN MONOLITHIC REINFORCED CONCRETE STRUCTURES, *ACI Journal*, vol. 85, no. 6, Nov.–Dec., pp. 675–696

ACI-ASCE Committee 426, 1977
SUGGESTED REVISIONS TO SHEAR PROVISIONS FOR BUILDING CODES, *ACI Journal*, vol. 74, no. 9, Sept., pp. 458–469

Agarwal, R. K., and Gardner, N. J., 1974
FORM AND SHORE REQUIREMENTS FOR MULTISTORY FLAT SLAB TYPE BUILDINGS, *ACI Journal*, vol. 71, no. 11, Nov., pp. 559–569

Ahmad, S. H., and Shah, S. P., 1982
STRESS-STRAIN CURVES OF CONCRETE CONFINED BY SPIRAL REINFORCE-MENT, *ACI Journal*, vol. 79, no. 6, Nov.–Dec., pp. 484–490

Ahmad, S. H., and Shah, S. P., 1985
STRUCTURAL PROPERTIES OF HIGH STRENGTH CONCRETE AND ITS IMPLI-CATIONS FOR PRECAST PRESTRESSED CONCRETE, *PCI Journal*, Nov.–Dec., pp. 92–119

Ahmad, S. H., et al., 1986
SHEAR CAPACITY OF REINFORCED HIGH-STRENGTH CONCRETE BEAMS, *ACI Journal*, vol. 83, March–April, pp. 297–305

AIJ, 1982
REINFORCED CONCRETE STRUCTURES. DESIGN CODE AND INTERPRETA-TION (COMMENTARY), Architectural Institute of Japan, Tokyo

Aktan, A. E., Pecknold, D. A. W., and Sozen, M. A., 1973
EFFECT OF TWO-DIMENSIONAL EARTHQUAKE MOTION ON A REINFORCED CONCRETE COLUMN, Civil Engineering Studies, Structural Research Series no. 399, University of Illinois, Urbana, May

Anderson, J. C., and Townsend, W. H., 1977
MODELS FOR RC FRAMES WITH DEGRADING STIFFNESS, *ASCE Journal of the Structural Division*, vol. 103, no. ST12, Feb., pp. 2361–2376

ANSI A10.9, 1983
AMERICAN NATIONAL STANDARD FOR CONSTRUCTION AND DEMOLITION OPERATIONS—CONCRETE AND MASONRY WORK SAFETY REQUIREMENTS (ACI 10.9), American National Standard Institute, New York, 22 pp.

ASTM C39, 1921
TEST METHOD FOR COMPRESSIVE STRENGTH OF CYLINDRICAL CONCRETE SPECIMENS, American Society for Testing and Materials

ASTM C309, 1989
SPECIFICATION FOR LIQUID MEMBRANE FORMING COMPOUNDS FOR CUR-ING CONCRETE

ASTM C1018, 1984
STANDARD TEST METHOD FOR FLEXURAL TOUGHNESS OF FIBER REIN-FORCED CONCRETE, ASTM Standards for Concrete and Mineral Aggregates, vol. 04.02, American Society for Testing and Materials, Aug., pp. 637–644

ASTM C1018, 1989
STANDARD TEST METHOD FOR FLEXURAL TOUGHNESS AND FIRST-CRACK STRENGTH OF FIBER REINFORCED CONCRETE (USING BEAM WITH THIRD POINT LOADING), ASTM Standards for Concrete and Mineral Aggregates, vol. 04.02, American Society for Testing and Materials, April, p. 7

ASTM C597-83, 1983
STANDARD TEST METHOD FOR PULSE VELOCITY THROUGH CONCRETE, American Society for Testing and Materials, Dec.

ASTM C803, 1983
STANDARD TEST METHOD FOR PENETRATION RESISTANCE OF HARDENED CONCRETE, American Society for Testing Materials, Jan.

ASTM C805, 1985
STANDARD TEST METHOD FOR REBOUND NUMBER OF HARDENED CONCRETE, American Society for Testing and Materials, Dec.

ASTM C873-85, 1985
STANDARD TEST METHOD FOR COMPRESSIVE STRENGTH OF CONCRETE CYLINDERS CAST IN PLACE IN CYLINDRICAL MOLDS, American Society for Testing and Materials, June.

ASTM C900, 1982
PULLOUT STRENGTH OF HARDENED CONCRETE, American Society for Testing Materials.

ASTM C900-87, 1987
STANDARD TEST METHOD FOR PULLOUT STRENGTH OF HARDENED CONCRETE, American Society for Testing and Materials, June.

ASTM C1074-87, 1987
STANDARD PRACTICE FOR ESTIMATED CONCRETE STRENGTH BY THE MATURITY METHOD, American Society for Testing and Materials, April.

ATC 3-06, 1978
TENTATIVE PROVISIONS FOR THE DEVELOPMENT OF SEISMIC REGULATION FOR BUILDINGS, Applied Technology Council, Publication ACT 3-06, p. 505

ATC 11, 1983
SEISMIC RESISTANCE OF REINFORCED CONCRETE SHEAR WALLS AND FRAME JOINTS: IMPLICATIONS OF RECENT RESEARCH DESIGN ENGINEERS, Applied Technology Council, Report C1018, ATC-11

Bakoss, S. L., Burfitt, A., Cridland, L., and Heiman, J. L., 1985
MEASURED AND PREDICTED LONG-TERM DEFORMATIONS IN A TALL BUILDING, *Deflections of Concrete Structures,* ACI Special Publication SP-86, American Concrete Institute, Detroit, Mich., pp. 63–94

Banthia, N. F., et al., 1987
STEEL FIBER REINFORCED CONCRETE UNDER IMPACT (International Symposium on Fiber Reinforced Concrete, Madras, India, Dec.), Oxford and IBH Publishing, New Delhi, pp. 4.29–4.39

Barney, G. B., Carley, W. G., Hanson, J. M., and Parmelee, R. A., 1977
BEHAVIOR AND DESIGN OF PRESTRESSED CONCRETE BEAMS WITH LARGE WEB OPENINGS, *PCI Journal,* vol. 22, no. 6, Nov.–Dec., pp. 32–61

Batson, G., 1985
USE OF STEEL FIBERS FOR SHEAR REINFORCEMENT AND DUCTILITY, Elsevier Applied Science Publishers, June, pp. 377–399

Batson, G., et al., 1972
FLEXURAL FATIGUE STRENGTH OF STEEL FIBER REINFORCED CONCRETE BEAMS, *ACI Journal,* vol. 69, no. 11, Nov., pp. 673–677

Baumann, T., 1972
ZUR FRAGE DER NETZBEWEHRUNG VON FLÄCHENTRAGWERKEN (ON THE PROBLEM OF NET REINFORCEMENT OF SURFACE STRUCTURES), *Bauingenieur,* vol. 47, no. 10, Oct., pp. 367–377

Bazant, Z. P., and Kim, T. K., 1984
SIZE EFFECT IN SHEAR FAILURE OF LONGITUDINALLY REINFORCED BEAMS, *ACI Journal,* vol. 81, Sept.–Oct., pp. 456–467

Beck, H., 1962
CONTRIBUTION TO THE ANALYSIS OF COUPLED SHEAR WALLS, *ACI Journal,* vol. 59, pp. 1055–1070

Bertero, V. V., 1980
SEISMIC BEHAVIOUR OF REINFORCED CONCRETE WALL STRUCTURAL SYS-
TEMS, Proceedings of the 7th World Conference on Earthquake Engineering, Istanbul,
Turkey, vol. 6, pp. 323–330

Bertero, V. V., Popov, E. P., Wang, T. Y., and Vallenas, J., 1977
SEISMIC DESIGN IMPLICATIONS OF HYSTERETIC BEHAVIOUR OF REIN-
FORCED CONCRETE STRUCTURAL WALLS, Proceedings of the 6th World Confer-
ence on Earthquake Engineering, New Delhi, India, vol. 5, pp. 159–165

Bickley, J. A., 1971
THE BUILDING COLLAPSE AT 2000 COMMONWEALTH AVE., BOSTON, MAS-
SACHUSETTS, Report to the Mayor's Investigative Commission

Bickley, J. A., 1982
CONCRETE OPTIMIZATION, Concrete International, pp. 38–41

Birss, G. R., Paulay, T., and Park, R., 1978
THE ELASTIC BEHAVIOR OF EARTHQUAKE RESISTANT REINFORCED CON-
CRETE INTERIOR BEAM-COLUMN JOINTS, Report no. 78-13, Department of Civil
Engineering, University of Canterbury, Christchurch, New Zealand, Feb.

Blakeley, R. W. G., Cooney, R. C., and Megget, L. M., 1975
SEISMIC SHEAR LOADING AT FLEXURAL CAPACITY IN CANTILEVER WALL
STRUCTURES, Bulletin of the New Zealand National Society for Earthquake Engineer-
ing, vol. 8, no. 4, pp. 278–290

Bobrowski, J., 1982
ORIGINS OF SAFETY IN CONCRETE STRUCTURES, Ph.D. Thesis, University of
Surrey, England, June, 276 pp.

Bobrowski, J., and Bardham-Roy, B. K., 1969
A METHOD OF CALCULATING THE ULTIMATE STRENGTH OF REINFORCED
AND PRESTRESSED CONCRETE BEAMS IN COMBINED FLEXURE AND
SHEAR, The Structural Engineer, vol. 47, no. 5, May, pp. 197–209

Braestrup, M. W., 1974
PLASTIC ANALYSIS OF SHEAR IN REINFORCED CONCRETE, Magazine of Concrete Research, vol. 26, no. 89, Dec., pp. 221–228

BSI, 1985
CODE OF PRACTICE FOR DESIGN AND CONSTRUCTION, (BS 8110), British Standards Institution, London, England, part 1, 154 pp.

Carrasquillo, R. L., Nilson, A. H., and Slate, F. O., 1981a
MICROCRACKLING AND BEHAVIOR OF HIGH STRENGTH CONCRETE SUB-
JECTED TO SHORT-TERM-LOADS, ACI Journal, May–June, pp. 179–186

Carrasquillo, R. L., Slate, F. O., and Nilson, A. H., 1981b
PROPERTIES OF HIGH STRENGTH CONCRETE SUBJECT TO SHORT-TERM
LOADS, ACI Journal, May–June, pp. 171–178

CEB-FIP, 1978
MODEL CODE FOR CONCRETE STRUCTURES, 3d edition, vols. 1, 2, Comité Euro-
International du Béton/Fédération Internationale de la Precontrainte, Paris, France, 348
pp.

CEB-FIP, 1982
SEISMIC DESIGN OF CONCRETE STRUCTURES. SECOND DRAFT OF AN AP-
PENDIX TO THE CEB-FIB MODEL CODE, Bulletin d'Information, no. 149, Comité
Euro-International du Béton, Paris, France, March

CEB, 1983
MODEL CODE FOR SEISMIC DESIGN OF CONCRETE STRUCTURES, Bulletin
d'Information, no. 162, Comité Euro-International du Béton, Paris, France, p. 117

Cerruti, L. M., and Marti, P., 1987
STAGGERED SHEAR DESIGN OF CONCRETE BEAMS: LARGE SCALE TESTS,
Canadian Journal of Civil Engineering, vol. 14, no. 2, April, pp. 257–268

Chen, R. C., et al., 1985
BEHAVIOR OF HIGH-STRENGTH CONCRETE UNDER UNIAXIAL AND BIAXIAL COMPRESSION, *High Strength Concrete*, ACI Special Publication SP-87, American Concrete Institute, Detroit, Mich., pp. 251–273

CIRIA, 1977
THE DESIGN OF DEEP BEAMS IN REINFORCED CONCRETE, Construction Industry Research and Information Association, Guide 2, London, England

Colaco, J. P., 1970
END MOMENTS FOR FLOOR BEAMS FRAMING INTO SPANDRELS, *ACI Proceedings*, vol. 67, no. 10, Oct.

Colaco, J. P., 1975
HAUNCHED-GIRDER CONCEPT FOR HIGH RISE OFFICE BUILDINGS IN REINFORCED CONCRETE, ACI Special Publication SP72-14, American Concrete Institute, Detroit, Mich.

Collins, M. P., 1978
TOWARDS A RATIONAL THEORY FOR REINFORCED CONCRETE MEMBERS IN SHEAR, *ASCE Journal of the Structural Division*, vol. 104, no. ST4, April, pp. 649–666

Collins, M. P., and Mitchell, D., 1980
SHEAR AND TORSION DESIGN OF PRESTRESSED AND NON-PRESTRESSED CONCRETE BEAMS, *PCI Journal*, vol. 25, no. 5, Sept.–Oct., pp. 32–100; also, Discussion, vol. 26, no. 6, Nov.–Dec., pp. 96–118

Collins, M. P., and Mitchell, D., 1986
A RATIONAL APPROACH TO SHEAR DESIGN—THE 1984 CANADIAN CODE PROVISIONS, *ACI Journal*, vol. 83, no. 6, Nov.–Dec., pp. 925–933

Collins, M. P., and Mitchell, D., 1987
PRESTRESSED CONCRETE BASICS, Canadian Prestressed Concrete Institute, Ottawa, Ont., 614 pp.

Cook, W. D., and Mitchell, D., 1988
STUDIES OF DISTURBED REGIONS NEAR DISCONTINUITIES IN REINFORCED CONCRETE MEMBERS, *ACI Structural Journal*, vol. 85, no. 2, March–April, pp. 206–216

Coull, A., and Choudhury, J. R., 1967
ANALYSIS OF COUPLED SHEAR WALLS, *ACI Journal*, vol. 64, pp. 587–593

Council on Tall Buildings, Group CB, 1978
STRUCTURAL DESIGN OF TALL CONCRETE AND MASONRY BUILDINGS, vol. CB, *Monograph on Planning and Design of Tall Buildings*, ASCE, New York

Council on Tall Buildings, Committee 43, 1979
CONNECTIONS, chapter SB-7, vol. SB, *Monograph on Planning and Design of Tall Buildings*, ASCE, New York

Council on Tall Buildings, Committee 6, 1980
EARTHQUAKE LOADING AND RESPONSE, chapter CL-2, vol. CL, *Monograph on Planning and Design of Tall Buildings*, ASCE, New York

Council on Tall Buildings, Committee 11, 1980
FOUNDATION SYSTEMS, chapter SC-7, vol. SC, *Council on Tall Buildings*, ASCE, New York

Council on Tall Buildings, 1983
DEVELOPMENTS IN TALL BUILDINGS, *Council on Tall Buildings*, Van Nostrand Reinhold, New York

Council on Tall Buildings, 1986
ADVANCES IN TALL BUILDINGS, *Council on Tall Buildings*, Van Nostrand Reinhold, New York

Council on Tall Buildings, 1988
SECOND CENTURY OF THE SKYSCRAPER, *Council on Tall Buildings*, Van Nostrand Reinhold, New York

Council on Tall Buildings, 1990
TALL BUILDINGS: 2000 AND BEYOND, Proceedings of Fourth World Congress held
November 5–9, 1990, in Hong Kong, Council on Tall Buildings, Bethlehem

CSA, 1984
DESIGN OF CONCRETE STRUCTURES FOR BUILDINGS (CAN3-A23.3-M84), Canadian Standards Association, Rexdale, Ont., 281 pp.

Culver, G. C., and Kushner, J., 1975
A PROGRAM FOR SURVEY OF FIRE AND LIVE LOADS IN OFFICE BUILDINGS,
Technical Note no. 858, National Bureau of Standards, Washington, D.C.

Cusens, A. R., 1966
ANALYSIS OF SLABLESS STAIRS, Concrete and Constructional Engineering, vol. 61,
no. 10, pp. 359–364

Cusens, A. R., and Kuang, J. G., 1965
ANALYSIS OF FREE STANDING STAIRS UNDER SYMMETRICAL LOADING,
Concrete and Constructional Engineering, vol. 60, no. 5, pp. 167–172

Cusens, A. R., and Santathadaporn, S., 1966
DESIGN CHARTS FOR HELICAL STAIRS WITH FIXED SUPPORTS, Concrete Publications, Ltd., Cement and Concrete Association, London, England

Daniel, H. R., and McMullen, A. E., 1977
TORSION IN CONCRETE BEAMS CONTAINING AN OPENING, ASCE Journal of
the Structural Division, vol. 103, no. ST3, March, pp. 607–617

Dunstan, A. T., 1987
JOINT PERFORMANCE OF RC STEPPED BEAMS SUBJECTED TO PURE MO-
MENT, B.A.Sc. Thesis, University of Toronto, Ont. Canada, April, 126 pp.

Durrani, A. J., and Wight, J. K., 1982
EXPERIMENTAL AND ANALYTICAL STUDY OF INTERNAL BEAM TO COL-
UMN CONNECTIONS SUBJECTED TO REVERSED CYCLIC LOADINGS, Report
no. UMEE-82R3, Department of Civil Engineering, University of Michigan, July

Ehsani, M. R., and Wight, J. K., 1982
BEHAVIOR OF EXTERNAL REINFORCED CONCRETE BEAM TO COLUMN
CONNECTION SUBJECTED TO EARTHQUAKE TYPE LOADING, Report no.
UMEE-82R5, Department of Civil Engineering, University of Michigan, July

El-Shakra, Z. M., 1989
TOUGHNESS AND FLEXURAL RESPONSE OF FIBER REINFORCED CON-
CRETES, Master Thesis, University of Missouri-Columbia, Dec., p. 189

El-Shakra, Z. M., and Gopalaratnam, V. S., 1990
EFFECT OF DEFLECTION MEASUREMENTS ON TOUGHNESS EVALUATIONS
OF FIBER REINFORCED CONCRETE, submitted for publication, March

El-Sheikh, M., and Chen, W. F., 1988
EFFECTS OF FAST CONSTRUCTION ON DEFLECTIONS OF R.C. BUILDINGS,
ASCE Journal of Structural Engineering, vol. 114, no. ST10, Oct., pp. 2225–2238

Elzanaty, A. H., Nilson, A. H., and Slate, F. O., 1986
SHEAR CAPACITY OF REINFORCED CONCRETE BEAMS UNDER HIGH-
STRENGTH CONCRETE, ACI Journal, vol. 83, March–April, pp. 290–296

ENR, 1973
COLLAPSE KILLS FIVE AND DESTROYS LARGE PORTION OF 26-STORY
APARTMENT BUILDING, Engineering News Record, March 8, p. 12

Fafitis, A., 1984
RESPONSE OF CONFINED CONCRETE SUBJECTED TO EARTHQUAKE TYPE
LOADINGS, Dissertation, Northwestern University, Evanston, Ill., Aug., p. 483

Fafitis, A., and Shah, S. P., 1982
DISCUSSION ON: A COMPARATIVE STUDY OF CONFINEMENT MODELS, ACI
Journal, July–Aug., pp. 260–265

Fafitis, A., and Shah, S. P., 1985a
PREDICTIONS OF ULTIMATE BEHAVIOR OF CONFINED COLUMNS SUB-
JECTED TO LARGE DEFORMATIONS, *ACI Journal*, vol. 82, July–Aug., pp. 423–433

Fafitis, A., and Shah, S. P., 1985b
LATERAL REINFORCEMENT FOR HIGH-STRENGTH CONCRETE COLUMNS,
ACI Special Publication SP-87, American Concrete Institute, Detroit, Mich., pp. 213–232

Fanella, D., and Naaman, A. E., 1985
STRESS-STRAIN PROPERTIES OF FIBER REINFORCED CONCRETE IN COM-
PRESSION, *ACI Journal*, vol. 82, July–Aug., pp. 475–483

Feineck, 1988
THEORETICAL CONSIDERATIONS AND EXPERIMENTAL EVIDENCE ON WEB
COMPRESSION FAILURE OF HIGH-STRENGTH CONCRETE BEAMS, Design As-
pects of High-Strength Concrete, Dubrovnic, Yugoslavia, Sept., pp. 19–31

Fenwick, R. C., and Paulay, T., 1968
MECHANISMS OF SHEAR RESISTANCE OF CONCRETE BEAMS, *ASCE Journal of
the Structural Division*, vol. 94, no. ST10, Oct., pp. 2325–2350

Ferguson, P. M., 1973
REINFORCED CONCRETE FUNDAMENTALS, 3d edition, John Wiley and Sons,
New York, pp. 85–125

Ferguson, P. M., Breen, J. E., and Jirsa, J. O., 1988
REINFORCED CONCRETE FUNDAMENTALS, 5th edition, John Wiley and Sons,
New York

Fintel, M., Derecho, A. T., Freskasis, G. N., Fugelso, L. E., and Gosh, S. K., 1975
STRUCTURAL WALLS IN EARTHQUAKE RESISTANT STRUCTURES, Progress
Report to the National Science Foundation (RANN), Portland Cement Association,
Skokie, Ill., p. 261

Fintel, M., and Ghosh, S. K.
CASE STUDY OF EFFECTS OF POST-TENSIONING THE BEAMS IN A 45-STORY
BUILDING, Portland Cement Association, Skokie, Ill.

Fintel, M., and Khan, F. R., 1965
EFFECTS OF COLUMN EXPOSURE IN TALL STRUCTURERS—TEMPERATURE
VARIATIONS AND THEIR EFFECTS, *ACI Journal*, Dec., vol. 62

Fintel, M., and Khan, F. R., 1969
EFFECTS OF COLUMN CREEP AND SHRINKAGE IN TALL STRUCTURES—
PREDICTION OF INELASTIC COLUMN SHORTENING, *ACI Journal*, Dec.

Fintel, M., and Khan, F. R., 1971
EFFECTS OF COLUMN CREEP AND SHRINKAGE IN TALL STRUCTURES—
ANALYSIS FOR DIFFERENTIAL SHORTENING OF COLUMNS AND FIELD OB-
SERVATION OF STRUCTURES, *Designing for Effects of Creep and Shrinkage in
Concrete Structures*, ACI Special Publication SP-27, American Concrete Institute, De-
troit, Mich., pp. 95–119

Forell, N. F., and Nicoletti, J. P., 1980
MEXICO EARTHQUAKES, OAXACA—NOVEMBER 29, 1978, GUERREO—MARCH
14, 1978, Earthquake Engineering Research Institute, Oct.

Franz, G. C., and Breen, J. E., 1980
DESIGN PROPOSAL FOR SIDE FACE CRACK CONTROL REINFORCEMENT FOR
LARGE REINFORCED CONCRETE BEAMS, *Concrete International: Design and
Construction*, vol. 2, no. 10

Franz, G., and Niedenhoff, H., 1963
REINFORCEMENT FOR BRACKETS AND SHORT BEAMS, *Beton und
Stahlbetonbau* (Berlin), vol. 58, no. 5, pp. 112–120

Freeman, S. A., Szarwecki, R. M., and Honda, K. K., 1980
SIGNIFICANCE OF STIFFNESS ASSUMPTIONS ON LATERAL FORCE CRITE-
RIA, *Reinforced Concrete Structures Subjected to Wind and Earthquake Forces*, ACI
Special Publication SP-63, American Concrete Institute, Detroit, Mich., pp. 437–457

Frenay, J. W., 1990
THEORY AND EXPERIMENTS ON THE BEHAVIOR OF CRACKS IN CONCRETE SUBJECTED TO SUSTAINED SHEAR LOADING, *Hedron,* vol. 35, no. 1, Delft University of Technology, The Netherlands, p. 80

Frenay, J. W., Pruijssers, A. F., Reinhardt, H. W., and Walraven, T. C., 1987
SHEAR TRANSFER IN HIGH-STRENGTH CONCRETE, *Stavanger,* June, pp. 225–236

Furlong, R. W., 1967
STRENGTH OF STEEL-ENCASED CONCRETE BEAM COLUMNS, *ASCE Journal of the Structural Division,* vol. 93, no. ST5, Oct., pp. 113–124

Furlong, R. W., 1989
PERSONAL COMMUNICATION, Nov.

Galeotti, G., Lang, L. D., Saiidi, M., and Zaidi, S. T. H., 1983
ACI Concrete International, vol. 5, no. 6, June, pp. 58–61

Gardner, N. J., 1985
SHORING, RESHORING AND SAFETY, *Concrete International: Design and Construction,* vol. 7, no. 4, April, pp. 28–34

Gates, W. E., 1978
THE ART OF MODELING BUILDINGS FOR DYNAMIC SEISMIC ANALYSIS, Proceedings of a Workshop on Earthquake-Resistant Reinforced Concrete Building Construction, University of California, Berkeley, vol. II, pp. 857–886

Ghali, A., Dilger, W., and Neville, A. M., 1969
TIME-DEPENDENT FORCES INDUCED BY SETTLEMENT OF SUPPORTS IN CONTINUOUS REINFORCED CONCRETE BEAMS, *ACI Journal,* vol. 66, no. 11, Nov., pp. 907–915

Gopalaratnam, V. S., and Shah, S. P., 1985a
SOFTENING OF PLAIN OF CONCRETE IN DIRECT TENSION, *ACI Journal,* vol. 82, May–June, pp. 310–323

Gopalaratnam, V. S., and Shah, S. P., 1986
PROPERTIES OF STEEL FIBER REINFORCED CONCRETE SUBJECTED TO IMPACT LOADING, *ACI Journal,* vol. 83, no. 1, Jan.–Feb. Pp. 117–126

Gopalaratnam, V. S., and Shah, S. P., 1987a
FAILURE MECHANISMS AND FRACTURE OF FIBER REINFORCED CONCRETE, *Fiber Reinforced Concrete—Properties and Applications,* ACI Special Publication SP-105, American Concrete Institute, Detroit, Mich., pp. 1–25

Gopalaratnam, V. S., and Shah, S. P., 1987b
TENSILE FAILURE OF STEEL FIBER REINFORCED MORTAR, *ASCE Journal of the Engineering Mechanics Division,* vol. 113, no. 5, May, 635–653

Gopalaratnam, V. S., et al., 1990
FRACTURE TOUGHNESS OF FIBER REINFORCED CONCRETE, Interuniversity Study Report by the Task Group on CMRC/NSF Research, ACI Committee, 544—Fiber Reinforced Concrete, Jan., p. 69

Gopalaratnam, V. S., 1985
FRACTURE AND IMPACT RESISTANCE OF STEEL FIBER REINFORCED CONCRETE, Ph.D. Thesis, Northwestern University, Evanston, Ill., June, p. 240

Gopalaratnam, V. S., and Shah, S. P., 1985b
STRENGTH, DEFORMATION AND FRACTURE TOUGHNESS OF FIBER CEMENT COMPOSITES AT DIFFERENT RATES OF FLEXURAL LOADING, Steel Fiber Concrete, Elsevier Publishers, June, pp. 299–331

Gopalaratnam, V. S., and Abu-Mathkour, H. J., 1987
EXPERIMENTAL INVESTIGATION OF PULL-OUT CHARACTERISTICS OF SHORT STEEL FIBERS FROM MORTAR MATRIX, Proceedings of the International Symposium on Fiber Reinforced Concrete, Madras, India, December, Oxford and IHB Publishing, New Delhi, pp. 2.201–2.211

Gopalaratnam, V. S., and Jin-Cheng, 1988
ON THE MODELING OF INELASTIC INTERFACES IN FIBROUS COMPOSITES,
Proceedings of the MRS Symposium on Bonding in Cementitious Composites, vol. 114,
pp. 225–232

Gopalaratnam, V. S., and Sahudin, A. H., 1990
AXISYMMETRIC FINITE ELEMENT STUDY OF NONLINEAR FIBER PULL-OUT,
submitted for publication, Jan.

Gosh, S. K., 1982
DEFLECTIONS OF A TWO-WAY REINFORCED CONCRETE SHORING SYSTEM,
Forming Economical Concrete Buildings, Portland Cement Association, Skokie, Ill., pp.
29.1–29.21

Grob, J., and Thurlimann, B., 1976
ULTIMATE STRENGTH AND DESIGN OF REINFORCED CONCRETE BEAMS
UNDER BENDING AND SHEAR, Memo, International Association of Bridge and
Structural Engineering, Zurich, Switzerland, 11:105

Gross, J. L., and Lew, A., 1986
ANALYSIS OF SHORING LOADS AND SLAB CAPACITY FOR MULTISTORY
CONCRETE CONSTRUCTION, 2nd International Conference on Forming Economical
Concrete Buildings, ACI Special Publication SP-90, American Concrete Institute, De-
troit, pp. 109–130

Goutama, M., 1988
TESTS ON REINFORCED CONCRETE STEPPED BEAMS, M.A.Sc. Thesis, University of Toronto, Toronto, Ont., Canada, 258 pp.

Grundy, P., and Kabaila, A., 1963
CONSTRUCTION LOADS ON SLABS WITH SHORED FORMWORK IN MULTI-
STORY BUILDINGS, ACI Journal, vol. 60, no. 12, Dec., pp. 1729–1738

Guralnick, S. A., Singh, S., and Erber, T., 1984
ENERGY METHODS FOR INCREMENTAL COLLAPSE ANALYSIS OF FRAMED
STRUCTURES, ASCE Journal of Structural Engineering, vol. 114, no. 1, Jan., pp. 31–
49

Gustaferro, A. H., 1972
FIRE RESISTANCE OF POST-TENSIONED STRUCTURES, Post-Tensioning Division, Prestressed Concrete Institute, Chicago, Ill.

Hagberg, Th., 1966
ON THE DESIGN OF BRACKETS, (in German) Beton und Stahlbetonbau (Berlin), vol.
61, no. 3, pp. 68–72

Hagberg, Th., 1977
DESIGN OF CONCRETE BRACKETS (in Norwegian), Lectural Notes, Nordic Sympo-
sium on Shear in Concrete Structures, Technical University of Norway, Trondheim,
April, p. 26

Hagberg, Th., 1983
DESIGN OF CONCRETE BRACKETS: ON THE APPLICATION OF THE TRUSS
ANALOGY, ACI Journal, vol. 80, no. 1, Jan.–Feb., pp. 3–12

Hawkins, N. M., and Mitchell, D., 1979
PROGRESSIVE COLLAPSE OF FLAT-PLATE STRUCTURES, ACI Journal, vol. 76,
no. 7, July, pp. 775–808

Hermansen, B. R., and Cowan, J., 1974
MODIFIED SHEAR-FRICTION THEORY FOR BRACKET DESIGN, ACI Journal,
vol. 71, no. 2, Feb., pp. 55–60

Hetenyi, M., 1946
BEAMS ON ELASTIC FOUNDATIONS, University of Michigan Press, Ann Arbor,
Mich.

Hillerborg, A., 1980
ANALYSIS OF FRACTURE BY MEANS OF THE FICTITIOUS CRACK MODEL, *International Journal of Cement Composite*, vol. 2, pp. 177–184

Hoff, G. C., 1987
BIBLIOGRAPHY ON FIBER REINFORCED CONCRETE, Proceedings of International Symposium on Fiber Reinforced Concrete, Madras, India, December, Oxford and IHB Publishing, New Delhi, pp. 8.3–8.163

Hognestad, E., 1951
A STUDY OF COMBINED BENDING AND AXIAL LOADING IN REINFORCED CONCRETE MEMBERS, Bulletin no. 399, Engineering Experiment Station, University of Illinois, Urbana, Nov.

Holmes, M., and Martin, L. H., 1983
ANALYSIS AND DESIGN OF STRUCTURAL CONNECTIONS, REINFORCED CONCRETE AND STEEL, Ellis Horwood Ltd., West Sussex, England

Hsu, T. T. C., 1988
SOFTENED TRUSS MODEL THEORY FOR SHEAR AND TORSION, *ACI Structural Journal*, vol. 85, no. 6, Nov.–Dec., pp. 624–635

Hurd, M. K., 1979
FORMWORK FOR CONCRETE, 4th edition, ACI Special Publication SP-4, American Concrete Institute, Detroit, Mich.

Hurd, M. K., and Courtois, P. D., 1986
METHOD OF ANALYSIS FOR SHORING AND RESHORING IN MULTISTORY BUILDINGS, *2nd International Conference on Forming Economical Concrete Buildings*, ACI Special Publication, SP-90, American Concrete Institute, Detroit, Mich., pp. 91–100

IABSE, 1979
COLLOQUIUM ON PLASTICITY IN REINFORCED CONCRETE, International Association of Bridge and Structural Engineers, Copenhagen, Introductory Report, vol. 28, 172 pp; Final Report, vol. 29, 360 pp.

IAEE, 1984
EARTHQUAKE RESISTANT REGULATIONS—A WORLD LIST, International Association for Earthquake Engineers, Tokyo, Japan, p. 904

Iqbal, M., and Derecho, A. T., 1980
INERTIAL FORCES OVER HEIGHT OF REINFORCED CONCRETE STRUCTURAL WALLS DURING EARTHQUAKES, *Reinforced Concrete Structures Subjected to Wind and Earthquake Forces*, ACI Special Publication SP-63, American Concrete Institute, Detroit, mich., pp. 173–196

Japan Concrete Institute, 1983
METHOD OF TEST FOR FLEXURAL STRENGTH AND FLEXURAL TOUGHNESS OF FIBER REINFORCED CONCRETE (SF4), JCI Standards for Test Methods of Fiber Reinforced Concrete, Japan Concrete Institute, pp. 45–51

Jenq, Y. S., and Shah, S. P., 1986
CRACK PROPAGATION IN FIBER-REINFORCED CONCRETE, *ASCE Journal of Structural Engineering*, vol. 112, no. ST1, Jan., pp. 19–34

Johnston, C. D., 1980
PROPERTIES OF STEEL FIBER REINFORCED MORTAR AND CONCRETE, Proceedings of an International Symposium on Fibrous Concrete, CI, The Construction Press Ltd., Lancaster, England

Johnston, C. D., 1982a
DEFINITION AND MEASUREMENTS OF FLEXURAL TOUGHNESS PARAMETERS OF FIBER REINFORCED CONCRETE, Cement, Concrete, and Aggregates, CCAGDP, vol. 4, no. 2, American Society for Testing and Materials, Winter, pp. 53–60

Johnston, C. D., 1982b
STEEL FIBER REINFORCED CONCRETE—PRESENT AND FUTURE IN ENGI-
NEERING CONSTRUCTION, Composites, April, pp. 113–121

Jonsson, E., and Savre, T. I., 1976
TESTS ON BRACKETS IN CONCRETE (in Norwegian), Norwegian Building Research
Institute, Oslo, Report no. 2/1976, p. 31

Kaba, S. A., and Mahin, S. A., 1984
REFINED MODELING OF REINFORCED CONCRETE COLUMNS FOR SEISMIC
ANALYSIS, Earthquake Engineering Research Center, University of California, Berke-
ley, Report no. UCB/EERC-84/03, April

Kani, G. N. J., 1964
THE RIDDLE OF SHEAR AND ITS SOLUTION, ACI Journal, vol. 61, no. 4, April, pp.
441–467

Karshenas, S., and Ayoub, H., 1989
AN INVESTIGATION OF LIVE LOADS ON CONCRETE STRUCTURES DURING
CONSTRUCTION, Proceedings of I COSSAR '89, 5th International Conference on
Structural Safety and Reliability, San Francisco, Calif., pp. 1807–1814

Kato, B., Akiyama, H., and Kitazawa, S., 1978
DEFORMATION CHARACTERISTICS OF BOX-SHAPED STEEL MEMBERS IN-
FLUENCED BY LOCAL BUCKLING (in Japanese), Transactions of the Architectural
Institute of Japan, no. 268, June, pp. 71–76

Kienberger, H., 1975
DIAPHRAGM WALLS AS LOAD BEARING FOUNDATIONS, Institution of Civil Engineers, London, England

Kemp, E. L., and Mukherjee, P. R., 1968
INELASTIC BEHAVIOR OF CORNER KNEE JOINTS, The Consulting Engineer,
Oct., pp. 44–48

Knowles, R. B., and Park, R., 1969
STRENGTH OF CONCRETE FILLED STEEL TUBULAR COLUMNS, ASCE Journal
of the Structural Division, vol. 95, no. ST12, Dec., pp. 2565–2587

Kollegger, J., and Mehlhorn, G., 1987
MATERIAL MODEL FOR CRACKED REINFORCED CONCRETE, Proc. IABSE
Colloquium on Computational Mechanics of Concrete Structures, Delft, The Nether-
lands, Aug., pp. 63–74

Kong, F. K., Editor, 1990
REINFORCED CONCRETE DEEP BEAMS, Blackie, Glasgow; Van Nostrand
Reinhold, New York

Kong, F. K., and Evans, R. H., 1980
REINFORCED AND PRESTRESSED CONCRETE, 2d edition, The English Language
Book Society and Nelson, pp. 162–179

Kong, F. K., Robins, P. J., and Cole, D. F., 1970
WEB REINFORCEMENT EFFECTS ON DEEP BEAMS, ACI Journal, vol. 67, pp.
1010–1017

Kong, F. K., et al., 1975
DESIGN OF REINFORCED CONCRETE DEEP BEAMS IN CURRENT PRACTICE,
Structural Engineering, vol. 53, no. 4

Kormeling, H. A., et al., 1980
STATIC AND FATIGUE PROPERTIES OF CONCRETE BEAMS REINFORCED
WITH CONTINUOUS BARS AND WITH FIBERS, ACI Journal, vol. 77, no. 1, Jan.–
Feb., pp. 36–43

Kotsovos, M. D., 1979
FRACTURE PROCESSES OF CONCRETE UNDER GENERALIZED STRESS
STATES, Materials and Structures (RILEM), vol. 12, no. 72, Nov.–Dec., pp. 431–437

Kotsovos, M. D., 1981
AN ANALYTICAL INVESTIGATION OF THE BEHAVIOR OF CONCRETE UNDER CONCENTRATION OF LOAD, *Materials and Structures* (RILEM), vol. 14, no. 83, Sept.–Oct., pp. 341–348

Kotsovos, M. D., 1982
A FUNDAMENTAL EXPLANATION OF THE BEHAVIOUR OF RC BEAMS IN FLEXURE BASED ON THE PROPERTIES OF CONCRETE UNDER MULTIAXIAL STRESS, *Materials and Structures* (RILEM), vol. 15, Nov.–Dec., pp. 529–537

Kotsovos, M. D., 1983a
EFFECT OF TESTING TECHNIQUES ON THE POST-ULTIMATE BEHAVIOUR OF CONCRETE IN COMPRESSION, *Materials and Structures,* (RILEM), vol. 16, pp. 3–12

Kotsovos, M. D., 1983b
MECHANISMS OF 'SHEAR' FAILURE, *Magazine of Concrete Research,* vol. 35, no. 123, June, pp. 99–106

Kotsovos, M. D., 1984a
BEHAVIOR OF RC BEAMS WITH SHEAR SPAN TO DEPTH RATIOS BETWEEN 1.0 AND 2.5, *ACI Journal,* vol. 81, no. 3, May–June, pp. 279–286

Kotsovos, M. D., 1984b
DEFORMATION AND FAILURE OF CONCRETE IN A STRUCTURE, International Conference on Concrete under Multiaxial Conditions (RILEM-CEB-CNRS), Toulous, France, May

Kotsovos, M. D., 1986
BEHAVIOUR OF REINFORCED CONCRETE BEAMS WITH A SHEAR SPAN TO DEPTH RATIO GREATER THAN 2.5, *ACI Journal,* vol. 83, pp. 1026–1034

Kotsovos, M. D., 1987a
SHEAR FAILURE OF REINFORCED CONCRETE BEAMS, *Engineering Structures,* vol. 9, pp. 32–38

Kotsovos, M. D., 1987b
SHEAR FAILURE OF RC BEAMS: A REAPPRAISAL OF CURRENT CONCEPTS, *Bulletin, d'Information,* no. 178/179, Comité Euro-International du Béton, Paris, France, pp. 103–112

Kotsovos, M. D., 1988a
COMPRESSIVE FORCE PATH CONCEPT: BASIS FOR ULTIMATE LIMIT STATE REINFORCED CONCRETE DESIGN, *ACI Journal,* vol. 85, pp. 68–75

Kotsovos, M. D., 1988b
DESIGN OF REINFORCED CONCRETE DEEP BEAMS, *The Structural Engineer,* vol. 66, pp. 28–32

Kotsovos, M. D., to be published, a
DESIGNING RC BEAMS IN COMPLIANCE WITH THE CONCEPT OF THE COM-PRESSIVE FORCE PATH, in preparation

Kotsovos, M. D., to be published, b
BEHAVIOUR OF RC BEAMS DESIGNED IN COMPLIANCE WITH THE COM-PRESSIVE FORCE PATH, in preparation

Kotsovos, M. D., to be published, c
SHEAR FAILURE OF RC BEAMS, in preparation

Kotsovos, M. D., to be published, d
BEHAVIOUR OF RC BEAMS WITH SHEAR SPAN TO DEPTH RATIOS GREATER THAN 2.5 in preparation

Kotsovos, M. D., to be published, e
THE USE OF FUNDAMENTAL PROPERTIES OF CONCRETE FOR THE DESIGN OF RC STRUCTURAL MEMBERS, Research Project sponsored by Nuffield Foundation, Award No. 890BA, Imperial College.

Kotsovos, M. D., Bobrowski, J., and Eibl, J., 1987
BEHAVIOUR OF RC T-BEAMS IN SHEAR, *The Structural Engineer,* vol. 65B, pp. 1–10

Kotsovos, M. D., and Newman, J. B., 1981a
FRACTURE MECHANICS AND CONCRETE BEHAVIOUR, *Magazine of Concrete Research,* vol. 33, no. 113, June, pp. 103–112

Kotsovos, M. D., and Newman, J. B., 1981b
EFFECT OF BOUNDARY CONDITIONS UPON THE BEHAVIOUR OF CONCRETE UNDER CONCENTRATIONS OF LOAD, *Magazine of Concrete Research,* vol. 33, no. 116, Sept., pp. 161–170

Kriz, L. B., and Raths, C. H., 1965
CONNECTION IN PRECAST CONCRETE STRUCTURES—STRENGTH OF COR-BELS, *PCI Journal,* vol. 10, no. 1, Feb., pp. 16–61

Kupfer, H., 1964
ERWEITERUNG DER MÖRSCH'SCHEN FACHWERKANALOGIE MIT HILFE DES PRINZIPS VOM MINIMUM DER FORMÄNDERUNGSARBEIT (GENERALIZA-TION OF MOERSCH'S TRUSS ANALOGY USING THE PRINCIPLE OF MINI-MUM STRAIN ENERGY), *Bulletin d'Information,* no. 40, Comité Euro-International du Béton, Paris, France, Jan., pp. 44–57

Lai, S. S., Will, G. T., and Otani, S., 1984
MODEL FOR INELASTIC BIAXIAL BENDING OF REINFORCED CONCRETE MEMBERS, *ASCE Journal of the Structural Division,* vol. 110, no. ST11, Nov., pp. 2563–2584

Lampert, P., and Thurlimann, B., 1971
ULTIMATE STRENGTH AND DESIGN OF REINFORCED CONCRETE BEAMS IN TORSION AND BENDING, International Association for Bridge and Structural Engineering, *Publications,* vol. 31-I, pp. 107–131

Lankard, D. R., 1975
FIBER CONCRETE APPLICATIONS, RILEM Symposium on Fiber Reinforced Cement and Concrete, Sheffield, England, pp. 3–19

Lawrence, P., 1972
SOME THEORETICAL CONSIDERATIONS OF FIBER PULL-OUT FROM AN ELASTIC MATRIX, *Journal of Materials Science,* vol. 7, pp. 1–6

Leonhardt, F., 1977
CRACK CONTROL IN CONCRETE STRUCTURES, IABSE surveys, no. S-4/77, Zurich, Switzerland

Leonhardt, F., and Monning, E., 1974
LECTURES ON THE DESIGN OF CONCRETE STRUCTURES: PART 3—BASIS FOR DESIGN OF REINFORCEMENT (in German), Springer-Verlag, Berlin-Heidelberg

Leonhardt, F., and Walther, R., 1961–62
THE STUTTGART SHEAR TEST, 1961, *Cement and Concrete Association Library,* 134 pp. (Translation by C. V. Amerongen of the articles that appeared in *Beton- und Stahlbetonbau,* vol. 56, no. 12, 1961; vol. 57, nos. 2, 3, 6, 7, and 9, 1962)

Leonhardt, F., and Walther, R., 1966
WANDARTIGE TRÄGER, Deutscher Ausschuss Für Stahlbeton; Wilhelm Ernst and Sohn, Berlin, Germany, 1978

Leslie, K. E., Rajagopalan, K. S., and Everard, N. J., 1976
FLEXURAL BEHAVIOR OF HIGH-STRENGTH CONCRETE BEAMS, *ACI Journal,* vol. 73, Sept., pp. 517–521

Lew, H. S., 1976
SAFETY DURING CONSTRUCTION OF CONCRETE BUILDINGS—A STATUS RE-PORT (in Japanese), *Transactions of the Architectural Institute of Japan,* no. 345, Nov., pp. 70–78, NBS Building Science Series no. 80, National Bureau of Standards, Washington, D.C.

Lew, H. S., 1980
WEST VIRGINIA COOLING TOWER COLLAPSE CAUSED BY INADEQUATE
CONCRETE STRENGTH, Civil Engineering, ASCE, vol. 50, no. 2, Feb., pp. 62–67

Lew, H. S., 1985
CONSTRUCTION LOADS AND LOAD EFFECTS IN CONCRETE BUILDING CON-
STRUCTION, Concrete International: Design and Construction, vol. 7, no. 4, April, pp.
20–23

Lew, H. S., Carino, N. J., and Fattal, S. G., 1982
CAUSE OF THE CONDOMINIUM COLLAPSE IN COCOA BEACH, FLORIDA, Concrete International: Design and Construction, vol. 4, no. 8, Aug., pp. 64–73

Linbeck, L. E. III, 1984
BEHAVIOR OF REINFORCED CONCRETE COLUMNS SUBJECTED TO CYCLIC
AXIAL AND LATERAL LOAD REVERSALS, Masters Thesis, University of Texas at
Austin, May

Liu, X., Chen, W., and Bowman, M. D., 1985
CONSTRUCTION LOAD ANALYSIS FOR CONCRETE STRUCTURES, ASCE Journal of Structural Engineering, vol. 111, no. ST5, May, pp. 1019–1036

Lorensten, M., 1965
HOLES IN REINFORCED CONCRETE GIRDERS, Portland Cement Association,
Skokie, Ill., Feb.

Lorensten, M., 1972
HOLES IN REINFORCED CONCRETE GIRDERS (in Swedish), Byggmastaven
(Stockholm).

Lyn, T. Y., 1963
LOAD BALANCING METHODS FOR DESIGN AND ANALYSIS OF PRE-
STRESSED CONCRETE STRUCTURES, ACI Journal, vol. 60, no. 6, June, pp. 719–
742

Ma, S. Y., Bertero, V. V., and Popov, E. P., 1976
EXPERIMENTAL AND ANALYTICAL STUDIES ON THE HYSTERETIC
BEHAVIOUR OF REINFORCED CONCRETE RECTANGULAR AND T-BEAMS,
Report no. 76-2, Earthquake Engineering Research Center, University of California, Ber-
keley

Mailhot, G., 1984
EXPERIMENTS ON THE STAGGERING CONCEPT FOR SHEAR DESIGN, M.Eng.
Thesis, McGill University, Montreal, Que., Canada, 96 pp.

Mander, J. B., Priestley, M. J. N., and Park, R., 1984
SEISMIC DESIGN OF BRIDGE PIERS, Research Report no. 84-2, Department of Civil
Engineering, University of Canterbury, Christchurch, New Zealand, p. 442, plus Appen-
dices, Feb.

Mansur, M. A., 1983
COMBINED BENDING AND TORSION IN REINFORCED CONCRETE BEAMS
WITH RECTANGULAR OPENINGS, Concrete International: Design and Construc-
tion, vol. 5, no. 11, Nov., pp. 51–58

Mansur, M. A., and Hasnat, A., 1979
CONCRETE BEAMS WITH SMALL OPENINGS UNDER TORSION, ASCE Journal
of the Structural Division, vol. 105, no. ST11, Nov., pp. 2433–2447

Mansur, M. A., and Paramasivam, P., 1984
REINFORCED CONCRETE BEAMS WITH SMALL OPENING IN BENDING AND
TORSION, ACI Journal, vol. 81, no. 2, March–April, pp. 180–185

Mansur, M. A., et al., 1983a
TORSION TESTS OF R/C BEAMS WITH LARGE OPENINGS, ASCE Journal of Structural Engineering, vol. 109, no. 8, Aug., pp. 1780–1791

Mansur, M. A., et al., 1983b
ULTIMATE TORQUE OF R/C BEAM WITH LARGE OPENINGS, *ASCE Journal of Structural Engineering*, vol. 109, no. 8, Aug., pp. 1887–1902

Mansur, M. A., et al., 1984
COLLAPSE LOADS OF R/C BEAMS WITH LARGE OPENINGS, *ASCE Journal of Structural Engineering*, vol. 110, no. 11, Nov., pp. 2602–2618

Mansur, M. A., et al., 1985
DESIGN METHOD FOR REINFORCED CONCRETE BEAMS WITH LARGE OPENINGS, *ACI Journal*, vol. 82, no. 4, July–Aug., pp. 517–524

Marti, P., 1980
ZUR PLASTISCHEN BERECHNUNG VON STAHLBETON (ON PLASTIC ANALYSIS OF REINFORCED CONCRETE), Institute of Structural Engineering, ETH Zurich, Switzerland, Report no. 104, 176 pp.

Marti, P., 1982
STRENGTH AND DEFORMATIONS OF REINFORCED CONCRETE MEMBERS UNDER TORSION AND COMBINED ACTIONS, *Bulletin d'Information*, no. 146, Comité Euro-International du Béton, Jan., pp. 97–138

Marti, P., 1985a
BASIC TOOLS OF REINFORCED CONCRETE BEAM DESIGN, *ACI Journal*, vol. 82, no. 1, Jan.–Feb., pp. 46–56; also, Discussion, vol. 82, no. 6, Nov.–Dec., pp. 933–935

Marti, P., 1985b
TRUSS MODELS IN DETAILING, *Concrete International: Design and Construction*, vol. 8, no. 10, Oct., pp. 66–68

Marti, P., 1986a
STAGGERED SHEAR DESIGN OF SIMPLY SUPPORTED CONCRETE BEAMS, *ACI Journal*, vol. 83, no. 1, Jan.–Feb., pp. 36–42

Marti, P., 1986b
STAGGERED SHEAR DESIGN OF CONCRETE BRIDGE GIRDERS, Proceedings of the International Conference on Short and Medium Span Bridges, Ottawa, Ont., Canada, Aug., vol. 1, pp. 139–149

Marti, P., 1989
DESIGN OF CONCRETE SLABS FOR TRANSVERSE SHEAR, *ACI Structural Journal*, submitted for publication

Marti, P., 1990
PERSONAL COMMUNICATION

Marti, P., and Kong, K., 1987
RESPONSE OF REINFORCED CONCRETE SLAB ELEMENTS TO TORSION, *ASCE Journal of Structural Engineering*, vol. 113, no. ST5, May, pp. 976–993

Martinez, S., Nilson, A. H., and Slate, F. O., 1982
SPIRALLY-REINFORCED HIGH-STRENGTH CONCRETE COLUMNS, *ACI Journal*, vol. 81, Sept.–Oct., pp. 431–442; Research report no. 82-10, Department of Structural Engineering, Cornell University, Ithaca, N.Y., Aug.

Mast, R. F., 1968
AUXILIARY REINFORCEMENT IN CONCRETE CONNECTIONS, *ASCE Proceedings*, vol. 94, no. ST6, June, pp. 1485–1504

Matsui, C., 1985a
STRENGTH AND BEHAVIOUR OF FRAMES WITH CONCRETE FILLED SQUARE STEEL TUBULAR COLUMNS UNDER EARTHQUAKE LOADING, Proceedings of the International Specialty Conference on Concrete Filled Steel Tubular Structures, Harbin, China, Aug., pp. 104–111

Matsui, C., 1985b
LOCAL BUCKLING OF CONCRETE FILLED STEEL SQUARE TUBULAR COLUMNS, IABSE-ECCS Symposium, Luxembourg, Sept., pp. 269–276

Mattock, A. H., 1976
DESIGN PROPOSALS FOR REINFORCED CONCRETE CORBELS, *PCI Journal,* vol. 21, no. 3, May–June, pp. 18–42

Mattock, A. H., et al., 1976
THE BEHAVIOR OF REINFORCED CONCRETE CORBELS, *PCI Journal,* vol. 21, no. 2, March–April, pp. 52–77

Mayfield, B., Kong, F. K., Bennison, A., and Davies, J. C. D. T., 1971
CORNER JOINT DETAILS IN STRUCTURAL LIGHTWEIGHT CONCRETE, *ACI Journal,* vol. 68, no. 5, May, pp. 366–372

McCormac, C. W., 1986
DESIGN OF REINFORCED CONCRETE, 2d edition, Harper & Row, New York, chapter 14

Mehmel, A., and Freitag, W., 1967
TESTS ON THE LOAD CAPACITY OF CONCRETE BRACKETS (in German), *Der Bauingenieur* (Heidelberg), vol. 42, no. 10, pp. 362–369

Meinheit, D. F., and Jirsa, J. O., 1983
SHEAR STRENGTH OF REINFORCED CONCRETE BEAM-COLUMN CONNECTIONS, *ASCE Journal of the Structural Division,* vol. 107, no. ST11, pp. 2227–2244

Meyers, V. J., 1983
MATRIX ANALYSIS OF STRUCTURES, Harper & Row, New York

Mindess, S., 1983
THE FRACTURE OF FIBER REINFORCED AND POLYMER IMPREGNATED CONCRETES: A REVIEW, *Fracture Mechanics of Concrete,* Elsevier Applied Science Publishers, Amsterdam, The Netherlands, pp. 481–501

Mindess, S., and Young, J. F., 1981
CONCRETE, Prentice-Hall, Englewood Cliffs, N.J., chapter 18

Mitchell, D., and Collins, M. P., 1974
DIAGONAL COMPRESSIONS FIELD THEORY—A RATIONAL MODEL FOR STRUCTURAL CONCRETE IN PURE TORSION, *ACI Journal,* vol. 71, no. 8, Aug., pp. 396–408

Mitchell, D., and Cook, W. D., 1984
PREVENTING PROGRESSIVE COLLAPSE OF SLAB STRUCTURES, *ASCE Journal of Structural Engineering,* vol. 110, no. ST7, July, pp. 1513–1532

Moehle, J. P., Diebold, J. W., and Zee, H. L., 1984
EXPERIMENTAL STUDY OF A FLAT-PLATE BUILDING MODEL, Proceedings of the Eighth World Conference on Earthquake Engineering, San Francisco, Calif., July, vol. IV, pp. 355–362

Moersch, E., 1908, 1922
DER EISENBETONBAU—SEINE THEORIE UND ANWENDUNG (REINFORCED CONCRETE CONSTRUCTION—THEORY AND APPLICATION), 3d edition, K. Wittwer, Stuttgart, 1908; 5th edition, vol. 1, part 2, 1922

Moersch, E., 1909
CONCRETE STEEL CONSTRUCTION, English translation by E. P. Goodrich, McGraw-Hill, New York, 368 pp. (Translation from 3d edition of *Der Eisenbetonbau;* 1st edition 1902)

Mohammadi, J., and Yazbeck, G. J., 1990
STRATEGIES FOR BRIDGE INSPECTION USING PROBALISTIC MODELS, in *Structural Safety and Reliability,* vol. 3, A. H.-S. Ang, M. Shinozuka, and G. I. Schueller, editors, American Society of Civil Engineers, New York, pp. 2115–2122

Mokhtar, A. S., et al., 1985
STUD SHEAR REINFORCEMENT FOR FLAT CONCRETE PLATES, *ACI Journal,* vol. 82, no. 5, Sept.–Oct.

Moretto, O., 1971
REINFORCED CONCRETE COURSE (Curso de Hormigon Armado), 2d ed., Libreria
El Ateneo, Buenos Aires, Argentina

Moretto, O., 1971
DEEP FOUNDATIONS—SELECTED SYNTHESIS OF THE PRESENT STATE OF
THE KNOWLEDGE ABOUT SOIL INTEGRATION, Revista Latinoamericana de
Geotecnia, Caracas, Venezuela, July–Sept. 1971

Moretto, O., 1975
FOUNDATIONS OF THE BRIDGES OVER THE PARANA RIVER IN ARGENTINA,
Proceedings of the 5th Panamerican Conference on Soil Mechanics and Foundation En-
gineering, Buenos Aires, Argentina, vol. V

Morishita, Y., Tomii, M., and Yoshimura, K., 1979a
EXPERIMENTAL STUDIES ON BOND STRENGTH IN CONCRETE FILLED CIR-
CULAR STEEL TUBULAR COLUMNS SUBJECTED TO AXIAL LOADS, Transac-
tions of the Japan Concrete Institute, vol. 1, pp. 351–358

Morishita, Y., Tomii, M., and Yoshimura, K., 1979b
EXPERIMENTAL STUDIES ON BOND STRENGTH IN CONCRETE FILLED
SQUARE STEEL TUBULAR COLUMNS SUBJECTED TO AXIAL LOADS, Trans-
actions of the Japan Concrete Institute, vol. 1, pp. 359–366

Morishita, Y., and Tomii, M., 1982
EXPERIMENTAL STUDIES ON BOND STRENGTH BETWEEN SQUARE STEEL
TUBE AND ENCASED CONCRETE CORE UNDER CYCLIC SHEARING FORCE
AND CONSTANT AXIAL FORCE, Transactions of the Japan Concrete Institute, vol.
4, pp. 363–370

Morrison, D. G., and Sozen, M. A., 1981
RESPONSE OF REINFORCED CONCRETE PLATE-COLUMN CONNECTIONS TO
DYNAMIC AND STATIC HORIZONTAL LOADS, Civil Engineering Studies, Struc-
tural Research Series no. 490, University of Illinois, Urbana, April

Morrison, J. K., et al., 1988
ANALYSIS OF THE DEBONDING AND PULL-OUT PROCESS IN FIBER COMPOS-
ITES, ASCE Journal of the Engineering Mechanics Division, vol. 114, no. EM2, Feb.,
pp. 277–294

Mphonde, A. C., and Frantz, G. C., 1985
SHEAR TEST OF HIGH- AND LOW-STRENGTH CONCRETE BEAMS WITH STIR-
RUPS, ACI Special Publication SP-87, American Concrete Institute, Detroit, Mich., pp.
179–196

Mueller, P., 1976
FAILURE MECHANISMS FOR REINFORCED CONCRETE BEAMS IN TORSION
AND BENDING, International Association for Bridge and Structural Engineering, Pub-
lications, vol. 36-II, pp. 147–163

Mueller, P., 1978
PLASTICHE BERECHNUNG VON STAHLBETONSCHEIBEN UND -BALKEN
(PLASTIC ANALYSIS OF REINFORCED CONCRETE WALLS AND BEAMS), In-
stitute of Structural Engineering, ETH Zurich, Switzerland, Report no. 83, 160 pp.

Naaman, A. E., and Shah, 1976
PULL-OUT MECHANISM IN STEEL FIBER REINFORCED CONCRETE, ASCE
Journal of the Structural Division, vol. 102, no. ST8, Aug., pp. 1537–1548

Naaman, A. E., et al., 1974
PROBABILISTIC ANALYSIS OF FIBER REINFORCED CONCRETE, ASCE Journal
of the Engineering Mechanics Division, vol. 100, no. EM2, April, pp. 397–413

Nasser, K. W., Acavalos, A., and Daniel, H. R., 1967
BEHAVIOR AND DESIGN OF LARGE OPENINGS IN REINFORCED CONCRETE
BEAMS, ACI Journal, vol. 64, no. 1, Jan., pp. 25–33

National Research Council of Canada, 1988
PROCEEDINGS, SYMPOSIUM/WORKSHOP ON SERVICEABILITY OF BUILD-
INGS (MOVEMENTS, DEFLECTIONS, VIBRATIONS), vol. 1, University of Ottawa,
Ottawa, Ont., May

Nawy, E. G., and Balaguru, P. N., 1983
HIGH-STRENGTH CONCRETE, *Structural Concrete Handbook,* McGraw-Hill, New
York

Neville, A. M., 1970
CREEP OF CONCRETE: PLAIN, REINFORCED AND PRESTRESSED, North Hol-
land, Amsterdam, The Netherlands

Ngab, A. S., et al., 1980
BEHAVIOR OF HIGH-STRENGTH CONCRETE UNDER SUSTAINED COMPRES-
SIVE STRESS, Department of Structural Engineering Research Report no. 80-2, Cornell
University, Ithaca, N.Y., Feb., p. 201

Ngab. A. S., Nilson, A. H., and Slate, J. D., 1981a
SHRINKAGE AND CREEP OF HIGH STRENGTH CONCRETE, *ACI Journal,* July–
Aug., pp. 255–261

Ngab, A. S., Slate, F. O., and Nilson, A. H., 1981b
MICROCRACKING AND TIME-DEPENDENT STRAINS IN HIGH STRENGTH
CONCRETE, *ACI Journal,* July–Aug., pp. 262–267

Niedenhoff, H., 1961
STUDIES ON THE STRUCTURAL BEHAVIOR OF BRACKETS AND SHORT
BEAMS, Doctoral Thesis, Technische Hochschule, Karlsruhe, Germany

Nielsen, M. P., 1971
ON THE STRENGTH OF REINFORCED CONCRETE DISCS, *Civil Engineering and
Building Construction Series,* no. 70, Acta Polytechnica Scandinavia, Copenhagen, Den-
mark, 261 pp.

Nielsen, M. P., 1984
LIMIT ANALYSIS AND CONCRETE PLASTICITY, Prentice-Hall, Englewood Cliffs,
N.J., 420 pp.

Nielsen, M. P., et al., 1978
CONCRETE PLASTICITY: BEAM SHEAR—SHEAR IN JOINTS—PUNCHING
SHEAR, Special Publication, Danish Society for Structural Science and Engineering,
Technical University of Denmark, Lyngby

Nilson, A. H., 1985
DESIGN IMPLICATIONS OF CURRENT RESEARCH ON HIGH STRENGTH CON-
CRETE, *High Strength Concrete,* ACI Special Publication SP-87, American Concrete In-
stitute, Detroit, Mich., pp. 85–118

NRCCND, 1983
EL-ASNAM, ALGERIA EARTHQUAKE OF OCTOBER 10, 1980, Earthquake Engi-
neering Research Institute, National Research Council Committee on Natural Disasters,
Jan.

Nylander, H., 1967
DEEP BEAMS, I. EFFECTS PRODUCED ON STRESS DISTRIBUTION UNDER
CONCENTRATED LOADS BY TRANSVERSE REINFORCEMENT DESIGNED TO
PREVENT BURSTING (Hoga Balkar. I. Inverkan Av Klyvningsforhindrande armering
pa spanningsfordelningen under koncentrerad last), Reprint from Nordisk Betong, no. 1,
Stockholm, Sweden, pp. 53–64

Nylander, H., and Nylander, J. O., 1967
DEEP BEAMS. II. MOMENT AND STRESS DISTRIBUTION IN CONTINUOUS
DEEP BEAMS (Hoga Balkar. II. Moment-Ock Spanningsfordelning 1 Kontinuerlig Hog
Balk), Reprint from Nordisk Betong, no. 1, Stockholm, Sweden, pp. 65–78

Oesterle, R. G., Fiorato, A. E., and Corley, W. G., 1980
REINFORCEMENT DETAILS FOR EARTHQUAKE-RESISTANT STRUCTURAL
WALLS, Concrete International: Design and Construction, vol. 2, no. 12, pp. 55–66

OSHA, 1983
SAFETY AND HEALTH REGULATIONS FOR CONSTRUCTION (29 CFR Part 1926/
1910), U.S. Department of Labor, Bureau of Labor Standards, Washington, D.C.

Park, R., 1977
COLUMNS SUBJECTED TO FLEXURE AND AXIAL LOAD, Bulletin of the New
Zealand National Society for Earthquake Engineering, vol. 10, no. 2, pp. 95–105

Park, R., and Leslie, P. D., 1977
CURVATURE DUCTILITY OF CIRCULAR REINFORCED CONCRETE COLUMNS
CONFINED BY THE ACI SPIRAL, Proceedings of the 6th Australian Conference on
the Mechanics of Structures and Materials, Christchurch, New Zealand, vol. 1, pp. 342–
349

Park, R., and Norton, J. A., 1974
EFFECTS OF CONFINING REINFORCEMENT ON THE FLEXURAL DUCTILITY
OF RECTANGULAR REINFORCED CONCRETE COLUMNS WITH HIGH
STRENGTH STEEL, Symposium on Design and Safety of Reinforced Concrete Com-
pression Members, Reports of Working Commissions, vol. 16, International Association
for Bridge and Structural Engineering, Quebec, Que., Canada, pp. 267–275

Park, R., and Paulay, T., 1975
REINFORCED CONCRETE STRUCTURES, John Wiley and Sons, New York, p. 769

Park, R., Priestley, M. J. N., and Gill, W. D., 1982
DUCTILITY OF SQUARE-CONFINED CONCRETE COLUMNS, ASCE Journal of the
Structural Division, vol. 108, no. ST4, April, pp. 929–950

Park, R. J. T., Priestley, M. J. N., and Walpole, W. R., 1982
THE SEISMIC PERFORMANCE OF STEEL ENCASED REINFORCED CONCRETE
BRIDGE PILES, Report no. 82-12, Department of Civil Engineering, University of
Canterbury, Christchurch, New Zealand, Feb.

Park, R., and Sampson, R. A., 1972
DUCTILITY OF REINFORCED CONCRETE COLUMN SECTIONS IN SEISMIC DE-
SIGN, ACI Journal, vol. 69, no. 9, pp. 543–551

Paulay, T., 1980
DETERMINISTIC DESIGN PROCEDURE FOR DUCTILE FRAMES IN SEISMIC
AREAS, ACI Special Publication SP-63, American Concrete Institute, Detroit, Mich.,
pp. 357–381

Paulay, T., 1981
LAPPED SPLICES IN EARTHQUAKE RESISTING COLUMNS, ACI Journal, vol. 79,
no. 6, pp. 458–469

Paulay, T., and Goodsir, W. J., 1985
THE DUCTILITY OF STRUCTURAL WALLS, Bulletin of the New Zealand National
Society for Earthquake Engineering, vol. 18, no. 3, pp. 269–280

Paulay, T., and Goodsir, W. J., 1986
THE CAPACITY DESIGN OF REINFORCED CONCRETE HYBRID STRUCTURES
FOR MULTI-STOREY BUILDINGS, Bulletin of the New Zealand Society for Earth-
quake Engineering, vol. 19, no. 1, pp. 1–17

Paulay, T., and Park, R., 1984
JOINTS IN REINFORCED CONCRETE FRAMES DESIGNED FOR EARTHQUAKE
RESISTANCE, Research Report no. 84-9, Department of Civil Engineering, University
of Canterbury, Christchurch, New Zealand, p. 80

Paulay, T., Park, R., and Priestley, M. J. N., 1978
REINFORCED CONCRETE BEAM-COLUMN JOINTS UNDER SEISMIC ACTIONS,
ACI Journal, vol. 75, no. 11, pp. 585–593

Paulay, T., Priestley, M. J. N., and Synge, A. J., 1982
DUCTILITY IN EARTHQUAKE RESISTING SQUAT SHEAR WALLS, *ACI Journal*, vol. 79, no. 4, pp. 257–269

Paulay, T., and Santhakumar, A. R., 1976
DUCTILE BEHAVIOUR OF COUPLE SHEAR WALLS, *ASCE Journal of the Structural Division*, vol. 102, no. ST1, pp. 93–108

Paulay, T., and Taylor, R. G., 1981
SLAB COUPLING OF EARTHQUAKE RESISTING SHEAR WALLS, *ACI Journal*, vol. 78, no. 2, pp. 130–140

Paulay, T., and Uzumeri, S. M., 1975
A CRITICAL REVIEW OF THE SEISMIC DESIGN PROVISIONS FOR DUCTILE SHEAR WALLS OF THE CANADIAN CODE AND COMMENTARY, *Canadian Journal of Civil Engineering*, vol. 2, no. 4, pp. 592–601

Pfeifer, D. W., Magura, D. D., Russell, H. G., and Corley, W. G., 1971
TIME DEPENDENT DEFORMATIONS IN A 70 STORY STRUCTURE, *Designing for Effects of Creep and Shrinkage in Concrete Structures*, ACI Special Publication SP-76, American Concrete Institute, Detroit, Mich., pp. 159–185

Portland Cement Association, 1980
DESIGN OF DEEP GIRDERS, Publication ISO79.01D, PCA, Skokie, Ill.

Potucek, W., 1977
DIE BEANSPRUCHUNG DER STEGE VON STAHLBETONPLATTENBALKEN DURCH QUERKRAFT UND BIEGUNG (STRESSES IN WEBS OF REINFORCED CONCRETE T-BEAMS SUBJECTED TO FLEXURE AND SHEAR), *Zement und Beton*, vol. 22, no. 3, pp. 88–98

Potyondy, J. G., 1985
CONCRETE FILLED TUBULAR STEEL STRUCTURES IN MARINE ENVIRONMENT, Proceedings of the International Specialty Conference on Concrete Filled Steel Tubular Structures, Harbin, China, Aug., pp. 27–31

Priestley, M. J. N., and Park, R., 1984
STRENGTH AND DUCTILITY OF BRIDGE SUBSTRUCTURES, Research Report 84-20, Department of Civil Engineering, University of Canterbury, Christchurch, New Zealand, p. 120

Priestley, M. J. N., and Park, R. J. N., 1985
CONCRETE FILLED STEEL TUBULAR PILES UNDER SEISMIC LOADING, Proceedings of the International Specialty Conference on Concrete Filled Steel Tubular Structures, Harbin, China, Aug., pp. 96–103

Priestley, M. J. N., Park, R., and Potangaroa, R. T., 1981
DUCTILITY OF SPIRALLY-CONFINED CONCRETE COLUMNS, *ASCE Journal of the Structural Division*, vol. 107, no. ST1, Jan., pp. 181–202

PTI, 1984
DESIGN OF POST-TENSIONED SLABS, Post-Tensioning Institute, Glenview, Ill.

Ragan, H. S., and Warwaruk, J., 1967
TEE MEMBERS WITH LARGE WEB OPENINGS, *PCI Journal*, vol. 12, no. 4, Aug., pp. 52–65

Ramakrishnan, V., and Ananthanarayana, Y., 1968
ULTIMATE STRENGTH OF DEEP BEAMS IN SHEAR, *ACI Journal*, vol. 65, pp. 87–98

Ramakrishnan, V., and Josifek, C., 1987
PERFORMANCE CHARACTERISTICS AND FLEXURAL FATIGUE STRENGTH ON CONCRETE STEEL FIBER COMPOSITES, Proceedings of International Symposium on Fiber Reinforced Concrete, Madras, India, December, Oxford and IBH Publishing, New Delhi, pp. 2.73–2.84

Ramakrishnan, V., et al., 1980
A COMPARATIVE EVALUATION OF CONCRETE REINFORCED WITH STRAIGHT STEEL FIBERS WITH DEFORMED ENDS GLUED TOGETHER IN BUNDLES, *ACI Journal*, vol. 77, no. 3, May–June, pp. 135–143

Rausch, E., 1922, 1931
DESIGN OF INCLINED REINFORCEMENT TO RESIST DIRECT SHEAR; DIRECT SHEAR IN CONCRETE STRUCTURES, *Der Bauingenieur* (Heidelberg); vol. 3, no. 7, April, pp. 211–212; vol. 12, no. 32/33, Aug., pp. 578–581

Rausch, E., 1963
DESIGN FOR SHEAR IN REINFORCED CONCRETE STRUCTURES, *Der Bauingenieur* (Heidelberg), vol. 38, p. 257

Rawdon de Paiva, H. A., and Siess, C. P., 1965
STRENGTH AND BEHAVIOUR OF DEEP BEAMS IN SHEAR, *ASCE Journal of the Structural Division*, vol. 91, pp. 19–41

Regan, P. E., 1969
SHEAR IN RC BEAMS, *Magazine of Concrete Research*, vol. 21, no. 66, March, pp. 31–42

Reinhardt, H. W., and Walraven, J. C., 1982
CRACKS IN CONCRETE SUBJECT TO SHEAR, *ASCE Journal of the Structural Division*, vol. 108, no. ST1, Jan., pp. 207–224

Rice, P. F., and Hoffman, E. S., 1985
STRUCTURAL DESIGN GUIDE TO THE ACI BUILDING CODE, Van Nostrand Reinhold, New York

Ritter, W., 1899
DIE BEAUWEISE HENNEBIQUE (HENNEBIQUE'S CONSTRUCTION METHOD), *Schweizerische Bauzeitung* (Zurich), vol. 17, pp. 41–43, 49–52, 59–61

Rogowsky, D. M., and MacGregor, J. G., 1986
THE DESIGN OF REINFORCED CONCRETE DEEP BEAMS, *Concrete International: Design and Construction*, vol. 8, no. 8, p. 49

Rogowsky, D. M., MacGregor, J. G., and Ong, S. Y., 1986
TESTS OF REINFORCED CONCRETE DEEP BEAMS, *ACI Journal*, vol. 83, no. 4, July–Aug., pp. 614–623

Roik, K., Bergmann, R., Bode, H., and Wagenknecht, G., 1975
TRAGFÄHIGKEIT VON AUSBETONIERTEN HOHLPROFILSTÜTZEN AUS BAUSTAHL, Technical Report no. 75-4, Institut für Konstruktiven Ingenieurbau, Ruhr-Universität Bochum, Germany, May

Romualdi, J. P., and Baston, G. R., 1963
MECHANICS OF CRACK ARREST IN CONCRETE, *ASCE Journal of the Engineering Mechanics Division*, vol. 89, no. EM3, June, pp. 147–168

Romualdi, J. P., and Mandel, J. A., 1964
TENSILE STRENGTH OF CONCRETE AFFECTED BY UNIFORMLY DISTRIBUTED AND CLOSELY SPACED SHORT LENGTHS OF WIRE REINFORCEMENT, *ACI Journal*, vol. 61, no. 6, June, pp. 657–670

Rosman, R., 1964
APPROXIMATE ANALYSIS OF SHEAR WALLS SUBJECTED TO LATERAL LOADS, *ACI Journal*, vol. 61, pp. 717–733

Russell, H. G., 1986
HIGH-RISE CONCRETE BUILDINGS: SHRINKAGE, CREEP, AND TEMPERATURE EFFECTS, Private Communication, 1986

Saenz, L. P., and Martin, I., 1961
SLABLESS TREAD-RISER STAIRS, *ACI Journal*, vol. 58, p. 353

Saiidi, M., 1986
CONSTRUCTABILITY OF REINFORCED CONCRETE JOINTS, ACI Publication
SCM-14(86), Sec. VI, March

Saiidi, M., Ghusn, G., and Jiang, Y., 1989
FIVE-SPRING ELEMENT FOR BIAXIALLY BENT R/C COLUMNS, *ASCE Journal of the Structural Division,* vol. 115, Feb., pp. 398–416

Saiidi, M., and Sozen, M. A., 1979
SIMPLE AND COMPLEX MODELS FOR NONLINEAR SEISMIC RESPONSE OF
REINFORCED CONCRETE STRUCTURES, Civil Engineering Studies, Structural Research Series no. 465, Department of Civil Engineering, University of Illinois, Urbana

Sakino, K., and Ishibashi, H., 1985
EXPERIMENTAL STUDIES ON CONCRETE FILLED SQUARE STEEL TUBULAR
SHORT COLUMNS SUBJECTED TO CYCLIC SHEARING FORCE AND CON-
STANT AXIAL FORCE, *Transactions of the Architectural Institute of Japan,* no. 353, July, pp. 81–89

Sakino, K., and Tomii, M., 1981
HYSTERETIC BEHAVIOR OF CONCRETE FILLED SQUARE STEEL TUBULAR
BEAM-COLUMNS FAILED IN FLEXURE, *Transactions of the Japan Concrete Institute,* vol. 3, pp. 439–446

Sakino, K., Tomii, M., and Watanabe, K., 1985
SUSTAINING LOAD CAPACITY OF PLAIN CONCRETE STUB COLUMNS CON-
FINED BY CIRCULAR STEEL TUBE, Proceedings of the International Specialty Conference on Concrete Filled Steel Tubular Structures, Harbin, China, Aug., pp. 112–118

SANZ, 1982
CODE OF PRACTICE FOR THE DESIGN OF CONCRETE STRUCTURES (NZS 3101
PART 1), Standards Association of New Zealand, Wellington

Sargin, M., 1971
STRESS-STRAIN RELATIONSHIPS FOR CONCRETE AND ANALYSIS OF STRUC-
TURAL CONCRETE SECTIONS, Study no. 4, Solid Mechanics Division, University of Waterloo, Ont., Canada

Schickert, G., and Winkler, H., 1977
RESULTS OF TEST CONCERNING STRENGTH AND STRAIN OF CONCRETE
SUBJECTED TO MULTIAXIAL COMPRESSIVE STRESS, Die Bundesanstalt für Materialprüfung (BAM), Berlin, Germany, p. 123

Schlaich, J., et al., 1987
TOWARD A CONSISTENT DESIGN OF STRUCTURAL CONCRETE, *PCI Journal,* vol. 32, no. 3, p. 74

Schlaich, J., and Schaefer, K., 1984
KONSTRUIEREN IN STAHLBETONBAU (DETAILING IN REINFORCED CON-
CRETE DESIGN), *Betonkalender,* part 2, W. Ernst, Berlin, Germany, pp. 787–1005

Schlaich, J., Schaefer, K., and Jennewein, M., 1987
TOWARD A CONSISTANT DESIGN OF STRUCTURAL CONCRETE, *PCI Journal,* vol. 32, no. 3, May–June, pp. 74–150

Schlaich, J., and Weischede, D., 1981
DETAILING REINFORCED CONCRETE STRUCTURES, Proceedings of the Canadian Structural Concrete Conference, Department of Civil Engineering, University of Toronto, Toronto, Ont., pp. 171–198

Schmidt, W., and Hoffman, E. S., 1975
9000 PSI CONCRETE—WHY? WHY NOT?, *Civil Engineering,* ASCE, pp. 52–55

Schuster, J., 1964
HELICAL STAIRS, Julius Hoffman, Stuttgart, Germany

Scott, B. D., Park, R., and Priestley, M. J. N., 1982
STRESS-STRAIN BEHAVIOUR OF CONCRETE BY OVERLAPPING HOOPS AT LOW AND HIGH STRAIN RATES, *ACI Journal*, vol. 79, no. 1, Jan.–Feb., pp. 13–27

Scott, W. T., 1985
RESHORING A MULTISTORY CONCRETE FRAME: A PRACTICAL APPROACH, *Analysis and Design of High-Rise Concrete Buildings*, ACI Special Publication SP-97, American Concrete Institute, Detroit, Mich., 277–301

SEAOC, 1975
RECOMMENDED LATERAL FORCE REQUIREMENTS AND COMMENTARY, Structural Engineers' Association of California, San Francisco

Sekin, M., and Uzumeri, S. M., 1980
EXTERIOR BEAM-COLUMN JOINTS IN REINFORCED CONCRETE FRAMES, Proceedings of the Seventh World Conference on Earthquake Engineering, Istanbul, Turkey, Sept., vol. 6, pp. 183–190

Shah, S. P., 1974
NEW REINFORCING MATERIALS IN CONCRETE, *ACI Journal*, vol. 71, no. 10, Oct.

Shah, S. P. (Editor), 1982
FATIGUE OF CONCRETE STRUCTURES, ACI Special Publication SP-75, American Concrete Institute, Detroit, Mich., pp. 133–175

Shah, S. P., and Rangan, B. V., 1971
FIBER REINFORCED CONCRETE PROPERTIES, *ACI Journal*, vol. 68, no. 2, Feb., pp. 126–135

Shah, S. P., et al., 1983
CYCLIC LOADING OF SPIRALLY REINFORCED CONCRETE, *ASCE Journal of Structural Engineering*, vol. 109, no. ST7, July, pp. 1695–1710

Sheikh, S. A., and Uzumeri, S. M., 1979
PROPERTIES OF CONCRETE CONFINED BY RECTANGULAR TIES, *Bulletin d'Information*, no. 132, Comité Euro-International du Béton, Paris, France, pp. 53–60

Sheikh, S. A., and Uzumeri, S. M., 1980
STRENGTH AND DUCTILITY OF TIED CONCRETE COLUMNS, *ASCE Journal of the Structural Division*, vol. 106, ST5, May, pp. 1079–1102

Siev, A., 1962
ANALYSIS OF FREE STRAIGHT MULTIFLIGHT STAIRCASES, *ASCE Journal of the Structural Division*, vol. 88, no. ST3, pp. 207–232

Smith, K. N., and Vantsiotis, A. S., 1982
SHEAR STRENGTH OF DEEP BEAMS, *ACI Journal*, vo. 79, pp. 201–213

Somerville, G., 1974
THE BEHAVIOR AND DESIGN OF REINFORCED CONCRETE CORBELS, *Shear in Reinforced Concrete*, ACI Special Publication SP-42, American Concrete Institute, Detroit, Mich., pp. 477–502

Stang, H., and Shah, S. P., 1986
FAILURE OF FIBER REINFORCED COMPSITES BY PULL-OUT FRACTURE, *Journal of Materials Science*, 21, March, pp. 953–957

Stevens, R. F., 1965
ENCASED STANCHIONS, *The Structural Engineer*, vol. 43, no. 2, Feb., pp. 59–66

Suaris, W., and Shah, S. P., 1983
PROPERTIES OF CONCRETE AND FIBER REINFORCED CONCRETE SUBJECTED TO IMPACT LOADING, *ASCE Journal of the Structural Division*, vol. 103, no. ST7, July, pp. 1717–1741

Subedi, N. K., 1988
REINFORCED CONCRETE DEEP BEAMS: A METHOD FOR ANALYSIS, *Proceedings of the Institution of Civil Engineers* (London), vol. 85, pp. 1–30

Suzuki, T., Kimura, M. Aburakawa, M., and Ogata, T., 1985
ELASTO-PLASTIC BEHAVIORS OF CONCRETE-FILLED SQUARE STEEL TUBU-LAR COLUMNS AND THEIR CONNECTIONS WITH BEAMS—TENSION-TYPE CONNECTIONS WITH LONG THROUGH BOLTS (in Japanese), *Transactions of the Architectural Institute of Japan,* no. 358, Dec., pp. 63–70

Suzuki, T., Kimura, M., Ogawa, T., and Itoh, H., 1986
ELASTO-PLASTIC BEHAVIORS OF CONCRETE-FILLED SQUARE STEEL TUBU-LAR COLUMNS AND THEIR CONNECTIONS WITH BEAMS—OUTSTANDING DIAPHRAGM CONNECTIONS (in Japanese), *Transactions of the Architectural Institute of Japan,* no. 359, pp. 93–101

Suzuki, T., Kimura, M., Ogawa, T., Itoh, H, and Miyashita, S., 1984
ELASTO-PLASTIC BEHAVIORS OF CONCRETE-FILLED SQUARE STEEL TUBU-LAR COLUMNS AND THEIR CONNECTIONS WITH BEAMS—TENSION-TYPE CONNECTIONS WITH LONG THROUGH BOLTS (in Japanese), Transactions of the Architectural Institute of Japan, no. 358, pp. 63–70, Dec.

Swann, R. A., 1969
FLEXURAL STRENGTH OF CORNERS OF REINFORCED CONCRETE PORTAL FRAMES, Report no. TRA 434, Cement and Concrete Association, London, England, Nov

Swartz, S. E., et al., 1985
STRUCTURAL BENDING PROPERTIES OF HIGH STRENGTH CONCRETE, ACI Special Publication SP-87, American Concrete Institute, Detroit, Mich., pp. 147–178

Tan, K. H., 1982
ULTIMATE STRENGTH OF REINFORCED CONCRETE BEAMS WITH RECTAN-GULAR OPENINGS UNDER BENDING AND SHEAR, Thesis, National University of Singapore, Kent Ridge, Singapore

Tanaka, H., et al., 1985
ANCHORAGE OF TRANSVERSE REINFORCEMENT IN RECTANGULAR REIN-FORCED CONCRETE COLUMNS IN SEISMIC DESIGN, *Bulletin of the New Zealand Society for Earthquake Engineering,* vol. 18, no. 2, June, pp. 165–190

Taylor, H. P. J., 1968
SHEAR STRESSES IN RC BEAMS WITHOUT SHEAR REINFORCEMENT, Techni-cal Report TRA 407, Cement and Concrete Association, London, England, Feb., 23 pp.

Terzaghi, K., 1955
COEFFICIENTS OF SUBGRADE REACTIONS, Geotechnique, London, England, Dec.

Thurlimann, B., Grob, J., and Luchinger, P., 1975
TORSION, BEIGUNG UND SCHUB IN STAHLBETONTRÄGERN (TORSION, FLEXURE AND SHEAR IN REINFORCED CONCRETE GIRDERS), Institute of Structural Engineering, ETH Zurich, Switzerland, 170 pp.

Thurlimann, B., and Luchinger, P., 1973
STEIFIGKEIT VON GERISSENEN STAHLBETONBALKEN UNTER TORSION UND BIEGUNG (STIFFNESS OF CRACKED REINFORCED CONCRETE BEAMS SUBJECTED TO TORSION AND FLEXURE), *Beton und Stahlbetonbau,* vol. 68, no. 6, June, pp. 146–152

Thurlimann, B., Marti, P., Pralong, J., Ritz, P., and Zimmerli, B., 1983
ANWENDUNG DER PLASTIZITÄTSTHEORIE AUF STAHLBETON (APPLICA-TION OF THE THEORY OF PLASTICITY TO REINFORCED CONCRETE), Insti-tute of Structural Engineering, ETH Zurich, Switzerland, 252 pp.

Timoshenko, S., 1965
STRENGTH OF MATERIALS, Van Nostrand Co., New York, N.Y.

Tomii, M., 1984
BOND CHECK FOR CONCRETE-FILLED STEEL TUBULAR COLUMNS, Proceed-ings of the U.S./Japan Joint Seminar on Composite and Mixed Construction, Washing-ton, D.C., July, pp. 195–204

Tomii, M., Matsui, C., and Sakino, K., 1973
CONCRETE FILLED STEEL TUBE STRUCTURES, Proceedings of the National Conference on the Planning and Design of Tall Buildings, ASCE-IABSE, Tokyo, Japan, Aug., pp. 55–72

Tomii, M., and Sakino, K., 1979a
EXPERIMENTAL STUDIES ON THE ULTIMATE MOMENT OF CONCRETE FILLED SQUARE STEEL TUBULAR BEAM-COLUMNS, *Transactions of the Architectural Institute of Japan*, no. 275, Jan., pp. 55–63

Tomii, M., and Sakino, K., 1979b
ELASTO-PLASTIC BEHAVIOR OF CONCRETE FILLED SQUARE STEEL TUBULAR BEAM-COLUMNS, *Transactions of the Architectural Institute of Japan*, no. 280, June, pp. 111–120

Tomii, M., and Sakino, K., 1979c
EXPERIMENTAL STUDIES ON CONCRETE FILLED SQUARE STEEL TUBULAR BEAM-COLUMNS SUBJECTED TO MONOTONIC SHEARING FORCE AND CONSTANT AXIAL FORCE, *Transactions of the Architectural Institute of Japan*, no. 281, July, pp. 81–90

Tomii, M., Sakino, K., and Kiyohara, K., 1981
EXPERIMENTAL STUDIES ON PLAIN CONCRETE COLUMNS SUBJECTED TO MONOTONIC SHEARING FORCE AND CONSTANT AXIAL FORCE, *Transactions of the Architectural Institute of Japan*, no. 307, Sept., pp. 46–55

Tomii, M., Sakino, K., Watanabe, K., and Xiao, Y., 1985a
LATERAL LOAD CAPACITY OF REINFORCED CONCRETE SHORT COLUMNS CONFINED BY STEEL TUBE—EXPERIMENTAL RESULTS OF PRELIMINARY RESEARCH, Proceedings of the International Specialty Conference on Concrete Filled Steel Tubular Structures, Harbin, China, Aug., pp. 19–26

Tomii, M., Sakino, K., Xiao, Y., and Watanabe, K., 1985b
EARTHQUAKE-RESISTING HYSTERETIC BEHAVIOR OF REINFORCED CONCRETE SHORT COLUMNS CONFINED BY STEEL TUBE—EXPERIMENTAL RESULTS OF PRELIMINARY RESEARCH, Proceedings of the International Specialty Conference on Concrete Filled Steel Tubular Structures, Harbin, China, Aug., pp. 119–125

Tomii, M., Yoshimura, K., and Morishita, Y., 1977
EXPERIMENTAL STUDIES ON CONCRETE FILLED STEEL TUBULAR STUB COLUMNS UNDER CONCENTRIC LOADING, Proceedings of the International Colloquium on Stability of Structures under Static and Dynamic Loads, SSRC/ASCE, Washington, D.C., March, pp. 718–741

Tomii, M., Yoshimura, K., and Morishita, Y., 1980a
A METHOD OF IMPROVING BOND STRENGTH BETWEEN STEEL TUBE AND CONCRETE CORE CAST IN CIRCULAR STEEL TUBULAR COLUMNS, *Transactions of the Japan Concrete Institute*, vol. 2, pp. 319–326

Tomii, M., Yoshimura, K., and Morishita, Y., 1980b
A METHOD OF IMPROVING BOND STRENGTH BETWEEN STEEL TUBE AND CONCRETE CORE CAST IN SQUARE AND OCTAGONAL STEEL TUBULAR COLUMNS, *Transactions of the Japan Concrete Institute*, vol. 2, pp. 327–334

Trost, H., 1982
THE CALCULATION OF DEFLECTIONS OF REINFORCED CONCRETE MEMBERS—A RATIONAL APPROACH, *Designing for Creep and Shrinkage in Concrete Structures*, ACI Special Publication SP-76, American Concrete Institute, Detroit, Mich., pp. 89–108

UBC, 1982
UNIFORM BUILDING CODE (CHAPTER 23, SECTION 2312: EARTHQUAKE REGULATIONS) International Conference of Building Officials, Whittier, California

Umoto, K., and Fujino, 1981
SHEAR BEHAVIOR OF REINFORCED CONCRETE BEAMS WITH STEEL FIBER
AS SHEAR REINFORCEMENT, *Transactions of the Japan Concrete Institute*, vol. 3,
pp. 245–252

Underwriters' laboratories, 1971
BUILDING MATERIALS LIST, Chicago, Ill, Jan.

U.S. Department of the Interior, 1981
CONCRETE MANUAL, U.S. Department of the Interior, Washington, D.C.

Uzumeri, S. M., 1977
STRENGTH AND DUCTILITY OF CAST-IN-PLACE BEAM-COLUMN JOINTS, *Reinforced Concrete Structures in Seismic Zones,* ACI Special Publication SP-53, American
Concrete Institute, Detroit, Mich., pp. 293–350

Vallenas, J. M., Bertero, V. V., and Popov, E. P., 1979
HYSTERETIC BEHAVIOUR OF REINFORCED CONCRETE STRUCTURAL
WALLS, Report no. UCB/EERC-79/20, Earthquake Engineering Research Center, College of Engineering, University of California, Berkeley, p. 234

van Mier, J. G. M., 1986
FRACTURE OF CONCRETE UNDER COMPLEX STRESS, *Heron,* Delft University of
Technology, The Netherlands, vol. 31, no. 3, p. 90

Vecchio, F. J., and Collins, M. P., 1982
THE RESPONSE OF REINFORCED CONCRETE TO IN-PLANE SHEAR AND NORMAL STRESSES, Publication no. 82-03, Department of Civil Engineering, University of
Toronto, Toronto, Ont., Canada, March, 332 pp.

Vecchio, F. J., and Collins, M. P., 1986
THE MODIFIED COMPRESSION FIELD THEORY FOR REINFORCED CONCRETE ELEMENTS SUBJECTED TO SHEAR, *ACI Journal,* vol. 83, no. 2, March–
April, pp. 219–231

Virdi, K. S., and Dowling, P. J., 1975
BOND STRENGTH IN CONCRETE FILLED CIRCULAR STEEL TUBES, CESLIC
Report CC11, Engineering structures Laboratories, Civil Engineering Department, Imperial College, London, England, Dec

Visalvanich, K., and Naaman, A. E., 1982
FRACTURE MODEL FOR FIBER REINFORCED CONCRETE, *ACI Journal,* vol. 80,
no. 2, March–April, pp. 128–138

Wakabayashi, M., 1977
A NEW DESIGN METHOD OF LONG COMPOSITE BEAM-COLUMNS, Proceedings
of the International Colloquium on Stability of Structures under Static and Dynamic
Loads, SSRC/ASCE, Washington, D.C., March, pp. 742–756

Wakabayashi, M., 1986
DESIGN OF EARTHQUAKE RESISTANT BUILDINGS, McGraw-Hill, New York, p.
309

Want, P. T., et al., 1978
STRESS-STRAIN CURVES OF NORMAL AND LIGHTWEIGHT CONCRETE IN
COMPRESSION, *ACI Journal,* vol. 75, no. 11, Nov., pp. 603, 611

Wang, C. K., and Salmon, C. G., 1985
REINFORCED CONCRETE DESIGN, 4th edition, Harper & Row, New York, chapters
10 and 14

Warner, R. F., 1975
AXIAL SHORTENING IN REINFORCED CONCRETE COLUMNS, UNICIV Report
no. R-143, University of New South Wales, Sydney, Australia, July

Wecharatana, M., and Shah, S. P., 1983
A MODEL FOR PREDICTING FRACTURE RESISTANCE OF FIBER REINFORCED
CONCRETE, *Cement and Concrete Research,* vol. 13, no. 6, Nov., pp. 819–829

Wei, S., et al., 1986
STUDY OF THE INTERFACE STRENGTH IN STEEL FIBER-REINFORCED
CEMENT-BASED COMPOSITES, *ACI Journal*, July–August, pp. 597–605

Williamson, G. R., 1978
THE EFFECT OF STEEL FIBERS AS WEB REINFORCEMENT IN REINFORCED
CONCRETE, Proceedings of the U.S. Army Science Conference, West Point, N.Y.,
June, vol. 3, pp. 107–123

Wittman, F. H., 1982
FUNDAMENTAL RESEARCH ON CREEP AND SHRINKAGE OF CONCRETE,
Nijhoff Publ., London, England, pp. 149–170, 269–278

Wood, B. R., Beaulieu, D., and Adams, P. F., 1976
COLUMN DESIGN BY P DELTA METHOD, *ASCE Journal of the Structural Division*,
vol. 102, no. ST2, Feb., pp. 411–427

Yoshimura, M., and Kurose, Y., 1985
INELASTIC BEHAVIOUR OF THE BUILDING, *Earthquake Effects on Reinforced
Concrete Structures, US-Japan Research*, ACI Special Publication SP-84, American
Concrete Institute, Detroit, Mich., pp. 163–201

Yu, W. W., and Winter, G., 1960
INSTANTANEOUS AND LONG-TIME DEFLECTIONS OF REINFORCED CON-
CRETE BEAMS UNDER WORKING LOADS, *ACI Journal*, vol. 57, no. 1, July, pp.
29–50

Zhang, L, and Jirsa, J. O., 1982
A STUDY OF SHEAR BEHAVIOR OF REINFORCED CONCRETE BEAM-COLUMN
JOINTS, PMFSEL Report 82-1, Department of Civil Engineering, University of Texas at
Austin, Feb.

Zhong, S., 1985
THE USE OF CONCRETE FILLED STEEL TUBULAR STRUCTURES IN CHINA,
Proceedings of the International Specialty Conference on Concrete Filled Steel Tubular
Structures, Harbin, China, Aug., pp. 1–6

Zsutty, T. C., 1968
BEAM SHEAR STRENGTH PREDICTION BY ANALYSIS OF EXISTING DATA,
ACI Journal, vol. 65, Nov., pp. 943–951

Contributors

The following is a list of those who have contributed manuscripts for this Monograph. The names, affiliations, and countries of each author are given.

Aycardi, L. G., Aycardi Ingenieria, Bogota, Colombia
Bickley, J., John A. Bickley Associates, Ltd., Brampton, Ontario, Canada
Bobrowski, J., Jan Bobrowski + Partners, Middlesex, England
Colaco, J. P., CBM Engineers, Inc., Houston, Texas, USA
Cusens, A. R., University of Leeds, Leeds, England

Daniel, H. R., Consultant, Calgary, Alberta, Canada
El-Shakra, Z. M., University of Missouri-Columbia, Columbia, Missouri, USA
Fafitis, A., Arizona State University, Tempe, Arizona, USA
Gopalaratnam, V. S., University of Missouri-Columbia, Columbia, Missouri, USA
Hagberg, T., Consulting Engineer, Oslo, Norway

Hassoun, M. N., South Dakota State University, Brookings, South Dakota, USA
Karshenas, S., Marquette University, Milwaukee, Wisconsin, USA
Kotsovos, M. D., Imperial College, London, England
Kreger, M., University of Texas, Austin, Texas, USA
Mansur, M. A., National University of Singapore, Singapore

Marti, P., Institute of Structural Engineering, Zurich, Switzerland
Michael, D. Ove Arup Partnership, London, England
Mohammadi, J., Illinois Institute of Technology, Chicago, Illinois, USA
Moretto, D., Consultant, Buenos Aires, Argentina
Park, R., University of Canterbury, Christchurch, New Zealand

Paulay, T., University of Canterbury, New Zealand
Rogowsky, D., VSL International Ltd., Bern, Switzerland
Saiidi, M., University of Nevada-Reno, Reno, Nevada, USA
Sakino, K., Kyushi University, Fukuoka-shi, Japan
Sanders, D. H., University of Nevada-Reno, Reno, Nevada, USA

Tan, K. H., National University of Singapore, Singapore
Tomii, M., Aoki Corporation, Tokyo, Japan
Young, J. F., University of Illinois, Urbana, Illinois, USA

Name Index

The following list cites the page numbers on which the indicated names are mentioned. The list includes the authors as well as other individuals or organizations named in the text. Names followed by years refer to bibliographic citations that are included in the appendix entitled "References/Bibliography."

ACI 6, 7, 8, 14, 17, 43, 47, 48, 49, 50, 52, 57, 127, 135, 164, 196, 204, 205, 211, 219, 222, 244, 246
ACI (1973) 27
ACI (1978, 1988) 33
ACI (1989) 24, 232, 234, 236, 237, 238, 241, 242, 243, 246
ACI Committee 207 334
ACI Committee 209 (1982) 60
ACI Committee 228 342
ACI Committee 318 (1989) 104,125,126,133,158,161, 197, 201, 254, 255, 257, 259, 264, 269, 274, 295, 304, 305, 306, 309, 320, 324
ACI Committee 352 321
ACI Committee 363 40,47,54,57
ACI Committee 544 (1973) 36
ACI-ASCE Committee 352 (1985) 316, 321, 322, 324, 325
ACI-ASCE Committee 462 (1977) 320, 322
ACI/SEAOC 248
Agarwal and Gardner (1974) 8
Ahmad and Shah (1982) 48
Ahmad and Shah (1985) 41
Aktan et al. (1973), 199

American National Standards Institute 6,7,8,9
Anderson and Townsend (1977) 15
Applied Technology Council (1978) 296
Architectural Institute of Japan, 205, 207, 211, 218, 241
ASTM C309 (1989) 348
ASTM 22,24
ASTM (1986) 25
ASTM C900 (1982) 342, 346, 347
ASTM (1984, 1989) 33,57
ASTM C39 (1921) 341
ATC (1983) 319, 321

Bakoss et al. (1985) 61
Banthia et al. (1987) 36
Barney et al. (1977) 165,166,169
Batson et al. (1972) 36
Batson (1985) 36
Baumann (1972) 69,70
Beck (1962) 308
Bertero (1980) 296, 297
Bertero et al. (1977) 305
Bickley (1971) 341, 347
Blakeley et al. (1975) 304

Bobrowski and Bardham-Roy (1969) 97,
   155
Braestrup (1974) 69
British Standards Institution (1985)
   88,104,147

Carrasquillo (1981a) 44
Carrasquillo et al. (1981a, 1981b) 40
CEB 172
CEB (1983) 255
CEB-FIP (1978) 60, 68, 158, 161
CEB-FIP (1982) 238, 241
Cerruti and Marti (1987) 73
Chen et al. (1985) 44
CIRIA (1977) 161
Colaco 129
Colaco (1970) 126
Collins and Mitchell (1986) 70,71,74
Collins and Mitchell (1987) 73
Cook and Mitchell (1988) 73, 161
Coull and Choudhury (1967) 308
Council on Tall Buildings (1978) 1, 5, 123,
   195, 256, 257, 290, 306
CSA (1984) 68, 136, 255, 297
Culver and Kushner (1975) 7
Cusens (1966) 171
Cusens and Kuang (1965) 171
Cusens and Santathadaporn (1966) 171

Daniel and McMullen (1977) 170
de Saint Venant 72
Dunstan (1987) 73
Durrani and Wight (1982) 318

Ehsani and Wight (1982) 318
El-Shakra (1989) 34
El-Shakra and Gopalaratnam (1990) 34
El-Sheikh and Chen (1988) 61
Elzanaty et al. (1986) 52
ENR (1973) 324

Fatitis and Shah (1985a, 1985b) 50
Fatitis and Shah (1985a) 49
Fenwick and Paulay (1968) 88, 90, 147, 150
Fintel and Khan (1971) 61
Fintel and Khan (1965, 1969) 126
Fintel et al. (1975) 301
Forell and Nicoletti (1980) 316
Franz and Niedenhoff (1963) 173,183
Freeman et al. (1980) 302
Furlong (1967), 204
Furlong (1989), 202

Galeotti et al. (1983) 320
Gardner (1985) 9
Gates (1978) 302
Ghali et al. (1969) 60
Gopalaratnam (1985) 31
Gopalaratnam and Abu-Mathkour (1987)
   37,39
Gopalaratnam and Shah (1985c) 31
Gopalaratnam and Shah (1986) 36
Gopalaratnam and Shah (1987a) 30, 39
Gopalaratnam and Shah (1987a, 1987b) 31
Gopalaratnam et al. (1990) 34
Gosh (1982) 6
Goutama (1988) 73
Gross and Lew (1986) 9
Grundy and Kabaila (1963) 8

Hagberg (1966) 172
Hagberg (1983) 187
Hawkins and Mitchell (1979) 320
Hennebique 67
Hillerborg (1980) 31
Hoff (1987) 27
Hognestad (1951), 196
Holmes and Martin (1983) 316
Hsu (1988) 70
Hurd (1979) 8
Hurd and Courtois (1986) 9

IABSE (1979) 69
IAEE (1984) 253, 256
Iqbal and Derecho (1980) 301

Japan Concrete Institute (1983) 33, 34
Johnston (1982a) 33

Kaba and Mahin (1984), 199
Kani (1964) 96,97,150,152
Kato et al. (1978) 213
Keinberger (1975) 338
Knowles and Park (1969), 203, 204, 205
Kong (1990) 158
Kong and Evans (1980) 147
Kong et al. (1975) 161
Kormeling et al. (1980) 36
Kotsovos et al. (1987) 90
Kotsovos (1981) 152
Kotsovos (1979) 88, 94, 151, 156
Kotsovos (1982) 84
Kotsovos (1983) 147,149,151,153,157
Kotsovos (1983a) 86
Kotsovos (1983b, 1988) 95

Kotsovos (1984) 88
Kotsovos (1984a) 149
Kotsovos (1984b) 157
Kotsovos (1987a) 100
Kotsovos (1987a,1987b) 89
Kotsovos (1988a) 93,97
Kotsovos and Newman (1981) 88,94
Kotsovos and Newman (1981a) 151,156
Kotsovos and Newman (1981b) 154
Kotsovos (to be published) 96
Kriz and Raths (1965) 141, 171, 187
Kupfer (1964) 69,70
Kyushu University 222

Lai et al. (1984), 199
Lampert and Thurlimann (1971) 69
Leonhardt (1974) 183
Leonhardt and Walther (1961/62) 149
Leonhardt and Walther (1966) 159, 160
Lew (1980) 342
Lew et al. (1984) 320
Linbeck (1987), 199
Liu et al. (1985) 8
Lorensten (1965) 125,165,169
Lyn (1963) 136

Ma et al. (1976) 259
Mailhot (1984) 73
Mander et al. (1984) 227, 228, 272
Mansur and Hasnat (1979) 169
Mansur and Paramasivam (1984) 169
Mansur et al. (1983a) 170
Mansur et al. (1984) 165, 166, 169
Marti (1980) 69
Marti (1982) 70, 80
Marti (1985a) 81
Marti (1985a, 1985b) 69, 74, 77
Marti (1986a, 1986b) 69
Marti (1989) 80
Marti (1990) 162
Martinez et al. (1982) 47,48
Mast (1968) 171
Matsui (1985a) 216
Matsui (1985b) 213, 214, 215
Mattock et al. (1976) 183
McCormac (1986) 16
Meinheit and Jirsa (1983) 275
Meyers (1983) 12
Mindess (1983) 39
Mitchell and Collins (1974) 70
Mitchell and Cook (1984) 320
Moehle et al. (1984) 320

Moersch (1922) 69
Moersch (1909) 88
Moersch (1908,1922) 67
Mokhtar et al. (1982) 139
Moretto (1970) 336
Moretto (1975) 338
Morishita et al. (1979a, 1979b) 218
Morrison and Sozen (1981) 320
Mueller (1976, 1978) 69

Naaman and Shah (1976) 37
Naaman et al. (1974) 31
Nasser et al. (1967) 125,165,169
National Research Council of Canada
   (1988) 15
Nawy and Balaguru (1983) 41
Neville (1970) 345
Ngab et al. (1981a) 47
Ngab et al. (1981a, 1981b) 40
Niedenhoff (1961) 171
Nielsen (1971) 69
Nielsen (1984) 69, 73
Nielsen et al. (1978) 69
Nilson (1985) 41,44,50
NRCCND (1983) 316

Oesterle et al. (1980) 305
OSHA 6

Park (1977) 2728
Park and Leslie (1977) 272
Park and Paulay (1975) 228, 230, 231, 232,
   235, 236, 244, 249, 254, 268, 301, 306,
   316, 318
Park and Sampson (1972) 272
Park et al. (1972, 1975, 1977) 244
Paulay (1980) 256
Paulay (1982) 233
Paulay and Goodsir (1985) 291
Paulay and Goodsir (1986) 312
Paulay and Park (1984) 275, 279, 287, 288,
   319
Paulay et al. (1978) 275
Pfeifer et al. (1971) 61
PIT (1977) 136
Portland Cement Association 27
Portland Cement Association (1980) 160
Potucek (1977) 70
Preistley and Park (1984, 1985) 219, 244,
   272, 274
Preistley et al. (1981) 236
Prestressed Concrete Institute 134

Ragan and Warwaruk (1967) 165
Ramakrishnan and Josifek (1987) 36
Rausch (1922) 171
Regan (1969) 88,147,150
Reinhardt and Walraven (1982) 147
Rice and Hoffman (1985) 136
Ritter (1899) 67,88
Rogowsky and MacGregor (1986) 162
Rogowski et al. (1986) 73
Rogowsky et al. (1986) 159,160,161,162
Roik et al. (1975), 202
Romuldi and Batson (1963) 27
Romuldi and Mandel (1964) 27
Rosman (1964) 308

Saenz and Martin (1961) 171
Saiidi and Sozen (1979) 15
Saiidi et al. (1989), 199
Sakino and Ishibashi (1985) 208, 210, 211
Sakino and Tomii (1981) 208
Sakino et al. (1985) 221
SANZ (1982) 230, 232, 233, 236, 238, 241,
   242, 244, 246, 254, 257, 267, 272, 275,
   285, 295, 298, 301, 305, 321
Schlaich and Schaefer (1984) 72
Schlaich and Weischede (1981) 72
Schlaich et al. (1987) 72,74
Schmidt and Hoffman (1975) 40
Schuster (1964) 171
Scott (1985) 9
SEAOC (1975) 238, 241, 243, 244, 246,
   247, 264
Sekin and Uzumeri (1980) 320
Shah (1974) 27
Shiekh and Uzumeri (1979) 272
Sheikh and Uzumeri (1980) 49
Siev (1962) 171

Stevens (1965), 202
Suaris and Shah (1983) 36
Suzuki et al. (1985, 1986) 216

Tan (1982) 166
Tanaka et al. (1985) 242
Taylor (1968) 88,147,150
Terzaghi (1955) 332
Thurlimann and Luchinger (1973) 70
Thurlimann et al. (1983) 69, 73, 80
Tomii and Sakino (1979a), 204
Tomii and Sakino (1979c) 208, 213
Tomii et al. (1973), 202
Tomii et al. (1981) 211
Tomii et al. (1985a, 1985b) 221
Trost (1982) 62

UBC (1982) 253
Umoto and Fijino (1981) 36
Underwriters Laboratories (1971) 125
Uzumeri (1977) 319

Vallenas et al. (1979) 296, 305
Vecchio and Collins (1982) 70
Vecchio and Collins (1986) 70

Wakabayashi (1977), 206
Wakabayashi (1986) 275
Wang and Salmon (1985) 13,15
Warner (1975) 61
Water and Power Resources Service (1981)
   334
Wei et al. (1986) 37
Williamson (1978) 36

Yoshimura and Kurose (1985) 259
Yu and Winter (1960) 62

Subject Index

accelerated construction 346
acoustical rating 126
additives 57
admixtures 21, 57, 134
aggregate interlock 88, 147
anchorage 182, 284, 316, 322, 325
anchorage deformations 302
anchorage failure 238
anchorage of beam bars 316
anchorage zones 144
anchors 143
apartment buildings 132
approximate analysis methods 13
autogenous shrinkage 60
axial load-carrying capacity 272
axial load-moment interaction 195
axial strain versus lateral strain curve 84

balanced-load concept 136
balanced strain condition 196
bar anchorage 286
bar diameters 188
bars 22
Barton Oaks project 130
basement walls 251
beam and slab construction 123
beam bars 286
beam capacity 160
beam-column design 321
beam-column joints 275, 279, 316
beam depths 324
beam openings 164
beam overstrength factor 259
beam stubs 324
beam-to-column connections 216, 315
beam widths 324
beams 52, 53, 83, 257, 266, 268
beams, deep, behavior of 158
bearing plate 183

behavior of deep beams 158
behavior of connections 315
bending moment diagram 236
bending moments 256
Bernoulli's theorem 172
biaxial bending 325
bond 217, 328
bond characteristics, FRC 37
bond deterioration 284
bond failure 100, 117
bond strength 285
bracing of foundations 339
brackets 171
buckling mode 212

caissons 335, 337, 339
cantilever action 260
cantilever structural wall 291
cantilever walls 290, 297, 301
cap 336
capacity 176
capacity design 254, 306
capacity design principles 255
capacity design procedure 312
capacity formulas 174
carbonation shrinkage 60
ceiling construction 125
chemical admixtures 57
chord members 165
circular columns 52, 247
code provisions 147
code recommendations 281
codes and specifications 344
cohesionless soils 333
cohesive soils 330, 333
collapse 113, 157, 253, 341
collapse during construction 341
collapse load analysis 166, 170
collapse mechanism 16

column actions 232
column bars 287
column deformations 61
column design moments 263
column flexural strengths 231
column moment pattern 262
column moments 195
column shear forces 266
column shrinkage and creep 126
columns 47, 195, 228, 256, 261, 270, 274, 277, 284, 295
columns, high-strength concrete 47
columns, steel-encased reinforced concrete 218
columns failing in flexure 210
columns failing in shear 210
columns in frames 214
combined footing 331
composite action 217
composite column 205, 221
composite failure 29
composite fractures 29
composite material 21
compressed concrete 271, 298
compression failure 176, 181, 295
compression field theory 70
compression resistance 21
compressive behavior, FRC 31
compressive force 151
compressive force path 93, 96
compressive state of stress, 93
compressive stress 94, 197
compressive zone 90, 154
computer programs 136
concrete cantilever 150
concrete confinement 242
concrete crushing 88
concrete design code 238
concrete-filled steel tubes 202
concrete placement 134, 334
concrete transportation 134
confinement 50, 298, 319
confinement stress 49
confining steel 248
congestion 250
connections 315–326
    (See also beam-to-column connections)
construction delays 324
construction loads 5–9
construction sequence 135
continuous members 78
core concrete 272

corrosion 141
coupled walls 306, 307, 309
coupling beams 302, 307, 309
crack patterns 152, 209
cracking 90, 94, 105, 140, 151, 308, 334
cracking, beams 109
cracking, critical 15
creep 46, 59, 62, 345
critical cracking 15
critical live load combination 13
critical section 147
cross ties 324
curing 345, 347
curvature ductility 297
cyclic strain history 224
cylinder test 341

D-regions 81
damage 235
dead load 6, 14, 125
deep beams 157, 336
deep foundations 335
deflections, slab and beam 62
deformations 59, 125
design actions 228, 255
design axial forces 262
design axial loads 232, 243
design calculations, beams 118
design codes 241, 243, 321
design considerations 315
design criteria 125
design for anchorage 321
design for serviceability 14
design for shear 321
design implications 154
design methods 67–121
design methods, deep beams 160
design methods, shear 50
design objectives, implementation 14
design procedures 79, 289, 309, 312
design requirements 324
design shear forces 309
design, slab-column joints 323
design steps 256
design stress 183
detailing 62, 133, 222
detailing, frames 266
detailing of columns 270
detailing practices 324
diagonal bars 169
diagonal tension failure 305
diaphragm action 126

diaphragm walls 338
differential settlements 126
dimensioning 183
direct compression struts 158
displacement 312
discontinuities 71
double tees 131
drifts 302
drop panel 130
drying shrinkage 59
ductile frames 312
ductile structural walls 289
ductile wall response 295
ductility 294
ductility demand 296
ductility in walls 297, 308
dynamic load 14, 231
dynamic magnification 260

early stripping 345
earthquake tolerance 312
earthquake-incuded axial forces 262
earthquake-resistant design 228
earthquakes 207
eccentric joints 287
economic benefits 346
elastic analysis 78, 126, 253, 308
elastic coupled walls 302
elastic foundations 331
elastic joint 278
elastic modulus 44
elastic regions 306
elastic rotation 12
electronics 2
elevator pits 334
energy absorption 32
energy-dissipating mechanisms 253
envelopes, shear and moment 13
experimental program 149
exterior beam-column joints 283

failure 93, 100, 110, 152, 173, 184, 237, 290, 316
failure, anchorage zones 144
failure, causes 95
failure, compressive zone 108
failure, square columns 209
failure criteria 97, 115
failure load 112
failure mode, beams 107
fatigue resistance, FRC 36
fiber aspect ratio 28

fiber-reinforced concrete 25
fiber reinforcement history 27
fiber types 28
fiber volume fraction 28
filigree system 133
finite-element analysis 147, 161
finite-element method 15
fire endurance 145
fire rating 125
flat-plate construction 123
flat-plate system 132
flat plates 135
flat-slab construction 130
flat slabs 135
flexible footing 331
flexural analysis, beams 53
flexural behavior, FRC 33
flexural capacity 98, 106, 113
flexural capacity, beams 83
flexural cracks 94
flexural failure 88, 152
flexural overstrength 231, 257, 303, 310
flexural reinforcement 299
flexural strength 127, 291, 293
flexural strength, FRC 33
flexure 328
floor-framing systems, selection 127
floor systems 124, 128
floor vibration 15
floors 123
fly ash 58
flying-form system 124
flying forms 134
footing 328
form removal 343, 347
form-stripping strength 344
formwork loads 6
foundation beam 189
foundations 327–340
full composite action 217, 220

geomembranes 334
girder construction 134
glass fiber 29
granulated blast furnice slag 58
grid sizes 8
ground motion 253

haunched girder 134
haunched-girder system 129
haunches 276
high-strength concrete 40, 325

high-strength concrete, applications 56
hollow-cored planks 132
hook detail 324
hoops 225, 238, 247, 299
horizontal deflections and cracking 61
horizontal haunches 288
horizontal members 123–193
horizontal reinforcement 174
hotels 132

impact resistance, FRC 36
in-place strength 342
in-place testing 341, 342, 347
inclined crack 154
inclined reinforcement 180
inclined stirrups 176
incremental collapse 11
incremental collapse and shakedown 17
inelastic joint 278
inelastic lateral interstory displacements
   259
inelastic regions 304
instability criteria 296
interior joints 286, 288

joint behavior 319
joint continuity 11
joint failures 321
joint reinforcement 281
joint shear reinforcement 287
joint shear resistance 285
joint shear stress 279
joints 276, 287

kinks 143

lapped splices 233, 256, 270
large-diameter piles 337
large-scale testing 325
lateral displacement 12
lateral loads 7
limit analysis 16
limit analysis method 68
limit state modes of failure 11
linear approaches 69
live loads 5, 6, 8, 14, 125
load history 60
load prediction 155
load redistribution 308
load-carrying capacity 86, 149
load-carrying capacity, beams 90, 97, 100
load-deflection curves, beams 91

load-deformation behavior 204
load-deformation behavior, FRC 32
load-deformation response predictions 71
load-displacement loops 245
loading behavior 244
loads during construction 8
loads on brackets 172
loads on walls 250
long-term performance 1
longitudinal bars 225, 238
longitudinal reinforcement 232, 267, 270,
   299
longitudinal steel 55

main reinforcement 22
mat foundations 333
materials 21–65, 254
mathematical models 291
matrix cracking 29
matrix mix 28
maturity testing 342
maximum capacity 179
methods of analysis 127
mineral admixtures 58
modeling 96, 301
modulus of elasticity 24
moment-curvature analyses 244
moment distribution 136
moment magnifier method 200
moment-of-inertia formula 56
moment-resisting ductile frames 255
monolithic beam-column connections 315
movements, concrete 1
multiaxial stress 44, 81

nodal zones and fans 80
node failure 184
nodes 182
noncomposite action 217
nonlinear approaches 69
nonlinear stress-strain 40

office buildings 128
one-way frame 261, 266
openings, beams 164
out-of-plane buckling 295

P-delta method 201
pan-joist construction 123, 128
parking slab 136
path direction 117
pattern loading 13

perimeter footings 329
pile cap 336, 338
piles 335, 337
plane-sections theory 83
plastic hinge 212, 229, 257, 267, 275, 303
plastic hinge location 322
plastic hinge regions 236, 242, 248
plastic limit analysis 213
plastic shrinkage 59
point loading 100
Poisson's ratio 44
postpeak load-carrying capacity 37
posttensioned floor systems 135
posttensioned slabs and beams 135
posttensioning 162
pour strips 140
precast concrete details 134
precast concrete floors 131
precast slab 133
prestressing force 80
prismatic beams 275
progressive collapse 6, 125
pullout strength 37
pullout test 342, 347

quality control 341

raft 333
rectangular ties 234
reinforced concrete columns 222
reinforcement 21, 76, 134
reinforcing materials 1
reinforcing paramenters 28
reinforcing steel 24
research needs 9, 18, 39, 56, 62, 164, 325,
    340
reshoring 135
retaining walls 195, 250
reversed cyclic loading 280, 291
reversed lateral load 295
rigid connection 183
Ronan point disaster 125
round bars 22

San Fernando earthquake 235
second-order effects 201
secondary moments 199
secondary reinforcement 22
seismic behavior of beam-column joints
    316
seismic design 235, 253–313
seismic design loads 297

seismic design philosophy 208
seismic loading 237, 242, 268
seismic loading behavior 244
seismic resistance 289
seismicity 2
sequencing, reinforcing bars 134
serviceability 14, 199
serviceability requirement 11
set-modifying agents 57
set retarders 58
shallow foundations 327
shear 50, 303, 309, 321, 322, 328
shear and moment diagrams 136
shear capacity 88, 147
shear capacity, FRC 34
shear capitals 138
shear design 146, 157
shear failure 90, 148, 150, 154, 157, 304
shear force 118, 280
shear in interior joints 319
shear reinforcement 149, 269
shear resistance 157, 268, 274, 279
shear stresses 320
shear studs 138
shear walls 195, 310
shoring 135
short columns 195, 202, 208
short foundation beams 171, 187
short-term deflections 56
shrinkage 46, 59, 62, 335
shrinkage restraints 59
silica fume 58
simulating real-life loading 325
sizing structural elements 324
slab formwork loads 6
slab kinks 143
slab loads 8
slab-column connections 315
slab-column design 322
slab-column joints 322
slab-wall connections 325
slabs 53
slender columns 199, 200
slenderness effects 199
sliding shear 306
slip-forming 134
small-diameter piles 335
solid-slab construction 123
spacing, transverse reinforcement 237
special loads 7
specifications 342
spiral reinforcement 227, 234, 247

split ties 324
spread footings 328
square column 247
stability 250
stairs 170
state of stress 88
steel confinement 47
steel congestion at joints 324, 325
steel-fiber reinforced concrete 30
steel grades 23
steel strains 196
steel tubes 203
steel wires 25
stiff columns 141
stiffness 40, 125
stirrups 22, 100, 160
story shear 201
strength and ductility requirements 125
stress distribution 49
stress-strain characteristics 83, 224
stress-strain curves 24, 41, 43, 83, 223, 227
stressing boxes 142
stripping criteria 347
stripping times 135, 345
strong beam-weak column connections
    325
strong column-weak beam 230, 233, 243
structural analysis 11–19, 73, 78
structural engineer 324, 343
structural restraint 139
structural walls 290
strut and tie model 72, 160, 187
superplasticizers 58, 324
superreinforced concrete 221
support-strip method 130

tensile behavior, composites 30
tensile force 115
tensile stress 93
tensile stresses 21, 88, 153
tension failure 181
test procedures 341
test results 186
tests, stub columns 212
thermal effects 61
thermal movements 126
top-chord force variation 75
toughness, FRC 33
toughness measures 35
transverse reinforcement 97, 225, 233, 238,
    244, 267, 271, 299

transverse reinforcement, type II behavior
    115
transverse reinforcement, type III behavior
    116
transverse reinforcement for confinement
    249
transverse reinforcement for shear 250
transverse web reinforcement 106
triaxial stress 81
truss analogy 148, 172
truss models 67, 160, 162
tubular sections 202
two-way-banded posttensioning system 130
two-way frame 231, 261, 266, 281
two-way shear 137

ultimate limit state 95
ultimate shear capacity, beams 52
ultimate states 15
ultimate strength 204
ultimate strength, columns 211
ultimate strength design 40
ultimate strength design codes 126
uniaxial compressive strength 41
uniaxial tensile stress 43
unstable fracture propagation 156
unsymmetric connections 325
upper limit of capacity 176

vertical joint shear reinforcement 282
vertical loads 6
vertical members 195–252
vertical reinforcement 284
vertical slab deflections 61
vibration 302, 303
vierendeel panel 165

waffle construction 123
waffle system 131
wall footings 328
wall stability 295
walls 250
water infiltration 251
waterproofing 334
water-reducing admixtures 58
weak beam-strong column 256
web reinforcement 160
welded wire fabric 25
width-to-wall-thickness ratios 211
wire mesh 325
wires, yield strength 25